Grade **5**

Scott Foresman

# Reader's and Writer's Notebook
## Teacher's Manual

PEARSON

Glenview, Illinois • Boston, Massachusetts • Chandler, Arizona •
Upper Saddle River, New Jersey

ISBN-13:  978-0-328-48479-9
ISBN-10:     0-328-48479-2

5 6 7 8 9 10  V084  18 17 16 15 14 13 12 11
CC1

# Unit 1: Meeting Challenges

# Unit 2: Doing the Right Thing

# Unit 3: Inventors and Artists

# Unit 4: Adapting

# Unit 5: Adventurers

# Unit 6: The Unexpected

Name _____

# Unit 1 Independent Reading Log

| Reading Time | Title and Author | What is it about? | How would you rate it? | Explain your rating. |
|---|---|---|---|---|
| From ___ to ___ | | | Great 5 4 3 2 1 Awful | |
| From ___ to ___ | | | Great 5 4 3 2 1 Awful | |
| From ___ to ___ | | | Great 5 4 3 2 1 Awful | |
| From ___ to ___ | | | Great 5 4 3 2 1 Awful | |
| From ___ to ___ | | | Great 5 4 3 2 1 Awful | |

# Unit 2 Independent Reading Log

| Reading Time | Title and Author | What is it about? | How would you rate it? | Explain your rating. |
|---|---|---|---|---|
| From _____ to _____ | | | **Great** 5  4  3  2  1 **Awful** | |
| From _____ to _____ | | | **Great** 5  4  3  2  1 **Awful** | |
| From _____ to _____ | | | **Great** 5  4  3  2  1 **Awful** | |
| From _____ to _____ | | | **Great** 5  4  3  2  1 **Awful** | |
| From _____ to _____ | | | **Great** 5  4  3  2  1 **Awful** | |

Name _____

# Unit 3 Independent Reading Log

| Reading Time | Title and Author | What is it about? | How would you rate it? | Explain your rating. |
|---|---|---|---|---|
| From ____ to ____ | | | **Great** 5 4 3 2 1 **Awful** | |
| From ____ to ____ | | | **Great** 5 4 3 2 1 **Awful** | |
| From ____ to ____ | | | **Great** 5 4 3 2 1 **Awful** | |
| From ____ to ____ | | | **Great** 5 4 3 2 1 **Awful** | |
| From ____ to ____ | | | **Great** 5 4 3 2 1 **Awful** | |

Name _____

# Unit 4 Independent Reading Log

| Reading Time | Title and Author | What is it about? | How would you rate it? | Explain your rating. |
|---|---|---|---|---|
| From ___ to ___ | | | Great 5 4 3 2 1 Awful | |
| From ___ to ___ | | | Great 5 4 3 2 1 Awful | |
| From ___ to ___ | | | Great 5 4 3 2 1 Awful | |
| From ___ to ___ | | | Great 5 4 3 2 1 Awful | |
| From ___ to ___ | | | Great 5 4 3 2 1 Awful | |

Name _____

# Unit 5 Independent Reading Log

| Reading Time | Title and Author | What is it about? | How would you rate it? | Explain your rating. |
|---|---|---|---|---|
| From ____ to ____ | | | Great 5 4 3 2 1 Awful | |
| From ____ to ____ | | | Great 5 4 3 2 1 Awful | |
| From ____ to ____ | | | Great 5 4 3 2 1 Awful | |
| From ____ to ____ | | | Great 5 4 3 2 1 Awful | |
| From ____ to ____ | | | Great 5 4 3 2 1 Awful | |

Name _____

# Unit 6 Independent Reading Log

| Reading Time | Title and Author | What is it about? | How would you rate it? | Explain your rating. |
|---|---|---|---|---|
| From ____ to ____ | | | Great 5 4 3 2 1 Awful | |
| From ____ to ____ | | | Great 5 4 3 2 1 Awful | |
| From ____ to ____ | | | Great 5 4 3 2 1 Awful | |
| From ____ to ____ | | | Great 5 4 3 2 1 Awful | |
| From ____ to ____ | | | Great 5 4 3 2 1 Awful | |

Selection Title _____ Author _____

---

**Realistic Fiction** means that a story is possible or seems real. It consists of the same elements as other story genres, including setting, character, plot, and theme. Characteristics of realistic fiction include the following.

- Characters generally behave like real people.
- Settings may or may not be real.
- The plot, or events that happen in the story, may or may not seem real.

---

**Directions** As you read *Red Kayak,* look for examples of character, setting, and plot that make this story seem real. Write those examples below.

**Character** _____

_____

_____

**Setting** _____

_____

_____

**Plot** _____

_____

_____

# Explore the Genre

Think about another story you've read that is realistic fiction. What similarities and differences do you find between the characters in that story and *Red Kayak*? Write a summary of the similarites. Use a separate sheet of paper if you need more space.

_____

_____

Selection Title _____ Author _____

A **tall tale** is a humorous story that uses realistic details to tell a story about characters and events that are impossible. Characteristics of a tall tale include the following.

- Many details are from everyday life.
- Characters are greatly exaggerated.
- The events described could not really happen.

**Directions** As you read *Thunder Rose,* look for examples of realistic details, exaggerated characters, and impossible events that make the story a tall tale. Write those examples below.

**Realistic Details** _____

_____

_____

**Exaggerated Characters** _____

_____

_____

**Impossible Events** _____

_____

_____

# Explore the Genre

Think about another story you've read that's a tall tale. What similarities do you find between that story and *Thunder Rose*? Briefly paraphrase, or tell in your own words, the plot of both tall tales. Keep events in the order in which they happened. Use a separate sheet of paper if you need more space.

_____

_____

**Selection Title** _____ **Author** _____

When we **infer,** we use our background knowledge with information from the text to come up with our own ideas about what we're reading. To infer, or make inferences, try the following steps.

- Think about what you already know about the topics.
- Combine what you know with information from the text to make inferences.
- Based on your inferences, think about ideas, morals, lessons, or themes in the text.

**Directions** As you read the selection, use your background knowledge and clues from the text to make inferences. Use the chart below to show how you made your inferences. Then write a statement that summarizes the theme, moral, or lesson from the selection.

| What I Know | Information from the Text | What I Infer |
|---|---|---|
| | | |

**Statement that summarizes the theme, moral, or lesson** _____

_____

_____

_____

Selection Title _____ Author _____

A **biography** tells the story of all or part of a real person's life. Events in the person's life are generally told in the order that they happen. Characteristics of a biography include the following.

- The subject is part or all of the life of a real person.
- The events in the person's life are told in the order that they happen.
- Events are told in a third-person narration using *he, she, him,* or *her* when referring to the person.

**Directions** As you read *Satchel Paige,* look for examples of who the subject is, events in order, and third-person narration that make this selection a biography. Write those examples below.

**Subject** _____

_____

_____

**Events** _____

_____

_____

**Third-person Narration** _____

_____

_____

# Explore the Genre

Think about another selection you've read that is a biography. Briefly paraphrase, or tell in your own words, two important events from each biography. Keep events in the order in which they happened. Use a separate sheet of paper if you need more space.

_____

**Selection Title** _____ **Author** _____

---

**Text structure** refers to the way an author organizes a text. Cause and effect and compare and contrast are two types of text structure. Knowing how a text is structured can improve our comprehension. Here are ways to identify text structure.

- Before you read, preview the text. Make predictions, ask questions, and use titles, headings, and illustrations to try to identify the structure.
- As you read, look for language that gives clues to the organization.
- After reading, recall the organization and summarize the text.

---

**Directions** As you preview and read the selection, write down features of the text that help you identify the text structure. Remember to ask questions, use text features, and look for language clues to identify the text structure. After reading, write the name of the text structure and a brief summary of the selection.

**Before Reading** _____

_____

_____

_____

**During Reading** _____

_____

_____

_____

**Text Structure/Summary** _____

_____

_____

_____

**Selection Title** _____ **Author** _____

---

We **visualize** to create pictures in our minds as we read. Creating pictures can help us better understand what we're reading. To visualize, try the following.

- Combine what you already know with details from the text to make a mental image.
- Think about the events of the story or selection. Use your five senses to create pictures and to try to put yourself in the story or selection.

---

**Directions** As you read the selection, use your senses to help you visualize what's happening or the information the author provides. Write down what you can see, hear, taste, smell, and touch.

**See** _____

_____

_____

**Hear** _____

_____

_____

**Taste** _____

_____

_____

**Smell** _____

_____

_____

**Touch** _____

_____

_____

Name _____

Selection Title _____ Author _____

> **Literary nonfiction** tells the story of a true event or events. Elements that are found in fiction may be used in literary nonfiction as well. Characteristics of literary nonfiction include the following.
>
> • The plot centers around true events.
> • Characters may include people who really existed at the time that the events took place.
> • The story may include fiction elements such as dialogue, descriptions, and illustrations.

**Directions** As you read *Hold the Flag High,* look for examples of true events, real people, and dialogue, descriptions, and illustrations that make this selection literary nonfiction. Write those examples below.

**True Events** _____

_____

_____

**Real People** _____

_____

_____

**Dialogue, Descriptions, and Illustrations** _____

_____

_____

## Explore the Genre

Think about another selection you've read that is literary nonfiction. What differences do you find between the events in that selection and *Hold the Flag High*? Write a summary of the similarities between the events in both selections. Keep the events in the order in which they happen. Use a separate sheet of paper if you need more space.

_____

© Pearson Education, Inc., 5

Selection Title _____ Author _____

**Folk tales** are stories that were created by an unknown storyteller and handed down orally from generation to generation until someone wrote them down. Characteristics of folk tales include the following.

• The subject matter is often the customs or beliefs of a particular culture.

• Human and animal characters usually represent some human trait or aspect of human nature.

• Themes about human nature are expressed.

**Directions** As you read *The Ch'i-lin Purse,* look for examples of subject matter, characters, and theme that make this story a folk tale. Write those examples below.

**Subject Matter** _____

_____

_____

**Characters** _____

_____

_____

**Theme** _____

_____

_____

# Explore the Genre

Think about another story you've read that is a folk tale. What similarities and differences do you find between that story and *The Ch'i-lin Purse*? Write about it. Use a separate sheet of paper if you need more space.

_____

_____

Name _____

Selection Title _____ Author _____

Strategic readers **monitor** their understanding of what they've read and use fix-up strategies to **clarify** understanding. Ways to monitor and clarify include the following.

• Ask questions during and after reading and summarize to check your understanding.

• Adjust your reading rate, read on, or reread the section that caused confusion.

• Visualize what you are reading.

• Use text features and illustrations to help clarify the text.

**Directions**  As you read, write down the page numbers of places that you had trouble understanding. Then describe the fix-up strategy you used to clarify the meaning.

**Where in the text I had trouble:** _____  _____

_____

**Fix-up Strategies I Used**

_____

_____

_____

_____

_____

## Selection Summary

Write a two- or three-sentence summary of the selection. Use a separate sheet of paper if you need more space.

_____

_____

_____

_____

Selection Title _____ Author _____

**Poetry** is the careful selection and arrangement of words in lines that express a writer's thoughts and feelings. While many poems use a rhyming pattern, some poems do not. Characteristics of poetry include the following.

• Lines of poetry may rhyme in a pattern with rhymes occurring within or at the ends of lines.

• Some poems have a rhythmic pattern.

• Poets often use words that appeal to the senses to help the reader experience the poem.

**Directions** As you read *The Midnight Ride of Paul Revere,* look for examples of patterns of rhyme and rhythm and words that appeal to the senses that make this selection a poem. Write those examples below.

**Rhyme** _____

_____

_____

**Rhythm** _____

_____

_____

**Words That Appeal to Senses** _____

_____

_____

## Explore the Genre

Think about another selection you've read that is a poem. What similarities and differences do you find between that poem and *The Midnight Ride of Paul Revere?* Write about it. Use a separate sheet of paper if you need more space.

_____

_____

Name _____

Selection Title _____ Author _____

**Dramas,** or plays, are stories that are to be acted out for an audience. Dramas are divided into numbered acts and scenes consisting mainly of dialogue and stage directions for the actors. Characteristics of dramas include the following.

- Characters and setting
- Dialogue
- Scenes

**Directions**  As you read *The Fabulous Perpetual Motion Machine,* look for examples of characters and setting, dialogue, and scenes. Write those examples below.

**Characters and Setting** _____

_____

_____

**Dialogue** _____

_____

_____

**Scenes** _____

_____

_____

# Explore the Genre

Think about characters and setting, dialogue, and scenes in another drama that you've read. What similarities and differences do you find between that drama and *The Fabulous Perpetual Motion Machine*? Write about it. Use a separate sheet of paper if you need more space.

_____

_____

**Selection Title** _____ **Author** _____

We **visualize** to create pictures in our minds as we read. Creating pictures can help us better understand what we're reading. To visualize, try the following.

- Combine what you already know with details from the text to make a mental image.
- Think about the events of the story or selection. Use your five senses to create pictures and to try to put yourself in the story or selection.

**Directions** As you read the selection, use your senses to help you visualize what's happening or the information the author provides. Write down what you can see, hear, taste, smell, and touch.

**See** _____

_____

_____

**Hear** _____

_____

_____

**Taste** _____

_____

_____

**Smell** _____

_____

_____

**Touch** _____

_____

_____

**Selection Title** _____ **Author** _____

When we **predict,** we tell what we think might happen in a selection. Predictions are based on our preview or what we've already read. We **set a purpose** to guide our reading. We can do the following to predict and set a purpose.

- Read the title and the author's name. Look at the illustrations and other text features.
- Think about why you're reading and set a purpose.
- Use your prior knowledge—what you already know—to make a prediction.
- As you read, check and change your prediction based on new information.

**Directions** Preview the selection. Make a prediction and set a purpose for reading the selection. As you read, check your predictions and set a new purpose as necessary. When you finish reading, write a summary of the selection.

**Before Reading**
**Make a Prediction** _____

_____

**Purpose for Reading** _____

_____

**During Reading**
**Check and Change Prediction** _____

**Set a New Purpose** _____

_____

**After Reading**
**Write a Summary** _____

_____

_____

_____

**Selection Title** _____ **Author** _____

**Text structure** refers to the way an author organizes a text. Cause and effect and compare and contrast are two types of text structure. Sequential order and logical order are two more types of text structure. Knowing how a text is structured can improve our comprehension. Here are ways to identify text structure.

- Before you read, preview the text. Make predictions, ask questions, and use titles, headings, and illustrations to try to identify the structure.
- As you read, look for language that gives clues to the organization.
- After reading, recall the organization and summarize the text.

**Directions**  As you preview and read the selection, write down features of the text that help you identify the text structure. Remember to ask questions, use text features, and look for language clues to identify the text structure. After reading, write the name of the text structure and a brief summary of the selection.

**Before Reading** _____

_____

_____

_____

**During Reading** _____

_____

_____

_____

**Text Structure/Summary** _____

_____

_____

_____

Selection Title _____     Author _____

---

**Expository text** tells about real people and events. Expository text is a type of expository nonfiction. Characteristics of expository text include the following.

- The topic provides information about the real world and people.
- The information in the text is factual.
- Selections often include text features such as diagrams, maps, charts, and graphs.

---

**Directions**  As you read *Special Effects in Film and Television,* look for examples of expository text. Write those examples below.

**Selection Topic** _____

_____

_____

**Facts** _____

_____

_____

_____

**Text Features** _____

_____

_____

# Explore the Genre

Think about another selection you've read that is expository text. What similarities and differences do you find between that selection and *Special Effects in Film and Television*? Write about it. Use a separate sheet of paper if you need more space.

_____

_____

_____

**Selection Title** _____ **Author** _____

Good readers ask questions as they read. **Questioning** helps us monitor our comprehension and clarify anything that's confusing. Questioning also helps to make inferences, interpret the texts we read, and promote discussion. As you read, use the following questioning strategy.

- Preview the selection and think about any questions you have about the topic.
- Establish a purpose for reading by asking yourself what your teacher might expect you to learn by reading this text.
- Read with a question in mind and make notes when you find information that addresses the question.
- Write down other questions that come up as you read and look for answers in the text.
- Remember that not all questions are answered in the text. Sometimes we have to make inferences or interpretations based on the information the author provides.

**Directions** As you read the selection, use the chart below to write down any questions that you have about the text in the column on the left. Write down any answers you find or inferences you make in the right hand column.

| Questions | Answers, Inferences, Interpretations |
|---|---|
|  |  |
|  |  |
|  |  |
|  |  |
|  |  |

**Selection Title** _____ **Author** _____

---

**Realistic fiction** tells the story of imaginary people and events. Characteristics of realistic fiction include the following.

- The characters seem like real people that you might know.
- The setting is realistic, such as a city or town, a school, or other places you might know.
- The plot is possible and could happen in real life.

---

**Directions** As you read *Tripping Over the Lunch Lady,* look for examples of character, setting, and plot that make this story realistic fiction. Write those examples below.

**Character** _____

_____

_____

**Setting** _____

_____

_____

**Plot** _____

_____

_____

# Explore the Genre

Think about the plot in another story you've read that's realistic fiction. What similarities do you find between that story and *Tripping Over the Lunch Lady*? Write a summary of the similarities between both plots. Arrange your ideas in a logical order. Use a separate sheet of paper if you need more space.

_____

_____

_____

Selection Title _____ Author _____

---

**Important ideas** in nonfiction texts are the main ideas and details about a topic that the author wants the reader to understand. You can do the following to help identify important ideas and details as you read.

- Preview the selection and read the title, headings, and captions.
- Look for words in special type such as italics, boldface, and bulleted lists.
- Watch for signal words and phrases such as *for example* and *most important*.
- Use text features including photographs and illustrations, diagrams, charts, and maps.

---

**Directions** As you read the selection, use the chart below to write down any important ideas and details that you find. List any text features or signal words you used to locate these ideas. Then choose one important idea and paraphrase, or tell in your own words, that idea using details that you listed in the chart. Be sure to maintain a logical order.

| Important Ideas | Details |
| --- | --- |
|  |  |

**Paraphrase one important idea** _____

_____

_____

_____

Selection Title _____ Author _____

**Story structure** is the important parts of the story that happen at the beginning, middle, and end of a story. To identify story structure, strategic readers do the following.

- Look for the conflict, or problem, at the beginning of the story.
- Track the events of the plot in the order in which they happen as conflict builds.
- Recognize the climax when the characters face conflict.
- Identify how the conflict gets resolved.

**Directions** As you read the story, chart the story structure using the plot map below. When you are finished, briefly paraphrase the story, or retell it in your own words, on a separate sheet of paper. Make sure you keep the events in the order in which they happened.

**Characters**

**Setting**

**Climax**
**(Turning Point)**

**Rising Action**

**Problem**
**(Goal)**

**Solution**
**(Outcome)**

Selection Title _____ Author _____

---

An **autobiography** is a form of literary nonfiction. Like a biography, it tells the story of all or part of a real person's life. But with an autobiography, a person tells his or her own story. Characteristics of an autobiography include the following.

- The subject is part or all of the life of a real person.
- The events in the person's life are usually told in the order that they happen.
- Events are told as a first-person narration.

---

**Directions** As you read *The Gymnast,* look for examples of the subject, events in order, and first-person narration that make this selection a biography. Write those examples below.

**Subject** _____

_____

_____

**Events** _____

_____

_____

**First-person Narration** _____

_____

_____

# Explore the Genre

Think about another selection you've read that is an autobiography. Briefly paraphrase, or tell in your own words, two events from each autobiography. Write about the events in the order in which they happened. Use a separate sheet of paper if you need more space.

_____

_____

Name _____

Selection Title _____ Author _____

Fiction is a made-up story, either serious or humorous, of imaginary people who generally behave as we expect people to behave. Fiction might include real places and events, but the story is created from the author's imagination. Characteristics of fiction include the following.

- Characters generally behave like real people.
- Settings may or may not be real.
- The plot, or events that happen in the story, may or may not seem real.

**Directions** As you read *The Skunk Ladder,* look for examples of character, setting, and plot that make this story fiction. Write those examples below.

**Character** _____

_____

_____

**Setting** _____

_____

_____

**Plot** _____

_____

_____

# Explore the Genre

Think about the setting in another story you've read that is fiction. What differences do you find between that story and *The Skunk Ladder*? Write a summary of the differences between both settings. Arrange your ideas in a logical order. Use a separate sheet of paper if you need more space.

_____

_____

**Selection Title** _____ **Author** _____

When we **infer,** we use our background knowledge with information from the text to come up with our own ideas about what we're reading. To infer, or make inferences, try the following steps.

- Think about what you already know about the topics.

- Combine what you know with information from the text to make inferences.

- Based on your inferences, think about ideas, morals, lessons, or themes in the text.

**Directions** As you read the selection, use your background knowledge and clues from the text to make inferences. Use the chart below to show how you made your inferences. Then write a statement that summarizes the theme, moral, or lesson from the selection.

| What I Know | Information from the Text | What I Infer |
|---|---|---|
| | | |

**Statement that summarizes the theme, moral, or lesson** _____

_____

_____

© Pearson Education, Inc., 5

Selection Title _____ Author _____

Strategic readers **monitor** their understanding of what they've read and use fix-up strategies to **clarify** understanding. Ways to monitor and clarify include the following.

- Ask questions during and after reading and summarize to check your understanding.
- Adjust your reading rate, read on, or reread the section that caused confusion.
- Visualize what you are reading.
- Use text features and illustrations to help clarify the text.

**Directions**  As you read, write down the page numbers of places that you had trouble understanding. Then describe the fix-up strategy you used to clarify the meaning.

**Where in the text I had trouble:** _____  _____  _____

_____  _____  _____  _____

**Fix-Up Strategies I Used**

_____

_____

_____

_____

_____

# Selection Summary

Write a two- or three-sentence summary of the selection. Use a separate sheet of paper if you need more space.

_____

_____

_____

_____

Name _____

Selection Title _____ Author _____

When we **summarize** and **paraphrase,** we capture the important ideas or events of a selection in a few sentences. Paraphrasing is putting what we've read into our own words. Good readers summarize and paraphrase what they've read to check understanding and improve comprehension. Keeping important ideas and events in a logical order also improves comprehension. To summarize or paraphrase, do the following.

• In fiction, look for the important events of the plot, including the climax.

• In nonfiction, look for the important ideas that the author presents.

• Jot notes as you read to help you summarize or paraphrase, keeping events in a logical order.

• Restate important pieces of information in your own words.

**Directions** As you read the selection, use the chart below to write down any important ideas or plot events. Remember to record events in a logical order. When you're finished reading, use your notes to summarize or paraphrase the selection.

**Important Ideas or Events**

_____

_____

_____

_____

_____

**Summary**

_____

_____

_____

_____

_____

© Pearson Education, Inc., 5

Name _____

**Selection Title** _____ **Author** _____

Good readers ask questions as they read. **Questioning** helps us monitor our comprehension and clarify anything that's confusing. Questioning also helps to make inferences, interpret the texts we read, and promote discussion. As you read, use the following questioning strategy.

- Preview the selection and think about any questions you have about the topic.
- Read with a question in mind and make notes when you find information that addresses the question.
- Write down other questions that come up as you read and look for answers in the text.
- Remember that not all questions are answered in the text. Sometimes we have to make inferences or interpretations based on the information the author provides.

**Directions** As you read the selection, use the chart below to write down any questions that you have about the text in the column on the left. Write down any answers you find or inferences you make in the right hand column.

| Questions | Answers, Inferences, Interpretations |
|-----------|--------------------------------------|
|           |                                      |
|           |                                      |
|           |                                      |
|           |                                      |
|           |                                      |
|           |                                      |
|           |                                      |

Name _____

Selection Title _____ Author _____

---

**Important ideas** in nonfiction texts are the main ideas and details about a topic that the author wants the reader to understand. You can do the following to help identify important ideas and details as you read.

• Preview the selection and read the title, headings, and captions.

• Look for words in special type such as italics, boldface, and bulleted lists.

• Watch for signal words and phrases such as *for example* and *most important*.

• Use text features including photographs and illustrations, diagrams, charts, and maps.

---

**Directions** As you read the selection, use the chart below to write down any important ideas and details that you find. List any text features or signal words you used to locate these ideas. Use the important ideas and details to write a short summary of the selection.

| Important Ideas | Details |
|---|---|
|  |  |

**Write a Summary** _____

_____

_____

Name _____

Selection Title _____ Author _____

Text structure refers to the way an author organizes a text. Cause and effect and compare and contrast are two types of text structure. Knowing how a text is structured can improve our comprehension. Here are ways to identify text structure.

- Before you read, preview the text. Make predictions, ask questions, and use titles, headings, and illustrations to try to identify the structure.

- As you read, look for language that gives clues to the organization.

- After reading, recall the organization and summarize the text.

**Directions** As you preview and read the selection, write down features of the text that help you identify the text structure. Remember to ask questions, use text features, and look for language clues to identify the text structure. After reading, write the name of the text structure and a brief summary of the selection.

**Before Reading** _____

_____

_____

_____

**During Reading** _____

_____

_____

_____

**Text Structure/Summary** _____

_____

_____

_____

Selection Title _____ Author _____

**Myths** are old stories that have been passed down through word of mouth for hundreds of years. Some myths have many different versions depending on the culture. Characteristics of myths include the following.

- The beliefs of a particular culture are reflected in the story.
- Characters are usually gods, goddesses, and humans interacting with natural forces.
- The plot often centers around events that try to explain a force of nature.

**Directions** As you read *King Midas and the Golden Touch,* look for examples of a particular culture, characters such as gods, goddesses, and humans, and events that try to explain nature that make this story a myth. Write those examples below.

**Culture** _____

_____

_____

**Characters** _____

_____

_____

**Events** _____

_____

_____

# Explore the Genre

Think about the culture, characters, and events in another story you've read that's a myth. What similarities and differences do you find between that story and *King Midas and the Golden Touch*? Write about it. Use a separate sheet of paper if you need more space.

_____

**Selection Title** _____ **Author** _____

When we **predict,** we tell what we think might happen in a selection. Predictions are based on our preview or what we've already read. We **set a purpose** to guide our reading. We can do the following to predict and set a purpose.

- Read the title and the author's name. Look at the illustrations and other text features.
- Think about why you're reading and set a purpose.
- Use your prior knowledge—what you already know—to make a prediction.
- As you read, check and change your prediction based on new information.

**Directions** Preview the selection. Make a prediction and set a purpose for reading the selection. As you read, check your predictions and set a new purpose as necessary. When you finish reading, write a summary of the selection.

**Before Reading**
**Make a Prediction** _____

_____

**Purpose for Reading** _____

_____

**During Reading**
**Check and Change Prediction** _____

_____

**Set a New Purpose** _____

_____

**After Reading**
**Write a Summary** _____

_____

_____

_____

Selection Title _____ Author _____

**Background knowledge** is what we already know about a topic. Using background knowledge can help us better understand what we're reading. Activate your background knowledge by doing the following.

• Preview the selection to find out what it's about.

• Think about what you already know about the topic.

• Connect the selection to your own world—to people, places, and events you already know.

**Directions** Use the KWL chart below to chart your background knowledge about the selection. List what you already know in the K column. Then list what you want to learn in the W column. After reading, list what you learned in the L column. Write a brief summary of the selection on a separate sheet of paper.

| What We Know | What We Want to Know | What We Learned |
|---|---|---|
|  |  |  |

Name _____

**Book Talk Tips**
- Speak clearly.
- Make eye contact.
- Talk about a book YOU liked reading.
- Don't give away the ending.
- Talk for 2–4 minutes, sharing amusing or important information from the book.

**Directions** Use the talking points below to help organize your book talk.

1. What is the title of the book?

2. Who is the author?

3. What is the genre?

4. What other book has the author written?

## If your book is fiction...

5. What is the most exciting part of this book? The plot, characters, theme? Explain why.

6. Briefly describe a setting, scene, or character from this book.

## If your book is nonfiction...

7. What important information did you learn from this book?

8. Briefly describe an interesting part of the book.

9. Do you have a personal connection with the story or topic? Explain.

10. Explain why your listeners should read this book.

**Before writing**

- Help your partner brainstorm ideas for writing.

- Discuss the writing topic with your partner. Does he or she need to narrow the topic or expand it?

**After the first draft**

- Before you exchange papers, tell your partner what you would like him or her to look for when reading your writing.

- Using sticky notes or a piece of notebook paper, note any questions or comments you have about your partner's writing.

- Point out the information or ideas that are well written.

- Discuss any information that seems unneeded or confusing, but make sure your comments are helpful and considerate.

**Revision**

- Read your partner's paper out loud to listen for strengths as well as places for improvement.

- Always tell your partner what you think works well in his or her paper.

- Start with a compliment, or strength, and then offer suggestions for improvement. For example, "I liked how you _____. What if you also _____?"

- Remember also to look for correct spelling and grammar.

**Other areas you might comment on:**

- Title

- Introduction

- Conclusion

- Descriptions

- Examples

- Use of verbs, nouns, adjectives or adverbs

Name _____

**Name of Writing Product** _____

**Directions**  Review your final draft. Rate yourself on a scale from 4 to 1 (4 is a top score) on each writing trait. After you fill out the chart, answer the questions below.

| Writing Traits | 4 | 3 | 2 | 1 |
|---|---|---|---|---|
| Focus/Ideas | | | | |
| Organization | | | | |
| Voice | | | | |
| Word Choice | | | | |
| Sentences | | | | |
| Conventions | | | | |

**1.** What is the best part of this piece of writing? Why do you think so?

_____

_____

_____

_____

**2.** Write one thing you would change about this piece of writing if you had the chance to write it.

_____

_____

_____

_____

© Pearson Education, Inc., 5

# Plot and Character

- The **plot** is the pattern of events in a story.
- The person or animal who most affects a story's plot is the **main character**.
- A plot includes (1) a problem or **conflict** the **main character** will experience, (2) **rising action** as the conflict builds, (3) a **climax**, when the main character faces the conflict, and (4) **a resolution**, when the problem or conflict is solved.

**Directions** Read the following passage. Then complete the diagram by filling in the elements of the story.

Rafael was doing chores in the barn when his radio stopped. He walked into his house and discovered the lights wouldn't turn on. The power was out! Rafael knew all the milk in the refrigerator would spoil if it stayed warm too long. His family's dairy farm couldn't afford to lose that milk.

Then he remembered how his father kept soft drinks cold when they went fishing. Rafael carried 23 gallons of milk to the edge of the stream and placed them in the shallow water almost up to their caps. He knew the cool water would keep the milk chilled until the power came back on.

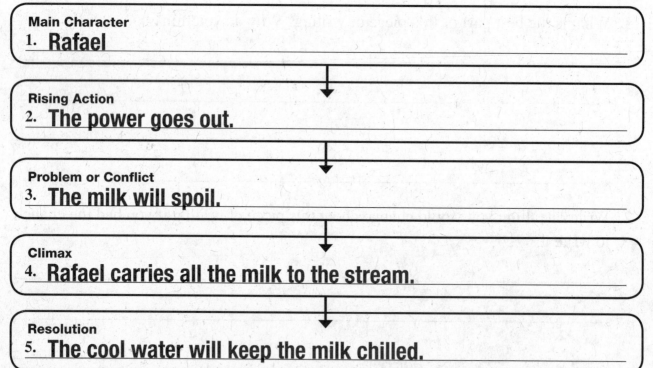

**Main Character**
1. **Rafael**

↓

**Rising Action**
2. **The power goes out.**

↓

**Problem or Conflict**
3. **The milk will spoil.**

↓

**Climax**
4. **Rafael carries all the milk to the stream.**

↓

**Resolution**
5. **The cool water will keep the milk chilled.**

© Pearson Education, Inc., 5

**Home Activity** Your child analyzed the plot of a short passage. Discuss a story with your child identifying characters, the problem or conflict, rising action, and resolution.

# Writing · Written Directions

### Key Features of Written Directions

- explains a process in steps and describes steps in order
- often are numbered or have clue words that show order

## Planting Flower Seeds

Flowers on a window sill add a nice touch to any home. Planting flower seeds in a cup or a small pot is a simple activity that brings great rewards. With the proper care, in a short time your seeds will sprout and become beautiful flowers.

To begin, you need a package of flower seeds, a flower pot, small rocks, potting soil, a spoon or scoop, and water. First, place small rocks at the bottom of your pot. These will help water drain away from the roots of your plant each time you water it. If a pot does not drain properly, the roots sit in too much water and could rot. Next, scoop soil into your pot. Fill it a little more than halfway to the top.

You are now ready to plant. Open your packet of seeds and sprinkle seeds into the soil. Since every plant will be different, read the instructions on your seed packet to find out how many seeds you can plant and how close together they should be. Press your seeds into the soil. Be sure that they are completely covered. Add more soil if you need to. Finally, water your seeds to make sure the soil is moist but not too wet. Be careful not to water your plant too much. There should not be puddles of water at the top of the pot.

When your seeds are planted, place your pot in a sunny area of your home. A window sill can work very well. Check your soil daily to make sure it does not dry out. If all goes well, by the end of the week you should begin to see small sprouts. If your flowers outgrow the original pot, you can either move them outside or move them to a bigger pot.

1. Read the directions. What process do these directions explain? What is the first step in the process?

   __The directions explain how to plant seeds. The first step is to put__

   __small rocks at the bottom of the pot for drainage.__

2. What is the second step in the process? What clue word tells you the order of step two? __Next, scoop soil into your pot. Fill it a little more than halfway to the top.__

   __next__

# Vocabulary

**Directions** Choose the word from the box that best matches each definition. Write the word on the line shown to the left.

insistently _____    1. in a way that demands attention

grumbled _____    2. muttered unhappily

minute _____    3. extremely small

compressions _____    4. pushes or presses against something

normally _____    5. regularly or usually the case

**Directions** Choose the word from the box that best completes the sentences below. Write the word on the line shown to the left.

neutral _____    6. Since the car was in _____, it didn't move when she pressed the gas pedal.

intentionally _____    7. I didn't hurt her feelings on purpose, or _____, but my words were careless.

grumbled _____    8. The workers _____, or muttered, when the boss told them they had to work faster.

insistently _____    9. The child tugged at my dress _____, wanting another cookie.

compressions _____    10. The rescue worker applied fifteen _____ to the man's chest, then breathed into his mouth twice.

## Write a Letter of Complaint

Pretend that you have returned from a store where you had a terrible experience. The clerks were so rude that you may never shop there again! On a separate piece of paper, write a letter to the store's manager describing the event. Use as many vocabulary words from this week as you can.

**Home Activity** Your child identified and used words from the story *Red Kayak*. Review the definitions of each of the vocabulary words with your child and work together to use the words in sentences.

# Four Kinds of Sentences

Each kind of sentence begins with a capital letter and has a special end mark.

A **declarative sentence** makes a statement. It ends with a period.
The creek goes through dense forests.

An **interrogative sentence** asks a question. It ends with a question mark.
Do you see a red kayak?

An **imperative sentence** gives a command or makes a request. It ends with a period.
The subject (*you*) does not appear, but it is understood.
Look in the marsh.

An **exclamatory sentence** shows strong feeling. It ends with an exclamation mark.
The water is freezing!
What a cold day it is!

**Directions** Rewrite each sentence. Make any needed corrections in capitalization and punctuation.

1. the creek is dangerous in winter?

    **The creek is dangerous in winter.**

2. he's not breathing.

    **He's not breathing!**

3. do you know how to perform CPR.

    **Do you know how to perform CPR?**

**Directions** Complete each sentence with words from the box. Then write whether the sentence is *declarative, interrogative, imperative,* or *exclamatory.*

think I see something!     make boating dangerous.
the opposite shore.        wear life jackets?

4. Strong winds and tides **make boating dangerous. declarative**

5. Did the boaters **wear life jackets? interrogative**

6. Drive toward **the opposite shore. imperative**

7. Gosh, I **think I see something! exclamatory**

**Home Activity** Your child learned about four kinds of sentences. Have your child write about an event at school using one example of each kind of sentence.

# Short Vowel VCCV, VCV

| Spelling Words | | | | |
|---|---|---|---|---|
| distance | method | anger | problem | butter |
| petals | enjoy | perhaps | figure | channel |
| admire | comedy | husband | tissue | mustard |
| shuttle | advance | drummer | regular | denim |

**Words in Context** Complete each sentence with a list word.

1. The _____ keeps the rhythm of the band.

2. Most people _____ the skills of talented artists.

3. Watching a _____ makes people laugh.

4. The _____ bus is the fastest way to get there.

5. I like _____ on my hot dog.

6. Her _____ was forty years old.

7. The shortest _____ between two points is a straight line.

8. The _____ fell off the flower one by one.

9. _____ we can have ice cream after dinner.

10. The skater practiced _____ eights on the ice.

1. **drummer**

2. **admire**

3. **comedy**

4. **shuttle**

5. **mustard**

6. **husband**

7. **distance**

8. **petals**

9. **Perhaps**

10. **figure**

**Word Meanings** Write the list word that has nearly the same meaning.

11. handkerchief

12. canal

13. lard

14. technique

15. like

16. proceed

17. rage

18. jeans

19. usual

20. difficulty

11. **tissue**

12. **channel**

13. **butter**

14. **method**

15. **enjoy**

16. **advance**

17. **anger**

18. **denim**

19. **regular**

20. **problem**

**Home Activity** Your child wrote words that have short vowels. Dictate words and have your child say and spell each word.

© Pearson Education, Inc., 5

# Steps in a Process

**Process** _____

Step 1

↓

Step 2

↓

Step 3

↓

Step 4

↓

Step 5

# Vocabulary · Homographs

- A **homograph** is a word that is spelled the same as one or more other words, has different meanings, and may have a different pronunciation.
- Pairs or groups of homographs often come from different parts of speech.
- When you look up a homograph in a dictionary, read each definition presented. The first definition listed may not be the meaning that matches the way the word is used in the sentence.

**bow**[1] (bou), *v.* to bend the head in greeting, respect, agreement, or obedience
**bow**[2] (bō), *n.* a knot made with two or more loops

**close**[1] (klōz), *v.* to shut
**close**[2] (klōs), *adj.* without much space between

**lead**[1] (led), *n.* a soft, bluish-white heavy metallic element
**lead**[2] (lēd), *adj.* most important

**minute**[1] (min´it), *n.* the 60th part of an hour of time
**minute**[2] (mī nüt´), *adj.* very small

**present**[1] (priz nt´), *v.* to bring before the public
**present**[2] (prez´nt), *n.* a gift

**rose**[1] (rōz), *v.* past tense of *rise*
**rose**[2] (rōz), *n.* a usually prickly, sometimes climbing shrub with colorful flowers

**Directions** Complete the following sentences using words from the list of homographs above.

1. Practicing for the school play was a lot of work. Our drama club was going to

   **present**_____ the tragedy *Romeo and Juliet* by William Shakespeare.

2. I didn't have the **lead**_____, or most important, role, but I was nervous!

3. My best friend, Emma, had the part of Juliet. When the show ended, the audience stood and

   applauded for at least a full **minute**_____.

4. When Emma took her **bow**_____, someone even threw a **rose**_____ on the stage!

5. We waited for the curtain to **close**_____, and then we went backstage to remove our makeup. The play was a success.

# Dictionary/Glossary

- A **dictionary** lists words in alphabetical order and gives their meanings, pronunciations, and other helpful information, including parts of speech—noun, verb, adjective, or adverb.

- A **glossary** is a list of important words and their meanings that are used in a book. Glossaries are located at the back of a book. Some glossary entries include a page reference noting the first appearance of the word in the book.

- When you see an unfamiliar word, and context clues do not help you figure out its meaning, you can use a dictionary or glossary to learn what it means.

**Directions** Read the dictionary and glossary entries.

### Dictionary Entry

**rep•u•ta•tion** (rep' ye ta' shen) **1.** *n.* what people think and say the character of someone or something is; character in the opinion of others; name; repute: *This store has an excellent reputation for fair dealing.* **2.** good name; good reputation: *Cheating ruined his reputation.* **3.** fame: *an international reputation.*

### Glossary Entry

**Ice Age** *n.* a cold period in which huge ice sheets spread outward from the polar regions, the last one of which lasted from about 1,600,000 to 10,000 B.C. (p. 107)

**Directions** Answer the questions below.

1. In the dictionary entry, what does the initial bold entry for the word *reputation* tell you?

   **It tells you how the word is broken down into syllables.**

2. In the dictionary entry, what does the representation of the word in parentheses tell you?

   **It tells you how to pronounce the word.**

3. Why do you think the dictionary provides sentence examples in the definition of the word?

   **The examples show how to use the word properly in a sentence.**

4. How many definitions does this dictionary list for *reputation*? Which is the most commonly used definition?

   **There are three; The first one is the most commonly used.**

5. What does the italicized *n.* stand for in both entries?

   **It stands for *noun*.**

6. What two things do you notice are missing from a glossary entry that you find in the dictionary entry?

   **The syllable and pronunciation guides are missing.**

7. What is the page number listed at the end of the glossary entry for?

   **It tells you on which page the glossary word is first used.**

8. What information do you get in both a dictionary and glossary entry?

   **Both give you a definition of the word.**

9. If you were reading a book about life in the desert, would you expect to find *Ice Age* in the glossary? Why or why not?

   **No; Glossaries only define the words in the book, and a book about desert life is unlikely to talk about an ice age.**

10. If you were reading a story and came across a word you did not know, where would be the first place you would look for a definition—a glossary or a dictionary?

   **Possible answer: I would look to see if the book had a glossary in the back first.**

© Pearson Education, Inc., 5

**Home Activity** Your child learned how to use a dictionary and a glossary. Make a list of all the possible times you might use a dictionary or glossary.

Name _____

# Short Vowel VCCV, VCV

**Proofread a Poster** Sarah made a poster for the school fair. Circle seven spelling errors. Find one capitalization error. Write the corrections on the lines.

**Spelling Words**

distance
method
anger
problem
butter
petals
enjoy
perhaps
figure
channel

admire
comedy
husband
tissue
mustard
shuttle
advance
drummer
regular
denim

Come (too) the village fair!
See the funny (comady) team show.
Milk a cow and churn some (buttar) at the farm exhibit.
Sample hot dogs with twenty choices of (musterd).
Make (tisseu) flower bouquets.
Decorate your denim jeans with a special new art method.
Enjoy fifty booths of crafts, fun, and games.
park at the Town Hall parking lot.
Ride the special (shuttal) bus to the fairgrounds.
Discount tickets are on sale in (advanse).

1. **to**
2. **comedy**
3. **butter**
4. **mustard**
5. **tissue**
6. **shuttle**
7. **advance**
8. **Park at the Town Hall parking lot.**

**Proofread Words** Circle the correct spelling of the word.

| 9. | channal | chanel | (channel) |
| 10. | (drummer) | drumer | drummor |
| 11. | metod | methid | (method) |
| 12. | parhaps | (perhaps) | pirhaps |
| 13. | (figure) | figger | figour |
| 14. | petles | petels | (petals) |
| 15. | problam | (problem) | problim |

**Frequently Misspelled Words**

and
to
too

**School + Home** **Home Activity** Your child found misspelled list words with VCCV and VCV patterns. Select a list word and ask your child to spell it.

## Four Kinds of Sentences

**Directions** Read the passage. Then read each question. Circle the letter of the correct answer.

# The Storm

    (1) The storm came up suddenly? (2) In a few short minutes, the sky turned dark. (3) Danny and Sherry were out in their sailboat within view of land! (4) Before they could reach harbor, however, the wind changed. (5) Sherry and Danny struggled to take down the sail. (6) The wind was too strong! (7) How could the pair get the boat to safety.

**1** What change, if any, should be made in sentence 1?

  **A**  Change *came up* to **come up**

  **B**  Change *suddenly?* to **suddenly.**

  **C**  Change *The storm* to **Storm**

  **D**  Make no change

**2** What change, if any, should be made in sentence 2?

  **A**  Change *minutes* to **minute's**

  **B**  Change the period to a question mark

  **C**  Remove the comma

  **D**  Make no change

**3** What change, if any, should be made in sentence 3?

  **A**  Change *were* to **was**

  **B**  Change the exclamation mark to a question mark

  **C**  Change the exclamation mark to a period

  **D**  Make no change

**4** What change, if any, should be made in sentence 4?

  **A**  Remove *however*

  **B**  Change *Before* to **before**

  **C**  Change the period to a comma

  **D**  Make no change

**5** What change, if any, should be made in sentence 7?

  **A**  Change the period to a question mark

  **B**  Change the period to an exclamation mark

  **C**  Change *How* to **How?**

  **D**  Make no change

**School + Home** **Home Activity** Your child prepared for taking tests on kinds of sentences. Have your child read part of a story to you and identify each sentence as declarative, interrogative, imperative, or exclamatory.

# Cause and Effect

- A **cause** is what makes something happen. An **effect** is what happens as a result of the cause.
- If there are no clue words, ask yourself, "What made this event happen? What happened as a result of this event?"
- An effect may become the cause of another effect.

**Directions** Read the following passage and complete the diagram below.

> By the third day of non-stop rain, no one on our street could keep the water out of their homes. The homes that had basements were hit hardest. Basements were flooded in spite of efforts to pump the water out. Toys, washing machines, and furniture in basements were soaked through completely.
>
> Our neighbor, Mrs. Chan, was so sad because all her photographs of her grandchildren had been in her basement. Her granddaughter May was my best friend, and I had May's school picture in my wallet. I wrapped it in a plastic bag, put on my raincoat, and ran to Mrs. Chan's house. Just as I handed Mrs. Chan May's picture, a ray of sun peeked out from behind a cloud.

## Possible answers given.

**Cause**

1. **non-stop rain**

**Effect**

flooded basements

**Cause**

flooded basements

**Effect**

2. **Mrs. Chan's pictures soaked**

**Cause**

Mrs. Chan's pictures are soaked.

**Effect**

3. **Mrs. Chan is sad.**

**Cause**

4. **Mrs. Chan is sad.**

**Effect**

5. **Neighbor gives Mrs. Chan picture of granddaughter.**

© Pearson Education, Inc., 5

**Home Activity** Your child identified causes and effects in a short passage. While working around the house, have your child explain to you the effects of one of the chores. Then ask your child to figure out if the effect becomes the cause of another effect.

# Writing • Writing for Tests

## The Winter of Blue Snow

It was the coldest winter Paul Bunyan had ever seen. It was so cold that the fish moved south, the trees begged to be cut down, and even the snow turned blue. The nights were so frosty that when Sourdough Sam called Paul Bunyan and the other lumberjacks to dinner, his words froze solid and hung in the air, so nobody heard him and the lumberjacks went hungry until morning.

To get his mind off his starving belly, Paul Bunyan went for a walk. He was just about to eat a valley-sized handful of blue snow when he heard a strange sound—like the snort of a bear crossed with the bleat of a lamb. Peering into his hands, Paul Bunyan saw the sorriest sight: a tiny baby ox, stained blue by the snow.

Well, Paul Bunyan took pity on the poor little ox and took him to Sourdough Sam for a few gallons of milk. While old Sourdough heated the milk over the fifty-burner stove, Paul Bunyan ate the dinner intended for fifty lumberjacks—he left not one spiral ham, bushel of mashed potatoes, or gallon of gravy on the massive table.

Soon it was clear that the little blue ox, which Paul Bunyan named Babe, had it in mind to take after its new owner. That first night, Babe drank the milk of a hundred cows, so the next morning Sourdough Sam had to make oatmeal for breakfast with melted blue snow. Babe soon grew so big that Paul Bunyan had to build an extra large barn to keep him in. When Babe was a week old, he started helping Paul Bunyan by hauling a hundred logs at a time by the strength of his massive neck.

The only trouble between Babe and Paul Bunyan was that Babe loved the winter and hated summer, so Paul Bunyan had to be mighty creative to keep Babe hauling logs in the summer heat. He even painted the roads white to make Babe think that they were covered in snow. Finally, Paul Bunyan hit on a grand idea: he introduced Babe to Bessie, the yellow cow. Bessie was almost a big as Babe and as beautiful as a summer day. She had a lovely yellow hide and warm brown eyes that nearly melted the blue right off Babe.

Now, being a summer cow and Sourdough Sam's best provider of milk and cream during the winter, Bessie could only work during the summer months. So during the winter, Babe hauled logs alone, thinking all the time about his Bessie, and during the summer, Babe and Bessie hauled logs together, which made Babe grow to love the summertime almost as much as Bessie did.

## Possible responses are underlined.

1. Find three improbable events in paragraph 1. Underline them.

2. Find two realistic details in paragraph 2. Underline them.

3. Find three exaggerated details in paragraph 5 that create humor. Underline them.

# Vocabulary

**Directions** Choose the word from the box that best matches each definition. Write the word on the line.

veins _____ 1. blood vessels that carry blood to the heart from all parts of the body

lullaby _____ 2. song for singing to a child

thieving _____ 3. stealing

pitch _____ 4. a thick, black, sticky substance made from tar or turpentine

constructed _____ 5. fitted together; built

**Check the Words You Know**

___branded
___constructed
___daintily
___devastation
___lullaby
___pitch
___resourceful
___thieving
___veins

**Directions** Choose the word from the box that best completes the sentences below. Write the word on the line shown to the left.

branded _____ 6. The rancher _____ his cattle with the symbol from his ranch so nobody else could claim them.

pitch _____ 7. The cracks in the roof were sealed with _____ .

daintily _____ 8. Grandma and Grandpa danced elegantly, or _____, in time with the music's gentle beat.

resourceful _____ 9. When no one else could think of how to solve the school's litter problem, Marisa impressed the principal with her_____ idea.

devastation _____ 10. The tornado caused a lot of _____, or destruction, when it whipped through town and ripped several homes from their foundations.

## Write a Friendly Letter

On a separate sheet of paper, write a friendly letter to someone living out of town about an event that happened where you live. Use as many vocabulary words as you can.

# Letter should include words from vocabulary list and details about an event that happened.

**Home Activity** Your child identified and used vocabulary words from *Thunder Rose*. Work with your child to learn the words and their definitions. Have your child create colorful flash cards to do so.

© Pearson Education, Inc., 5

# Subjects and Predicates

Every sentence has a subject and a predicate. The words that tell whom or what the sentence is about are the **complete subject.**

Many families moved west in the 1840s.

The words that tell what the subject is or does are the **complete predicate.**

The trip could take up to six months.

A **nominative** is a noun or pronoun that means the same as the subject. It explains or identifies something about the subject.

Joe was an experienced cowboy.     The nominative is *cowboy.*

A **fragment** is a group of words that lacks a subject or a predicate.

Had to carry everything with them.     This fragment lacks a subject.

A **run-on** is two or more complete sentences run together.

The settlers needed food they needed tools.

**Directions** Underline each complete subject once. Underline each complete predicate twice.

1. A tornado's shape is like a funnel.

2. The deadly funnel measures up to a mile wide.

3. They are unpredictable in their movements.

4. Settlers feared the awful twister.

**Directions** Write *F* after a fragment. Write *R* after a run-on. Then correct the sentence errors. Write a simple sentence or a compound sentence on the lines.     **Possible answers:**

5. The wind inside a tornado ____F____

**The wind inside a tornado can spin at up to 300 miles per hour.**

6. A tornado can be called a twister it is also sometimes called a cyclone. ____R____

**A tornado can be called a twister. It is also sometimes called a cyclone.**

**Home Activity** Your child learned about subjects and predicates. Talk about a storm you and your child have experienced. Have your child write several sentences about the storm and identify the complete subjects and predicates in each sentence.

# Long Vowel VCV

| Spelling Words | | | | |
|---|---|---|---|---|
| fever | broken | climate | hotel | basic |
| vocal | native | silent | labor | spider |
| label | icon | agent | motive | vital |
| acorn | item | aroma | ego | solo |

**Words in Context** Complete each sentence with a list word.

1. From a small ____, a large oak tree grows.

2. When you are sick, you may have a ____.

3. Your ____ is what you think of yourself.

4. Flying ____ means doing something alone.

5. A desert ____ may produce too little rain to support crops.

6. The two people were loud and ____ as they cheered.

7. The travel ____ helped plan a vacation.

8. We want to stay in the ____ that has a pool.

9. Have you ever watched a ____ spin its web?

10. The clothing ____ itches the back of my neck.

1. **acorn**
2. **fever**
3. **ego**
4. **solo**
5. **climate**
6. **vocal**
7. **agent**
8. **hotel**
9. **spider**
10. **label**

**Antonyms** Write the list word that has the opposite or nearly the opposite meaning.

11. fixed

12. advanced

13. alien

14. noisy

15. unimportant

11. **broken**
12. **basic**
13. **native**
14. **silent**
15. **vital**

**Synonyms** Write the list word that has the same or nearly the same meaning.

16. work

17. reason

18. object

19. scent

20. image

16. **labor**
17. **motive**
18. **item**
19. **aroma**
20. **icon**

**Home Activity** Your child wrote words with the long vowel VCV pattern. Have your child tell you one synonym or one antonym for a list word.

# Scoring Rubric: Tall Tale

|  | 4 | 3 | 2 | 1 |
|---|---|---|---|---|
| **Focus/Ideas** | Exaggerated character and events | Somewhat exaggerated character and events | Character and events hardly exaggerated | Character and events not exaggerated |
| **Organization/ Sequence** | Clear order of events | Mostly clear order of events | Confused order of events | No order of events |
| **Voice** | Engaging and original voice | Generally engaging voice | No clear original voice | Voice is not engaging or original |
| **Word Choice** | Writer uses strong sensory details | Writer uses good sensory details | Writer uses weak sensory details | Writer does not include sensory details |
| **Sentences** | Clear, complete sentences | Most sentences clear and complete | Some sentences unclear and incomplete | Many sentences incomplete |
| **Conventions** | Subjects and predicates used correctly | Most subjects and predicates used correctly | Some mistakes with subjects and predicates | Many errors with subjects and predicates |

# Vocabulary · Context Clues

- **Homonyms** are words that are spelled the same but have different meanings.
- Look for **context clues**—words and sentences around a word—to figure out which meaning is being used in the sentence.

**Directions** Read the following passage about a hurricane. Then answer the questions below. Look for homonyms as you read.

> As Pedro scaled the ladder to the roof, he felt the blood in his veins pumping through his body. He was the first person to get a look at the destruction the hurricane had created. He looked at the roof and reminded himself to bring up a bucket of pitch next time to repair the new cracks. Looking out over the countryside, he saw that many buildings would need to be constructed again. He started gathering broken branches to pitch, or throw, down to the ground below. Then he paused and took a deep breath, thinking about what this disaster had done to his community. He knew that none of his neighbors would have to pitch tents and live in their yards while repairs were made to their homes. The people of his town would help each other find shelter, and everyone would be fine.

1. *Vein* can mean "a blood vessel" or "a crack in a rock filled with a mineral deposit." How is it used in the passage? How can you tell?

   **a blood vessel; The sentence talks about blood.**

2. What does *pitch* mean in the third sentence of this passage? What clues help you understand the meaning used in this sentence?

   **It means a dark, sticky substance; bucket, repair, cracks**

3. What does *pitch* mean in the fifth sentence of this passage? What clues help you understand the meaning used in this sentence?

   **It means to throw; the word _throw_**

4. To *scale* something can mean "to climb up something" or "to measure something." How is it used in this passage? How can you tell?

   **to climb up; Pedro goes to the roof using a ladder.**

5. What does *pitch* mean in the second-to-last sentence of this passage? What clues help you understand the meaning used in this sentence?

   **to put up; tents**

**Home Activity** Your child read a short passage and used context clues to understand homonyms, words that are spelled the same but have different meanings. With your child, make a list of homonyms. Challenge your child to make up a sentence using each meaning.

# Almanac

An **almanac** is a yearly book that contains calendars, weather information, and dates of holidays. Almanacs also contain charts and tables of current information in subject areas such as populations of cities and nations, and lists of recent prize winners in science, literature, and sports.

**Directions** Read this almanac entry about the United States Census. Use the information to answer the questions on the next page.

## United States Census

Every ten years, the federal government conducts a census, or count, of the number of people who live in the United States. According to the federal Constitution, a census must be completed every ten years to determine the number of representatives each state may send to the U.S. House of Representatives.

The census shows how the populations of cities, regions, and states compare. This data helps government officials decide how and where to spend federal money. Traditionally, a census not only counts the number of citizens, but it also gathers other information, such as:

- the ethnic background of citizens
- the number of adults and children
- the number of employed people and unemployed people
- the income level of citizens and their type of housing

For many decades, the three largest cities have remained New York City, Los Angeles, and Chicago. However, other cities are growing more quickly than any of these three. Many sociologists, economists, and government officials find the growth rates of cities the most interesting information in the census. In recent years, the trend has been for great numbers of people to move from the North to the South—especially to states in the Southwest.

The federal government collects data every year, not just every decade. For instance, the chart below shows data from the 2000 census in one column, but it also includes data collected by the government in 2002. This chart shows the ten fastest growing cities of 100,000 people or more in the United States.

| CITY | 2000 Population | 2002 Population | Numerical Change | Percentage Change |
|------|-----------------|-----------------|------------------|-------------------|
| Gilbert, AZ | 109,920 | 135,005 | 25,085 | 22.8 |
| North Las Vegas, NV | 115,488 | 135,902 | 20,414 | 17.7 |
| Henderson, NV | 175,750 | 206,153 | 30,403 | 17.3 |
| Chandler, AZ | 176,652 | 202,016 | 25,364 | 14.4 |
| Peoria, AZ | 108,685 | 123,239 | 14,554 | 13.4 |
| Irvine, CA | 143,072 | 162,122 | 19,050 | 13.3 |
| Rancho Cucamonga, CA | 127,743 | 143,711 | 15,968 | 12.5 |
| Chula Vista, CA | 173,566 | 193,919 | 20,353 | 11.7 |
| Fontana, CA | 128,938 | 143,607 | 14,669 | 11.4 |
| Joliet, IL | 106,334 | 118,423 | 12,089 | 11.4 |

© Pearson Education, Inc., 5

1. According to the U.S. Constitution, what is the maximum number of years that can pass between federal censuses?

   **A census must be conducted every ten years.**

2. What is the purpose of conducting a federal census, according to the U.S. Constitution?

   **The purpose is to determine the number of representatives each state will send to the U.S. House of Representatives.**

3. In addition to population, what are two examples of other data a census provides?

   **the number of adults and children; the number of employed people and unemployed people**

4. What types of people consult the federal census?

   **Among others, sociologists, economists, government officials, and ordinary citizens consult the federal census.**

5. What are the three largest cities in the United States?

   **New York City, Los Angeles, and Chicago**

6. Which state has the most listings among the fastest-growing cities on the 2002 census?

   **California has the most, with four cities listed.**

7. Would an almanac be a good place to find information on why nine of ten fastest-growing U.S. cities are located in the Southwest or West? Why or why not?

   **Almanacs only provide statistics, so they are probably not the best resource for learning the reasons for the growth of cities.**

8. Which city had the highest numerical increase in population between 2000 and 2002?

   **Henderson, Nevada had the highest increase.**

9. Which city had the highest population in 2002? How much higher is its population than that of the city listed below it?

   **Henderson, Nevada has the highest population. Its population is 4,137 higher than Chandler, Arizona's population.**

10. Between 2000 and 2002, Los Angeles (population 3,503,532) saw a numerical increase in population of 104,239. Why do you think Los Angeles isn't listed on this chart?

    **Los Angeles was already a big city, so this is a low percentage change.**

**Home Activity** Your child learned about the contents of almanacs and analyzed data from an almanac. Together, look up information about your town or area of the country in an almanac. Read about population, weather forecast, historical sites, and so on. Discuss how the information in the almanac helps you better understand your own geographical area.

# Long Vowel VCV

**Proofread a Postcard** Yolanda wrote a postcard to her friend. Circle six spelling errors and one capitalization error. Write the corrections on the lines.

Spelling Words

(dear) Margaret,

I'm having a great time at the (hotle.) There are lemon trees everywhere and the (eroma) from the blossoms is awesome. Today, I'm going to (by) some gifts. There are many (nateve) crafts to choose from. It's very calm and (silant) here. The only noise comes from the wind and the ocean. Thank your travel (agant) for suggesting this place. It's now a family favorite!

Your friend,
Yolanda

| **Spelling Words** |
| --- |
| fever |
| broken |
| climate |
| hotel |
| basic |
| vocal |
| native |
| silent |
| labor |
| spider |
| |
| label |
| icon |
| agent |
| motive |
| vital |
| acorn |
| item |
| aroma |
| ego |
| solo |

1. **Dear** 2. **hotel**
3. **aroma** 4. **buy**
5. **native** 6. **silent**
7. **agent**

**Proofread Words** Circle the correct spelling of the word.

| 8. | vocle | (vocal) | vocel |
| --- | --- | --- | --- |
| 9. | (label) | laebel | labal |
| 10. | brokin | brokan | (broken) |
| 11. | basec | (basic) | basuc |
| 12. | ikon | (icon) | ican |
| 13. | (motive) | motife | motove |
| 14. | akorn | acern | (acorn) |
| 15. | (fever) | fevar | feaver |
| 16. | eego | (ego) | egho |

| **Frequently Misspelled Words** |
| --- |
| favorite |
| buy |

**Home Activity** Your child identified misspelled list words in a paragraph. Ask your child to name one list word with the long *a* sound and one with the long *o* sound.

## Subjects and Predicates

**Directions** Read the passage. Then read each question. Circle the letter of the correct answer.

# Cowboys of Texas

(1) Cowboys of Texas herded cattle to Kansas on the Abilene Trail. (2) The great herds moved along slowly. (3) These large animals must graze for hours each day. (4) They needed a vast supply of water. (5) Lean, tanned cowboys (6) They crossed dangerous rivers and slept under the light of the moon. (7) A cowboy's horse was his friend and co-worker.

**1** What is the complete subject of sentence 1?

  **A**  Cowboys

  **B**  Cowboys of Texas

  **C**  Kansas

  **D**  the Abilene Trail

**2** What is the complete predicate of sentence 2?

  **A**  moved

  **B**  moved along

  **C**  moved along slowly

  **D**  The great herds

**3** What is the complete subject of sentence 3?

  **A**  These large animals

  **B**  large animals

  **C**  hours each day

  **D**  animals must graze

**4** How can you best describe sentence 5?

  **A**  Has a subject and predicate

  **B**  Run-on sentence

  **C**  Has a complete subject

  **D**  Sentence fragment

**5** In sentence 6, what is the complete subject?

  **A**  They

  **B**  They crossed

  **C**  They crossed dangerous rivers

  **D**  rivers

© Pearson Education, Inc., 5

**School + Home**  **Home Activity** Your child prepared for taking tests on subjects, predicates, fragments, and run-ons. Circle a paragraph in the newspaper. Have your child identify the subject and predicate of teach sentence in the paragraph.

# Theme and Setting

- The **theme** is the underlying meaning of a story. It is often not stated. You can figure out a theme from events and other evidence in the story.

- The **setting** is where and when the story takes place. Writers use details, such as sights and sounds, to describe it.

**Directions** Read the following passage. Then complete the diagram with the sights, sounds, smells, or feelings expressed in the passage.

I love to go to the beach in the summer because a beach can excite the senses. I might hear the roaring waves or the squawk of seagulls. I might feel the gritty warmth of the sand underfoot. Even the mix of odors on the breeze—an airy freshness with a hint of rotting fish—can stay with me long after I've left the water's edge. When I look out toward the vast horizon over the water, I feel as free as the birds darting and diving above my head, and as small as the grains of sand blowing across my toes.

**Possible answers given for 1, 3–5.**

1. roaring waves

**Setting**
2. a beach in summer

3. gritty warmth of sand

smell of fish

seagulls' cries

4. What is the theme of the passage?

**A person's senses are awakened at the beach.**

5. Visualize that you are on a beach. On a separate piece of paper, list a few of the sights, sounds, smells, or feelings you included in your scene.

**I imagined the sound of people laughing, the smell of sunscreen, the coolness of the water, and the sight of children.**

**Home Activity** Your child identified the setting and theme in a fictional passage. Sit with your child in a familiar place and identify its sights, sounds, and smells.

# Writing · Invitation

**Key Features of an Invitation**

- may be informal or formal
- gives important information about an event or plan
- sometimes asks for a response

---

## Beach Party!

Dear Melissa,

To celebrate the last few days of summer, I'm going to have a beach party! Here are the details:

**What:** Beach Party!

**Where:** Kaiser Beach, 1409 Lakefront Way

**When:** 12:00 P.M., Saturday, August 22

This is the best beach in town! It's really big, so it's not usually too crowded.

To get to the beach, take a right off Sandy Point Rd. and go three blocks. We'll have a spot set up near the lifeguard stand on the beach. Look for the yellow beach umbrella.

Here are a few items you might want to bring with you:
Swimsuit
Sunscreen
Towel

Please tell me if you will be able to make it or not. You can call me at home. (222) 567-1234

Your friend,
Emily

---

1. Tell what the event is, where it is taking place, and when it is happening.

   **Beach party; Kaiser Beach; Aug. 22 at 12 P.M.**

2. Name three types of additional details the writer includes.

   **directions; what to bring; how to respond to the invitation**

Name_____

# Vocabulary

**Directions** Choose a word from the box that best matches each clue. Write the word on the line.

**headland**_____

1. This is a good place to build a lighthouse.

**kelp**_____

2. Some call it seaweed, others call it this.

**lair**_____

3. This could be considered a secret hiding spot.

**gnawed**_____

4. This is what the rabbit did to the carrot.

**sinew**_____

5. This works with your muscle to help you move.

> ## Check the Words You Know
>
> ____gnawed
> ____headland
> ____kelp
> ____lair
> ____ravine
> ____shellfish
> ____sinew

**Directions** Choose the word from the box that best completes each sentence. Write the word on the line.

The fox slowly emerged from its, den, or **1. lair**_____. Having **2. gnawed**_____

the last bone from an earlier meal, the fox headed down the hill toward the **3. ravine**_____,

or canyon, in search of more food. While foxes will occasionally eat **4. shellfish**_____,

they much prefer the **5. sinew**_____ and muscle of birds or small mammals.

## Write a Letter

On a separate sheet of paper, write a letter you might send off in a bottle if you were stranded on an island. Use as many vocabulary words as you can.

# Letters should include words from the vocabulary list and details about an island.

© Pearson Education, Inc., 5

**Home Activity** Your child identified and used vocabulary words from *Island of the Blue Dolphins*. With your child, work together to tell a story incorporating the vocabulary words. Take turns adding sentences to the story until all the words have been used.

Name _____

# Independent and Dependent Clauses

A related group of words with a subject and a predicate is called a **clause.** A clause that makes sense by itself is an **independent clause.** A clause that does not make sense by itself is a **dependent clause.** A **complex sentence** contains an independent and a dependent clause.

| | |
|---|---|
| **Independent Clause** | They came to the island in canoes. |
| **Dependent Clause** | even though it was a long trip |

If the dependent clause comes first, set it off with a comma: *Until they were attacked, Native Americans lived on the island.* If the independent clause is first, no comma is needed: *Native Americans lived on the island until they were attacked.*

**Directions** Write *I* if the underlined group of words is an independent clause. Write *D* if it is a dependent clause.

1. If you live on an island, you become independent. ___D___

2. Natives made their own clothes because they could not buy them. ___I___

3. Since there were no stores, they hunted for food. ___I___

4. A seal provided meat while people used its hide for clothes. ___D___

5. A hunting party paddled boats out to sea so that they could catch fish. ___I___

6. Women gathered berries and roots before winter came. ___D___

7. Because they needed containers for the food, they made baskets out of grasses. ___D___

**Directions** Underline the dependent clause in each sentence.

8. Because they cooked with fire, the natives kept live coals.

9. After food was prepared, they covered the embers with ashes.

10. While they slept through the night, the coals stayed warm.

11. The coals smoldered until morning came.

12. When the cook blew on the coals, they glowed brightly.

13. She fed wood to the coals so that the fire would catch again.

14. If her husband had caught fish that morning, they would eat well for breakfast.

© Pearson Education, Inc., 5

 **Home Activity** Your child learned about independent and dependent clauses. Ask your child to write a sentence about Native Americans using an independent clause and a dependent clause and explain the difference between the two.

# Long Vowel Digraphs

| Spelling Words | | | | |
|---|---|---|---|---|
| coast | feast | speech | wheat | Spain |
| paint | arrow | needle | charcoal | praise |
| faint | maintain | crease | grain | breeze |
| willow | appeal | bowling | complain | sneeze |

**Words in Context** Complete each sentence with a list word.

1. I am dizzy and may ____.

2. A perfect ____ score is 300.

3. I had multi-____ bread in my sandwich.

4. High ____ tells you that you did a great job.

5. Make a ____ in the paper to fold it in half.

6. Food grilled over a ____ fire tastes great.

7. It is generally better to be positive than to ____.

8. A sailboat needs a strong ____ to go fast.

9. Antique car owners spend time and money to ____ their vehicles so they will continue to run.

10. Two countries that border ____ are Portugal and France.

1. **faint**

2. **bowling**

3. **grain**

4. **praise**

5. **crease**

6. **charcoal**

7. **complain**

8. **breeze**

9. **maintain**

10. **Spain**

**Classifying** Write the list word that belongs in each group.

11. bow, feather, ____

12. sew, thread, ____

13. glide, cruise, ____

14. cold, cough, ____

15. corn, barley, ____

16. talk, lecture, ____

11. **arrow**

12. **needle**

13. **coast**

14. **sneeze**

15. **wheat**

16. **speech**

**Synonyms** Write the list word that has the same or nearly the same meaning.

17. request

19. tree

17. **appeal**

19. **willow**

18. banquet

20. color

18. **feast**

20. **paint**

**Home Activity** Your child wrote words with long vowel digraphs. Have your child tell you two ways to spell long *e*.

© Pearson Education, Inc., 5

**Four-Column Chart**

# Vocabulary • Unknown Words

- When you see an unknown word, use a dictionary or glossary to learn the word's meaning.
- A **dictionary** lists words in alphabetical order and gives their meanings, pronunciations, and other helpful information. A **glossary** is a list of important words and their meanings that are used in a book.

**Directions** Read the following passage about fishermen. Then answer the questions below. Look up unknown words in a dictionary or glossary.

People who make their living from the ocean need more than good fishing skills. Of course they need to know about what kinds of shellfish live in the area, and how much kelp floats in the waters they fish. They also need to know about water quality: how brackish is the water? Is it polluted? Knowing which are the best fishing coves and how near the shore the larger fish travel is essential.

We view a coastline from a headland and appreciate its beauty, but a fisherman sees a completely different world. He or she sees a deep-sea ravine, the lair of a myriad of different fish. Many fishing decisions are left to the brain of the person fishing, not his or her luck, muscle, or sinew.

1. What is *kelp?* Why should people who fish for a living know about kelp?

   **seaweed; Possible answer: Where there is kelp, there are likely to be fish.**

2. How do *shellfish* differ from other fish?

   **Shellfish have shells, whereas other fish do not.**

3. If you are standing on a *headland,* where is the water?

   **It is beneath you.**

4. What is a *lair?* How does it apply to schools of fish?

   **a hiding place; Possible answer: It is the place where the fish spend their time.**

5. What does *myriad* mean? Would a person who fishes for a living be pleased to see a myriad of fish?

   **many; Yes, because there would be many fish to catch.**

**Home Activity** Your child identified and used vocabulary words from a passage about fishermen. Read a nonfiction article with your child. Have him or her point out unknown words. Together, look up the words in a dictionary or glossary.

© Pearson Education, Inc., 5

# SPQ3R

**SPQ3R** is an acronym for a set of study skills that can help you when you read any text. It is especially helpful when reading nonfiction. Here's what it means: **Survey:** Look at the title, author name, chapter headings, and illustrations to get an idea of what you are about to read. **Predict:** Imagine what the story you're going to read is about. **Question:** Generate questions you want answered when reading the story. **Read:** Read the story, keeping your predictions and questions in mind. **Recite:** Recite or write down what you learned from reading the story. **Review:** Look back at the story, the predictions you made, the questions you posed, the answers you found in the text, and the information you learned from your reading.

**Directions** Use SPQ3R in reading the passage and answering the questions that follow.

**Hawaii: A Remote State**

Hawaii is a group of volcanic islands in the central Pacific Ocean some 2,300 miles west of San Francisco, California. Hawaii became the fiftieth state in the United States in 1959. It is an important military location of the U.S. because of its location in the ocean. Because it is so beautiful, it is also one of the most popular vacation spots for Americans even though the flight to Hawaii is long.

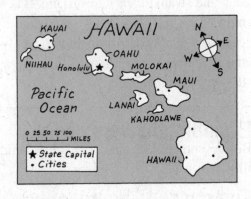

## Possible answers given.

1. Before you read this passage, what could you tell about the passage by surveying the map?

**The passage is going to be about Hawaii.**

2. Before you read this passage, what did you predict the passage would be about?

**the distance between Hawaii and other places**

3. What was a question you wanted the passage to answer before you read it?

**Where are Hawaii's best beaches?**

4. When did Hawaii become a state? What is one of the things that Hawaii is known for?

**1959; It is an important military location.**

5. Write a brief review of what you learned from this passage. In your review, discuss whether your questions were answered and whether your prediction was true.

**As I predicted, the passage was about Hawaii, but it didn't tell me where the beaches are. I learned when it became a state, that it has military bases, and that it is popular for vacations.**

**Directions** Use SPQ3R in reading the passage and answering the questions that follow.

**Assateague Island's Wild Horses**

Assateague Island is a 37-mile-long barrier island, a thin strip of land that helps to protect Maryland's shoreline. It has been an outpost for the U.S. Coast Guard for nearly 50 years. What is most unique about the island is the horses that roam freely on the beaches and marshland. While the origin of the horses is unclear, the popular myth claims the horses jumped from a sinking Spanish ship and swam to reach this island. It is more likely the horses were taken to the island by landowners trying not to pay taxes on livestock, perhaps as long ago as the seventeenth century.

## Possible answers given.

1. Before you read this passage, what could you tell about the passage by surveying the illustration?

   **The passage is probably about horses.**

2. Before you read this passage, what did you predict the passage would be about?

   **It will be about wild horses on an island.**

3. Before you read this passage, what questions did you want the passage to answer?

   **Do any people live on the island? What do the horses eat?**

4. What is most unique about Assateague Island?

   **There are horses that roam the island freely.**

5. Write a brief review of what you learned from this passage. In your review, discuss whether your questions were answered and whether your prediction was true.

   **As I predicted, the passage was about wild horses on an island.**

   **My questions were not answered. I learned that no one really**

   **knows how the horses got to the island.**

**Home Activity** Your child learned about the SPQ3R study skill and applied it to two nonfiction passages. Have your child explain the study skill to you. Then, with your child, apply it to a newspaper or magazine article.

# Long Vowel Digraphs

**Proofread a Report** Miguel wrote about his family's trip. Circle six spelling errors. Find one punctuation error. Write the corrections on the lines.

> This summer, my family traveled to Spain. We felt very lucky to stay in a hotel right on the (caost.) The weather was always beautiful with a light (breaze) blowing in off the ocean. Outside my window, the branches of a (wilow) tree dipped into a small pond. The sky was the same color as the baby blue color in my (pante) box. On our last night we had a wonderful (feest.) I thought I would (fante) at the sight of so much food! Everything was really delicious(?.) My stomach hurt before we got to dessert. Is that anything to complain about?

| | Spelling Words |
|---|---|
| | coast |
| | feast |
| | speech |
| | wheat |
| | Spain |
| | paint |
| | arrow |
| | needle |
| | charcoal |
| | praise |
| | faint |
| | maintain |
| | crease |
| | grain |
| | breeze |
| | willow |
| | appeal |
| | bowling |
| | complain |
| | sneeze |

1. **coast**
2. **breeze**
3. **willow**
4. **paint**
5. **feast**
6. **faint**
7. **Everything was really delicious.**

**Frequently Misspelled Words**

Halloween
really

**Proofread Words** Circle the correct spelling of the word.

8. weat        wheet        (wheat)
9. charcole     (charcoal)    charcol
10. (maintain)   maintane     mantain
11. boling      bolling      (bowling)
12. (complain)   complane     complan
13. creese      creaze       (crease)
14. arow        (arrow)      arro

**Home Activity** Your child corrected misspelled list words in a paragraph and selected the correctly spelled word in a group of words. Select three list words and ask your child to spell them.

# Independent and Dependent Clauses

**Directions** Read the passage. Then read each question. Circle the letter of the correct answer.

# Ancient Tools

(1) Natives used different kinds of natural materials as tools. (2) Carved to a point, a rock could serve as a knife. (3) Bones of some animals became tools too. (4) Because bone is so hard, it can pass through leather. (5) Artists might carve bone if the weather was bad. (6) Deerskin made soft, warm clothing after it was tanned. (7) They used every part of an animal so that nothing was wasted.

1 What is the independent clause in sentence 2?

   A   Carved to a point

   B   a rock

   C   a rock could serve

   (D)  a rock could serve as a knife

2 What is the dependent clause in sentence 3?

   A   Bones of some animals

   B   some animals

   C   became tools

   (D)  None of the above

3 In sentence 4, which word identifies a dependent clause?

   (A)  Because

   B   hard,

   C   , it

   D   leather.

4 What is the independent clause in sentence 6?

   A   Deerskin

   (B)  Deerskin made soft, warm clothing

   C   it was tanned

   D   after it was tanned

5 In sentence 5, what is the dependent clause?

   (A)  if the weather was bad

   B   the weather

   C   Artists might carve

   D   None of the above

© Pearson Education, Inc., 5

**School + Home** **Home Activity** Your child prepared for taking tests on independent and dependent clauses. Say a dependent clause (*after we eat dinner, before we leave home, when we go to the store*). Have your child add an independent clause to make a sentence.

# Fact and Opinion

- A **statement of fact** can be proved true or false.
- A **statement of opinion** is what someone thinks or feels. Statements of opinion often contain words that make judgments, such as *interesting* or *beautiful.*
- A single sentence might contain both a statement of fact and a statement of opinion.

**Directions**  Read the following passage.

Jackie Robinson was the first African American baseball player to play in the modern major leagues. I think he was very brave to do so. He played in the Negro Leagues until 1947 when he was signed to the Brooklyn Dodgers. Despite controversy about Robinson breaking the color barrier, he was an immediate success. At the end of his first season, Robinson was named Rookie of the Year. During his third season, he won the league's batting title and was later named the league's Most Valuable Player. He was probably the most valuable player of the entire twentieth century.

For each statement, circle *F* or *O* to tell whether it is a fact or an opinion. Circle the words in the sentence that tell you the statement is an opinion.

F **(O)** 1. (I think) Jackie Robinson was very brave to play in the major leagues.

**(F)** O 2. Jackie Robinson was the first African American baseball player to play in the modern major leagues.

F **(O)** 3. Jackie Robinson (was probably the most valuable player) of the twentieth century.

**(F)** O 4. Jackie Robinson was named the league's Most Valuable Player.

**(F)** O 5. The Brooklyn Dodgers signed Jackie Robinson.

**Home Activity** Your child read a short passage and identified whether statements were facts or opinions. Read a newspaper article and an editorial about the same current event with your child. Have your child analyze which statements are facts and which are opinions.

# Writing • Newsletter Article

**Key Features of a Newsletter Article**

- presents basic facts, and then adds details
- typically tells about an event, idea, or person
- includes direct quotations to enhance the article
- answers the questions: *Who? What? Where? When? Why? How?*

## Muhammad Ali

Muhammad Ali is a legendary fighter. He began boxing when we was twelve, and in 1960 he won a gold medal at the Olympics in Rome. After that, he became a professional boxer.

Ali's career is legendary, and with good reason: Not only did he not lose a professional fight until 1971, but Ali was a great showman. He taunted opponents and relied on his quick reflexes to dodge punches in the ring. He once spoke of an opponent, "Frazier is so ugly that he should donate his face to the US Bureau of Wild Life."

In 1964, Ali defeated Sonny Liston to become the heavyweight champion of the world. He lost few fights after that and truly earned his reputation as one of our country's greatest athletes. He had many fans of all races at a time when it was hard for black Americans to rise above racial discrimination. He once said, "I wish people would love everybody else the way they love me. It would be a better world."

Though he faced countless tough opponents during his boxing career, Ali faced his biggest challenge when he was diagnosed with Parkinson's disease. Parkinson's is a disease that affects the central nervous system and causes people to lose control of their movements. While the disease may have silenced Ali (he speaks rarely because of the way in which Parkinson's affects his voice), it has not stopped him from fighting for what he believes. He continues to battle against Parkinson's disease as well as other problems, such as world hunger, poverty, and human rights' abuses. Even in the face of his greatest challenge, Muhammad Ali remains a champion.

**1.** Read the article. Who is the article about? What is he known for?

**Muhammad Ali. He is a legendary professional boxer.**

**2.** Name three important events in Muhammad Ali's life.

**He won a gold medal in the Olympics.**

**He became the heavyweight champion of the world.**

**He was diagnosed with Parkinson's disease.**

Name_____

# Vocabulary

**Directions** Draw a line to match each word on the left with its definition on the right.

1. fastball          firm belief in yourself
2. unique           a pitch thrown at high speed
3. weakness        laughing at; making fun of
4. confidence      having no like or equal
5. mocking         a weak point; slight fault

## Check the Words You Know

___confidence
___fastball
___mocking
___outfield
___unique
___weakness
___windup

**Directions** Choose the word from the box to complete each clue and fill in the crossword puzzle.

**DOWN**

6. We have full _____ in his hitting.
7. Motions the pitcher makes before throwing the ball is called a _____.

**ACROSS**

8. If the ball is hit out of the diamond, it's in the _____.
9. A standout hitter like Hank Aaron is _____ among players.
10. Running too slowly is a player's major _____.

```
        6 c           7 w
      8 o u t f i e l d
        n           n
        f           d
        i         9 u n i q u e
        d           p
        e
   10 w e a k n e s s
        c
        e
```

## Write a News Report

On a separate sheet of paper, write a brief television news report about a baseball game, using as many vocabulary words as you can.

**News reports should include words from the vocabulary list and details about a baseball game.**

**Home Activity** Your child identified and used vocabulary words found in the biographical story *Satchel Paige*. Look in the sports pages of a newspaper and read a description of a sporting event with your child. See if you can identify any of the vocabulary words in the article.

© Pearson Education, Inc., 5

# Compound and Complex Sentences

A **simple sentence** expresses a complete thought. It has a subject and a predicate.
  The Negro League formed in 1920.

A **compound sentence** contains two simple sentences joined by a comma and a conjunction such as *and, but,* or *or.*
  The athletes played several games a day, and they traveled on a bus.

A **complex sentence** contains an independent clause, which can stand alone, and a dependent clause, which cannot stand alone. The clauses are joined by a word such as *if, when, because, until, before, after,* or *since.* In the following sentence, the independent clause is underlined once; the dependent clause is underlined twice.
  Many years would pass before the major leagues were integrated.

**Directions** Join each pair of simple sentences with *and, but,* or *or.* Write the compound sentence on the lines. Change punctuation and capital letters as necessary.

1. My sister can hit the ball hard. She pitches well too.

**My sister can hit the ball hard, and (*or* but) she pitches well too.**

2. The game should have started at one o'clock. A thunderstorm began at 12:45.

**The game should have started at one o'clock, but a thunderstorm began at 12:45.**

3. The teams will make up the game next Sunday. They will wait until the end of the season.

**The teams will make up the game next Sunday, or they will wait until the end of the season.**

**Directions** Write *compound* after each compound sentence. Write *complex* after each complex sentence. Underline the word that joins the two clauses in each sentence.

4. All players are important to a team, <u>but</u> the pitcher may be most important. **compound**

5. <u>If</u> a pitcher strikes out batters, the opposing team cannot score. **complex**

6. Outfielders must catch the ball <u>when</u> the batter hits a pop fly. **complex**

7. The game was tied, <u>and</u> no one left the bleachers. **compound**

8. The pitcher struck out two batters, <u>but</u> the third batter hit a home run. **compound**

 **Home Activity** our child learned about compound and complex sentences. Have your child write a paragraph about a baseball game, using at least one compound sentence and one complex sentence.

Name _____

# Adding -ed, -ing

## Spelling Words

| supplied | supplying | denied | denying | decided |
|----------|-----------|--------|---------|---------|
| deciding | included | including | admitted | admitting |
| occurred | occurring | qualified | qualifying | identified |
| identifying | delayed | delaying | satisfied | satisfying |

**Word Pairs** Write the best list words to complete each sentence pair.

Were you **(1)**____ with lunch? I found the food very **(2)**____.

1. __satisfied__                  2. __satisfying__

David **(3)**____ that he lost his key. **(4)**____ guilt was the best thing to do in his case.

3. __admitted__                  4. __Admitting__

Did you see the eclipse as it was **(5)**____? Last time one **(6)**____, I missed it.

5. __occurring__                  6. __occurred__

The runners lined up for the **(7)**____ race. After that race, only three runners **(8)**____ for the team.

7. __qualifying__                  8. __qualified__

My lost cat has an **(9)**____ number tattooed on her skin. She was easily **(10)**____ as mine when she was found.

9. __identifying__                  10. __identified__

I have so much trouble **(11)**____ between piano or karate lessons. Have you **(12)**____ on a choice yet?

11. __deciding__                  12. __decided__

The coach used many **(13)**____ tactics, such as time-outs, during the game. Then the final quarter was **(14)**____ by the rain.

13. __delaying__                  14. __delayed__

The school closet was fully **(15)**____ with pencils. Do you think the school will be **(16)**____ pencils for the big test?

15. __supplied__                  16. __supplying__

Stop **(17)**____ that you broke the window! Even though you **(18)**____ it, we all saw your ball break the window.

17. __denying__                  18. __denied__

Are you **(19)**____ olives on your shopping list? I've **(20)**____ carrots, celery, and pickles on my list.

19. __including__                  20. __included__

**Home Activity** Your child wrote words with -ed and -ing endings. Select a list word and ask your child to tell you its meaning.

**Five-Column Chart**

|  |  |
|---|---|
|  |  |
|  |  |
|  |  |
|  |  |
|  |  |

Name_____

# Vocabulary • Antonyms

- An **antonym** is a word that means the opposite of another word.
- Words such as *unlike, but,* and *instead* may indicate the presence of antonyms.
- A **thesaurus**, a book that lists words and their antonyms and synonyms (words that mean the same thing), may help bring *clarity,* instead of *confusion,* to your writing and reading.

**Directions** Read the following passage about an athlete. Then circle the words in the list below that complete antonym pairs. Use a thesaurus to help you.

Although Pete was born without legs, he refused the idea that his disability should slow him down. Unlike people who accepted misfortune as an excuse to give up, Pete tried to live life to the fullest. It was true that his wheelchair sometimes made him feel confined at school. But on the weekends, his favorite sport, rock climbing, made him feel completely free.

Pete always used caution when fastening his ropes and caring for his equipment. Two hundred feet above the rocky bottom of a canyon was no place for recklessness! Starting at the base of a cliff, he would pull his way up to the pinnacle. After straining for hours, he would reach the top, exhausted. Pete didn't feel that school was boring, but it didn't match the exhilarating feeling that came from the physical and mental challenge of rock-climbing.

| | | | |
|---|---|---|---|
| **1. refused** | disability | excuse | (accepted) |
| **2. free** | (confined) | completely | favorite |
| **3. caution** | (recklessness) | rocky | caring |
| **4. base** | cliff | reach | (pinnacle) |
| **5. boring** | mental | feeling | (exhilarating) |

**School + Home**

**Home Activity** Your child read a short passage and identified antonyms, words that mean the opposite of each other. Have your child describe a familiar person, place, or thing using words and their antonyms, using a dictionary, glossary, or thesaurus for help.

## Newspaper/Newsletter

- A **newspaper** is a daily (or weekly) periodical that contains timely news and information on current events and issues. Daily newspapers use various text features in providing local, regional, national, and international news. Most newspapers organize information from most important to least important. There are three basic kinds of articles found in a newspaper: news stories, editorials (opinions pieces), and feature stories.
- A **newsletter** is a brief publication by a group or organization that contains news of interest to that group's members.

**Directions**  Read the newspaper page and answer the questions below.

# HOMETOWN NEWS

JULY 17, 2004                                                                    **Cloudy, 72°**

# BARR HITS FOR THE CYCLE–AGAIN

Hometown hero Billy Barr has been having the kind of week baseball players can only dream of. Last night, for the third game in a row, Barr hit for the cycle, which means he hit a single, a double, a triple, and a home run.

"I guess my grandfather was looking out for me tonight," said Barr after the game, referring to his grandfather Alan Barr, one of the first Negro League players to break into Major League baseball in the 1950s. Billy Barr frequently makes reference to his grandfather, who inspired his grandson to play baseball.

The last time a Major League player hit for the cycle in three consecutive games was in 1971, when Sal Bando did it for the Oakland Athletics.

1. Where do you find the date on a newspaper's front page?

   **It is at the top under the name of the newspaper.**

2. How does the headline give you a clue to what the article will be about?

   **It tells you who the article is about and what that person did.**

3. Most newspapers give the daily weather forecast somewhere on the front page. What is the forecast for this day?

   **Cloudy, 72 degrees**

4. Why does the writer mention the last time this event occurred at the very end of the article?

   **Mentioning the last occurrence shows how rarely it happens.**

5. Which of the three basic types of articles is this one?

   **This article is a news story.**

**Directions** Read the selection from the newsletter and answer the questions below.

---

# EVANSTON SOCCER NEEDS VOLUNTEERS

**Hello Evanston soccer families!**

The new season starts soon, and we're busy getting our teams and coaches organized and ready to play. As you can imagine, it's a lot of work. So once again we are asking for volunteers to help us out for the new season. We are an all-volunteer organization. In 2006 we won the Regional Youth Soccer Organization of the year award because of the great support our volunteers gave us. We want to make it two in a row for this year!

Volunteering only requires a few hours of your time each week. Currently, we need about forty parents to volunteer to be coaches, referees, and board members.

We know how busy everyone's lives are, but our organization can only succeed if everyone pitches in. We hope you'll consider volunteering this year!

---

**6.** To whom is this newsletter story directed?

**It's directed to parents of Evanston youth soccer players.**

**7.** Who do you think would receive a copy of this newsletter?

**Families and individuals involved in the Evanston soccer program would receive it.**

**8.** Name two things this newsletter specifically asks soccer parents to volunteer to do.

**Possible answer: coach or referee**

**9.** Based on this newsletter article, who runs this youth soccer organization?

**The organization is run by volunteers.**

**10.** If you wanted to find out about a big event happening in your city, where would you go to find out the information—a newspaper or a newsletter? Why?

**A newspaper would be better because they cover important events for a big audience. Newsletters are written for specific groups.**

© Pearson Education, Inc., 5

School + Home

**Home Activity** Your child answered questions about newspapers and newsletters. With your child, sketch out the front page of a newspaper based on your family's activities for the day.

# Adding *-ed, -ing*

**Proofread a Newspaper Article** This is an article from a local weekly newspaper. Circle six spelling errors. Write the sentence with a punctuation error correctly. Write the corrections on the lines below.

Three Caught After Holdup
by Rosy Redeye

The crime (ocurred) after midnight. The store's videotape (identifyed) three suspects. The store owner (supplyed) the license plate number to the police department. (Geting) the results took no time. The police quickly located the car and suspects (.) They had trouble (admiting) their wrongdoing. However, in front of the judge, they (deceided) to admit everything. The police were satisfied that they had solved the case.

1. **occurred**
2. **identified**
3. **supplied**
4. **Getting**
5. **admitting**
6. **decided**
7. **The police quickly located the car and suspects.**

**Spelling Words**

supplied
supplying
denied
denying
decided
deciding
included
including
admitted
admitting

occurred
occurring
qualified
qualifying
identified
identifying
delayed
delaying
satisfied
satisfying

**Frequently Misspelled Words**

getting
decided
stopped

**Proofread Words** Circle the correct spelling of the word.

8. occured      (occurred)      ocured
9. (included)    includid        includ
10. qualifed     qualifide       (qualified)
11. deceided     (decided)       decieded
12. satesfying   (satisfying)    satisfiying
13. (admitted)   admited         admetted
14. suppliing    sapplying       (supplying)

**School + Home**

**Home Activity** Your child identified misspelled list words. Select three list words and ask your child to spell them.

**82 Spelling** Adding *-ed, -ing*

# Compound and Complex Sentences

**Directions** Read the passage. Then read each question. Circle the letter of the correct answer.

# Just For Fun

(1) Every day Ted and I play catch, or we join our friends in a game. (2) We love the game, but we aren't the best players. (3) They say that if you practice every day, you will do better. (4) Today, our game was fun because the crowd cheered us on. (5) Although our team played well, we still lost. (6) Because we have fun, we don't mind an occasional loss. (7) We keep score, but we really play just for fun.

**1** In sentence 1, *Every day Ted and I play catch* is what?

   **A** Dependent clause

   **(B)** Independent clause

   **C** Compound sentence

   **D** Complex sentence

**2** In sentence 2, which word is a conjunction?

   **A** We

   **B** aren't

   **(C)** but

   **D** best

**3** Sentence 4 is which type of sentence?

   **A** Compound sentence

   **(B)** Complex sentence

   **C** Simple sentence

   **D** Exclamatory sentence

**4** What is the dependent clause in sentence 5?

   **A** our team lost

   **B** we still lost

   **C** our team played well

   **(D)** Although our team played well

**5** Sentence 7 is which type of sentence?

   **(A)** Compound sentence

   **B** Complex sentence

   **C** Simple sentence

   **D** Exclamatory sentence

© Pearson Education, Inc., 5

**School + Home** **Home Activity** Your child reviewed compound and complex sentences. Ask your child to explain how a game is played using some compound and complex sentences.

# Cause and Effect

- A **cause** is what makes something happen. An **effect** is what happens as a result of the cause.
- An effect may have more than one cause, and a cause may have more than one effect.

**Directions** Read the following passage and complete the diagram below.

Colonists came to America seeking opportunities unavailable to them in Europe. England viewed America as a source of revenue and raw materials for its growing economy. As the colonies flourished, laws were enacted forcing them to buy finished products from England rather than allow colonists to make and sell their own. Laws including new taxes on tea, textiles, and sugar, made colonists resent the meddling in their everyday lives, and they felt restrained. When they protested, the king sent troops to enforce the laws and keep order. In response, colonists formed their own government and signed the Declaration of Independence. The king didn't accept this call for self-government, and soon the American Revolution began.

## Possible answers given.

**Causes**

**Effects**

1. **Colonists wanted more opportunities.**

→ Colonists settled in America.

→ 2. **England enjoyed a new source of revenue.**

3. **Declaration of Independence signed.**

4. **The Revolutionary War started.**

The English didn't accept America's call for independence. →

5. Summarize the passage in one or two sentences.

**Unfair taxes by the English and the colonists' desire for freedom caused the American Revolutionary War.**

© Pearson Education, Inc., 5

**Home Activity** Your child read a short passage and identified causes and effects. Look up an event in the U.S. Revolutionary War and discuss causes and effects described in the selection.

# Writing • Expository Composition

**Key Features of an Expository Composition**

- tells about real people and events
- provides a description or explanation of something
- includes a topic sentence, a body, and a closing sentence

## Education for All

Since our country's beginning, leaders of the United States have wanted to provide education for all citizens. When our nation was newly formed, schools were run by private groups and religious organizations. Thomas Jefferson thought that a government-run educational system was a good idea. Other leaders agreed.

The idea was a good one, but it seemed to be an impossible task. Who would pay for the schools and teachers? How would schools deal with the large numbers of immigrants that were coming into the U.S.? It was a difficult and confusing time, both politically and economically. Schools continued to serve only those students from wealthy families who could afford an education.

It was not until the 1800s that the modern idea of public education began to take shape. Horace Mann, of Massachusetts, was one of the first to reform the American educational system. He supported a public school system that provided education for all children. He extended the school year and worked to train teachers.

Over the years, other people worked to provide equal education for all students. Catherine Beecher worked to provide more educational opportunities for women. Booker T. Washington worked to provide education for African Americans.

Although today's educational system still faces challenges, we have come a long way since the Declaration of Independence. Students of every kind come together in schools and have the opportunity to receive an education. The impossible challenge of education for all has been overcome.

1. Circle the introduction and conclusion.

2. Underline the main idea of each body paragraph.

# Vocabulary

**Directions** Choose the word from the box that best completes each sentence. Write the word on the line.

The wagon 1. **lurched**_____ forward, swaying and

almost throwing me out the back. My father and mother sat on the

driver's bench, 2. **surveying**_____ the foothills of the

Sierra Nevada Mountains below us. Like many immigrant families,

we traveled west over miles of dry, 3. **barren**_____ lands.

Everything we could take from our past, or

4. **previous**_____, life back in Boston was now in our

covered wagon. We were headed to California to try our luck

5. **prying**_____ gold from the earth to make our fortune.

**Check the Words You Know**

____barren
____deafening
____lurched
____previous
____prying
____surveying

**Directions** Circle the word that has the same or nearly the same meaning as the first word in each group.

6. prying          (extracting)        attempting          bragging

7. surveying       wondering          planning           (measuring)

8. lurched         fumbled           (staggered)          belched

9. deafening       (loud)             empty              dry

10. previous        sinister           related            (earlier)

## Journal Entry

On a separate piece of paper, write a journal entry as if you have just moved to another country. Use as many vocabulary words as you can.

**Journal entry should include words from the vocabulary list and details about what it would be like to move to another country.**

© Pearson Education, Inc., 5

**Home Activity** Your child identified and used vocabulary words from *Ten Mile Day*. Together with your child, read an article about life in another country. Talk with your child about what it might be like to live in that country.

Name _____

# Common, Proper, and Collective Nouns

The names of particular persons, places, and things are **proper nouns.** Capitalize the first word and each important word of a proper noun.

I like <u>Brady Parks</u> in the book by <u>Priscilla Cummings</u>.

All other nouns are **common nouns**. They are not capitalized.

That <u>author</u> has written several exciting <u>novels</u>.

Capitalize the first word and all important words in a title.

*Reflections on a Gift of Watermelon Pickle*

Capitalize days of the week and months of the year.

Saturday, October 14

Capitalize the first letter of an abbreviated proper noun. Abbreviations often occur in addresses, titles and initials in names, and names of days and months. Most abbreviations end with a period. In addresses, state names are abbreviated using two capital letters and no period.

The envelope went to Mr. L. Cho, 11 E. 3rd St., Rochester, MN 55901.
It was postmarked Mon., Nov. 6.

A **collective noun** names a group, such as *family* or *class*.

**Directions** Write the proper noun from the box that matches each common noun. Add capital letters where they are needed.

> sears tower      *my side of the mountain*
> argentina        president jefferson
> rebecca          "america the beautiful"

| **Common Noun** | **Proper Noun** |
|---|---|
| 1. girl | **Rebecca** |
| 2. president | **President Jefferson** |
| 3. country | **Argentina** |
| 4. book | ***My Side of the Mountain*** |
| 5. building | **Sears Tower** |
| 6. song | **"America the Beautiful"** |

© Pearson Education, Inc., 5

**Home Activity** Your child learned about common, proper, and collective nouns. Take a walk with your child. Have him or her pick out collective and proper nouns on signs and buildings in your community and practice speaking and writing them using proper capitalization.

**Conventions** Common, Proper, and Collective Nouns   **87**

# Contractions

| Spelling Words | | | | |
|---|---|---|---|---|
| they're | you've | weren't | needn't | there'd |
| they've | mustn't | what'll | doesn't | hadn't |
| could've | would've | should've | might've | wouldn't |
| who've | shouldn't | who'd | this'll | couldn't |

**Contractions** Write the contraction that can be made from the underlined words.

1. <u>They are</u> going on a school trip to the museum.

2. The students <u>need not</u> bring lunch because the museum has a cafeteria.

3. <u>This will</u> be an educational and fun trip.

4. Students <u>must not</u> bring umbrellas or backpacks.

5. Those <u>who have</u> taken the tour can go to the bookstore.

6. Those <u>who would</u> rather not go, please report to Room 303.

7. Students <u>should not</u> talk during the tour.

8. We <u>could not</u> hear the tour guide.

9. Anyone who <u>does not</u> behave will not be allowed to go on the next trip.

10. Students <u>would not</u> want to disappoint their teacher.

1. **They're**

2. **needn't**

3. **This'll**

4. **mustn't**

5. **who've**

6. **who'd**

7. **shouldn't**

8. **couldn't**

9. **doesn't**

10. **wouldn't**

**Questions** Write the contraction that completes each answer.

11. Do they have any ice cream at the stand? No, ____ sold out.

12. Would they have eaten popcorn instead? Yes, they ____.

13. Should I have thrown the ball? Yes, you ____.

14. Could I have handed in my project yesterday? Yes, you ____.

15. Had the students worn these coats before? No, they ____.

16. Would there be another party? Yes, ____ be another party at a later date.

17. Might they have joined in the fun? They ____, but they had to go home.

18. Do you know what will happen tomorrow? No one knows ____ happen tomorrow.

19. Were the boys at the game? No, they ____ there.

20. Do you have my book? No, ____ put it in your locker.

11. **they've**

12. **would've**

13. **should've**

14. **could've**

15. **hadn't**

16. **there'd**

17. **might've**

18. **what'll**

19. **weren't**

20. **you've**

© Pearson Education, Inc., 5

**Home Activity** Your child wrote contractions. Say two words and have your child combine them into a contraction and spell the word.

**88 Spelling** Contractions

**Web B**

# Vocabulary • Multiple-Meaning Words

- Some words have more than one meaning. They are called **multiple-meaning words.**
- **Context clues,** words and phrases near the multiple-meaning word, may help identify what a word means in a particular context, or situation.

**Directions** Read the following passage. Then answer the questions below.

> Many things surprised Svetlana when she arrived with her family in America. Mostly, she was surprised at how many cars were on the road. Plenty of people had cars in Bulgaria, of course, but everyone here seemed to enjoy being mobile all the time. The sidewalks were clean and wide, but people would refuse to use them, even on sunny days. She noticed her neighbors getting in their cars just to go a half mile instead of walking.
>
> In Bulgaria, when Svetlana needed to go somewhere a few miles away, she would usually ride her bicycle. Occasionally, she would ride the moped she shared with her whole family. It used little gas, and she could park it anywhere. To what did Svetlana attribute people's addictions to their automobiles? She supposed they believed owning a car was a sign of success. She took pride in the exercise she got walking and bicycling!

1. *Mobile* can mean "capable of motion" or "a hanging sculpture whose parts are moved by air currents." How do you think these two meanings are related to one another?

   **Both meanings are related to the idea of movement.**

2. *Refuse* can mean "indicate unwillingness" or "garbage." Which of these definitions is meant in the fourth sentence?

   **"Indicate unwillingness"; Her neighbors are unwilling to walk.**

3. *Moped* can mean "acted as if drained of energy by sadness" or "a small two-wheeled vehicle that has both an engine and pedals." Use a dictionary to find out how to pronounce *moped*. Which meaning uses two syllables?

   **"a small two-wheeled vehicle that has both an engine and pedals"**

4. *Attribute* can mean "characteristic, quality, or trait" or "explain by suggesting a source or cause." Which definition is meant in the second paragraph?

   **"Explain by suggesting a source or cause"; Svetlana is looking for a cause for Americans' dedication to their cars.**

**Home Activity** Your child identified words with multiple meanings in a fictional passage. With your child, make a list of words you often use that have different meanings.

# Electronic Encyclopedia

An **encyclopedia** gives general information about many different subjects. An electronic encyclopedia can be found on a CD-ROM or on the Internet. They often have interactive graphics and maps, as well as audio files. They are organized alphabetically by **entries,** which are the topics. You can locate topics by using **keyword searches.** Keyword searches give you a list of topics to choose from. Cross-referencing is represented by hotlinks, which are underlined words.

**Directions** Read the entry from an online encyclopedia and answer the questions below.

---

**Online Student Encyclopedia**                              🏠 **home**

**Keyword Search** [_____]

Print Article          E-Mail Article to Friend          Bookmark Article

**Ellis Island**
Ellis Island is located in New York Harbor. It was named after its owner in the 1770s, Samuel Ellis. Sixteen million immigrants to the United States passed through Ellis Island between 1892 and 1954. In 1965 the island became part of the Statue of Liberty National Monument. The immigration processing center is no longer used; however, it was made into a museum in 1990. The museum houses 400 years' worth of documents and artifacts about American immigration.

See also **Immigration**.

**Back to top**

---

## Possible answers given.

1. How would you search for information about Samuel Ellis in this online encyclopedia?

   **You would enter "Samuel Ellis" in the Keyword Search box at the top of the screen.**

2. Can you e-mail this article to a friend? Why do you think e-mailing an article would be useful?

   **Yes; It would be useful for doing research with a project team.**

3. Why do you think you would bookmark this page?

   **It would be helpful for doing future research on the subject.**

4. When was Ellis Island made into a museum?

   **Ellis Island became a museum in 1990.**

5. What is a simple way you could learn more about immigration?

   **You could click on the underlined words *See also Immigration.***

**Directions** Read the entry from an online encyclopedia and answer the questions below.

---

# Online Student Encyclopedia

🏠 **home**

**Keyword Search** [_____]

Print Article          E-Mail Article to Friend          Bookmark Article

## Ethnic Diversity

Most contemporary societies are, to some extent, ethnically diverse. History has played a part in making societies more diverse. Conquerors brought people from different societies to live under their rule. Sometimes people were brought to a new society as slaves. When they are not forced to move, people are often motivated to move to new societies to pursue economic improvement or to flee political and religious persecution. See also ethnicity, immigration.

*Assimilation* occurs when a newly arrived group takes on some (or all) of the customs and values of the dominant group. Assimilation can occur voluntarily or it can be forced by the dominant group.

**Back to top**

---

## Possible answers given.

**6.** This selection is part of a larger topic entitled *Ethnic Groups*. What keywords would you use if you wanted to learn about how the Irish moved to America?

__*Irish immigrant* or *Irish immigration* would be possible keywords.__

**7.** If you wanted to learn about people who moved to flee religious persecution, what words would you use in the keyword search?

__*Immigration* and *religious persecution* are possible keywords.__

**8.** How would you print this article?

__**Click on *Print Article* at the top of the screen.**__

**9.** According to the entry, what are three reasons people leave their native lands?

__**Economic, political, and religious freedom are three reasons**__
__**people may move.**__

**10.** What is the difference between a dictionary and an encyclopedia?

__**Dictionaries provide definitions to words; Encyclopedias provide**__
__**in-depth information about a topic.**__

**Home Activity** Your child answered questions about electronic encyclopedias. With your child, search an encyclopedia for information about your family's ancestors and their native land or lands.

# Contractions

**Proofread a Conversation** Jack wrote this conversation between a waiter and a diner. Circle six spelling errors and one punctuation error. Write the corrections on the lines.

"(Whatll) you have for lunch?" asked the waiter.

"I'm not sure," said the diner.

"Maybe this'll tempt you—lima bean casserole!" said the waiter.

"(Who'ud) eat that for lunch?" asked the diner.

"That's a very popular dish around here," said the waiter. "(Theyr'e) already lining up outside the door for the beans."

"You (were'nt) kidding about a long line," said the diner.

"(You mustn't miss this tasty treat," said the waiter.

"Okay, I wouldn't want to miss your special dish!" said the diner. "Hey, this (doesnt) taste too bad at all!"

"See what you would've been missing if you (had'nt) tried our special dish!" said the waiter.

1. **What'll**     2. **Who'd**

3. **They're**     4. **weren't**

5. **doesn't**     6. **hadn't**

7. **"You mustn't miss this tasty treat," said the waiter.**

**Proofread Words** Circle the correct spelling of the word.

8. wood've    woud've    (would've)

9. dosn't    (doesn't)    dosen't

10. (weren't)    wearn't    wheren't

11. coudn't    culdn't    (couldn't)

12. (might've)    mihgt've    mitgth've

13. whatll    whatl'l    (what'll)

14. (who'd)    who'ld    whod'd

**School + Home**

**Home Activity** Your child identified misspelled list words. Select contractions and ask your child to tell you how they were formed.

## Common, Proper, and Collective Nouns

**Directions** Read the passage. Then read each question. Circle the letter of the correct answer.

# The Railroad

(1) Grenville Dodge was the chief engineer of the Transcontinental Railroad.
(2) The book *the transcontinental railroad* tells how the railroad was built.
(3) The Union Pacific laid its first rails in july 1865. (4) Dr. Thomas c. Durant
ran that railroad. (5) Groups of workers were brought from China and Ireland.
(6) They began in Iowa and met the Central Pacific workers in Promontory, Utah.
(7) Hundreds of miles of these tracks remain today.

1  What change, if any, should be made in sentence 1?

  A  Change *chief engineer* to **Chief Engineer**

  B  Change the period to an exclamation mark

  C  Change *engineer* to **engineer,**

  (D)  Make no change

2  What change, if any, should be made in sentence 2?

  (A)  Change *the transcontinental railroad* to **The Transcontinental Railroad**

  B  Change *the book* to the **book,**

  C  Capitalize railroad

  D  Make no change

3  What is the collective noun in sentence 5?

  (A)  Groups

  B  brought

  C  China

  D  Ireland

4  What change, if any, should be made in sentence 3?

  A  Change *Union Pacific* to **union pacific**

  (B)  Change *july* to **July**

  C  Change *its* to **it's**

  D  Make no change

5  What change, if any, should be made in sentence 4?

  A  Change the period to a question mark

  B  Change *Dr. Thomas c. Durant* to a collective noun

  (C)  Change *Dr. Thomas c. Durant* to **Dr. Thomas C. Durant**

  D  Make no change

Write your own sentences about railroads using common, proper, and collective nouns. Read the sentences aloud.

**Home Activity** Your child prepared for taking tests on common, proper, and collective nouns. Have your child read an interesting magazine or newspaper article. He or she can circle the proper nouns, underline the common nouns, and put a box around collective nouns.

# Short Vowel VCCV, VCV

| Spelling Words | | | | |
|---|---|---|---|---|
| distance | method | anger | problem | butter |
| petals | enjoy | perhaps | figure | channel |
| admire | comedy | husband | tissue | mustard |
| shuttle | advance | drummer | regular | denim |

**Alphabetize** Write the twelve list words below in alphabetical order.

| | |
|---|---|
| method | comedy |
| denim | anger |
| distance | enjoy |
| perhaps | advance |
| admire | figure |
| channel | regular |

1. __admire__
2. __advance__
3. __anger__
4. __channel__
5. __comedy__
6. __denim__

7. __distance__
8. __enjoy__
9. __figure__
10. __method__
11. __perhaps__
12. __regular__

**Hidden Words** Each of these small words can be found inside one of the list words. Write the list word that contains the small word.

13. sue __tissue__
14. rob __problem__
15. drum __drummer__
16. pet __petals__

17. ban __husband__
18. shut __shuttle__
19. but __butter__
20. tar __mustard__

© Pearson Education, Inc., 5

**School + Home**

**Home Activity** Your child learned to spell longer words with short vowel sounds. Find words with short vowel sounds in a magazine or newspaper and ask your child to spell them.

# Four Kinds of Sentences

**Directions** Write *D* if the sentence is declarative. Write *IN* if the sentence is interrogative. Write *IM* if the sentence is imperative. Write *E* if the sentence is exclamatory.

1. Keesha's family took a kayak trip in Alaska. ___**D**___

2. How do you make a kayak go? ___**IN**___

3. A kayaker uses a long paddle. ___**D**___

4. Please find out who invented kayaks. ___**IM**___

5. Eskimos used kayaks thousands of years ago. ___**D**___

6. Eskimo kayaks were made of sealskins. ___**D**___

7. A kayak weighs as little as 32 pounds. ___**D**___

8. Wow, that is really light! ___**E**___

9. Can you ride a kayak in rapids? ___**IN**___

10. Kayaking is so much fun! ___**E**___

**Directions** Complete each sentence with words from the box. Then write *D, IN, IM,* or *E* to identify the kind of sentence.

> can participate in races.   kayaking can be dangerous?
> include kayak races.   me how to kayak.
> exciting the rapids are!

11. Don't you think **kayaking can be dangerous?** ___**IN**___

12. Good kayakers **can participate in races.** ___**D**___

13. How **exciting the rapids are!** ___**E**___

14. Please teach **me how to kayak.** ___**IM**___

15. The Olympic Games **include kayak races.** ___**D**___

# Long Vowel VCV

| Spelling Words | | | | |
|---|---|---|---|---|
| fever | broken | climate | hotel | basic |
| vocal | native | silent | labor | spider |
| label | icon | agent | motive | vital |
| acorn | item | aroma | ego | solo |

**Analogies** Write the word that completes each comparison.

1. Mouth is to taste as nose is to **aroma** .
2. Loud is to deafening as quiet is to **silent** .
3. Cold is to chill as hot is to **fever** .
4. Robin is to bird as black widow is to **spider** .
5. Two is to duet as one is to **solo** .
6. Cottage is to house as inn is to **hotel** .
7. Vine is to grape as oak tree is to **acorn** .
8. Smart is to intelligent as self-esteem is to **ego** .
9. Friend is to enemy as stranger is to **native** .
10. Sleep is to rest as work is to **labor** .

**Word Clues** Write the list word that fits each clue.

11. This includes a place's temperatures and rainfall.     **climate**
12. You'll find one of these sewn into a piece of clothing.     **label**
13. You can't use something described as this.     **broken**
14. An actor or athlete might employ this person.     **agent**
15. A person who speaks up is described this way.     **vocal**
16. This explains why you did something.     **motive**
17. This describes something that is absolutely necessary.     **vital**
18. You can click on one of these on a Web site.     **icon**
19. This is another word for a thingamajig.     **item**
20. This describes something that is not advanced.     **basic**

**Home Activity** Your child learned to spell longer words with long vowel sounds. To practice at home, make up clues about words with long vowel sounds and ask your child to spell them.

# Subjects and Predicates

**Directions** Draw a line between the complete subject and the complete predicate in each sentence. Circle the simple subject and the simple predicate.

1. Many useful (tools) (are made) from metal.

2. (Steel) (is) an important metal for buildings and tools.

3. This (alloy) (contains) a mixture of iron and carbon.

4. An iron (bar) (will rust) over time.

5. (Oxygen) from the air (mixes) with the metal.

6. That orange (deposit) on the outside surface (is called) rust.

**tools/are**
**Steel/is**
**alloy/contains**
**bar/will**
**air/mixes**
**surface/is**

**Directions** Underline each simple subject once. Underline each simple predicate twice.

7. Many <u>ranchers</u> <u><u>mend</u></u> fences regularly.

8. The shiny thin <u>wires</u> <u><u>are stretched</u></u> from post to post.

9. <u>Someone</u> <u><u>hammers</u></u> the wire to the post.

10. The wooden <u>posts</u> <u><u>stretch</u></u> in a straight line.

11. This <u>job</u> <u><u>is</u></u> certainly hard work.

12. A work <u>crew</u> <u><u>will repair</u></u> the old fence today.

**Directions** Write *F* after a fragment. Write *R* after a run-on. Write *S* after a complete sentence.

13. Has been replaced by plastic in many products. ___**F**___

14. Plastic is hard and durable at the same time, it is lighter than metal. ___**R**___

15. Many parts of today's trucks and automobiles. ___**F**___

16. Plastic is not only lighter than metal it is cheaper too. ___**R**___

17. Just think about all the uses for plastic! ___**S**___

18. Many new materials from recycled products. ___**F**___

Name _____

# Long Vowel Digraphs

| Spelling Words | | | | |
|---|---|---|---|---|
| coast | feast | speech | wheat | Spain |
| paint | arrow | needle | charcoal | praise |
| faint | maintain | crease | grain | breeze |
| willow | appeal | bowling | complain | sneeze |

**Word Search** Circle ten hidden list words. Words are down, across, and diagonal.
Write the words on the lines.

```
F  B  W  S  P  P  A  D  E  Y
N  J  O  I  C  F  A  I  N  T
A  L  A  W  E  R  B  I  P  O
G  Q  W  I  L  L  O  W  N  M
R  T  U  A  E  I  S  U  G  T
A  E  S  P  A  I  N  N  W  Y
I  B  N  P  S  E  G  F  T
N  W  H  E  A  T  E  N  O  P
E  K  S  A  I  k  Z  E  N  l
H  E  E  L  C  R  E  A  S  E
```

1. **bowling**
2. **paint**
3. **faint**
4. **willow**
5. **Spain**
6. **wheat**
7. **crease**
8. **grain**
9. **appeal**
10. **sneeze**

**Scramble** Unscramble the list words and write them on the lines.

11. elende    **needle**
12. worar    **arrow**
13. sarpie    **praise**
14. zerbee    **breeze**
15. ascto    **coast**
16. timinana    **maintain**
17. shepec    **speech**
18. larhocca    **charcoal**
19. stafe    **feast**
20. aclimpon    **complain**

© Pearson Education, Inc., 5

**Home Activity** Your child learned to spell words with long vowel digraphs. Ask your child to give examples of and spell words with *ea*, *ee*, *ai*, *oa*, and *ow*.

Name _____

# Independent and Dependent Clauses

**Direction** Write *I* if the underlined group of words is an independent clause.
Write *D* if it is a dependent clause.

1. We visited the seashore when we went to California. ____**I**____

2. After we walked on the beach, we swam in the ocean. ____**D**____

3. Although the sun was warm, I shivered with cold. ____**I**____

4. The water seemed even colder because our skin was hot. ____**D**____

5. If you look far out, you can see dolphins swimming. ____**D**____

6. They leap out of the water as if they are playing. ____**I**____

7. While I was resting on the sand, I spied something. ____**I**____

8. When I looked through binoculars, I saw seals. ____**D**____

9. As I watched, some of them slid into the water. ____**I**____

10. Since I saw them, I have read more about seals. ____**D**____

**Directions** Complete each sentence by adding a clause from the box. Underline the dependent clause in each sentence.

> it is the exception to the rule        while a seal has none        it can weigh up to 8,800 pounds
> because walruses are usually much bigger        you will remember it

11. You can tell a walrus and a seal apart **because walruses are usually much bigger.**

12. In addition, a walrus has two large ivory tusks **while a seal has none.**

13. Because an elephant seal can grow very large, **it is the exception to the rule.**

14. If you run into an elephant seal, **you will remember it.**

15. When a male elephant seal is full grown, **it can weigh up to 8,800 pounds.**

# Adding -ed, -ing

| Spelling Words | | | | |
|---|---|---|---|---|
| supplied | supplying | denied | denying | decided |
| deciding | included | including | admitted | admitting |
| occurred | occurring | qualified | qualifying | identified |
| identifying | delayed | delaying | satisfied | satisfying |

**Antonyms** Write the list word ending in -ed that has the opposite or nearly the opposite meaning.

1. unhappy **satisfied**
2. on time **delayed**
3. denied **admitted**
4. excluded **included**
5. unsure **decided**

**Synonyms** Write the list word ending in -ed that has the same or nearly the same meaning.

6. happened **occurred**
7. named **identified**
8. furnished **supplied**
9. confessed **admitted**
10. able; competent **qualified**

**Word Clues** Write the list word that fits each clue.

11. what a lawbreaker is doing to avoid getting in trouble **denying**
12. what an athlete is doing in a regional track meet **qualifying**
13. what trucks full of food are doing at the supermarket **supplying**
14. what a jury is doing after a trial **deciding**
15. what an event is doing while it is underway **occurring**
16. what a detective is attempting by looking at fingerprints **identifying**
17. what a school is doing when it lets students in **admitting**
18. what an airline is doing to passengers when running late **delaying**
19. what a delicious meal is doing for your hunger **satisfying**
20. what you are doing when you put everything in **including**

© Pearson Education, Inc., 5

 **School + Home** **Home Activity** Your child learned to spell words with -ed and -ing. To practice at home, name three verbs that describe after-school activities. Ask your child to spell each word with an -ed ending and with an -ing ending.

# Compound and Complex Sentences

**Directions** Write *compound* if the sentence is a compound sentence. Write *complex* if the sentence is a complex sentence.

1. Great athletes seem superhuman, but they often begin humbly. **compound**

2. After they learned the basics, they practiced hard. **complex**

3. If they had failures, they did not give up. **complex**

4. They kept at it for years, and they steadily improved. **compound**

**Directions** Combine each pair of simple sentences using the conjunction in ( ). Write the compound sentence on the line.

5. I like swimming. My dad coaches track. (but)

**I like swimming, but my dad coaches track.**

6. I can jump like a rabbit. I can run like a racehorse. (and)

**I can jump like a rabbit, and I can run like a racehorse.**

7. I could choose one sport. I could do both. (or)

**I could choose one sport, or I could do both.**

8. According to Mom, I should decide. She is usually right. (and)

**According to Mom, I should decide, and she is usually right.**

**Directions** Write the word in ( ) that best connects the clauses. Underline the dependent clause in the complex sentence.

9. The players are tired **because** they have played two games. (because, if)

10. **After** they finish their games, they sleep on the bus. (Although, After)

11. They may travel for hours **before** they reach the next town. (before, since)

12. The driver will not wake them **until** the bus gets to the hotel. (after, until)

© Pearson Education, Inc., 5

# Contractions

| Spelling Words | | | | |
|---|---|---|---|---|
| they're | you've | weren't | needn't | there'd |
| they've | mustn't | what'll | doesn't | hadn't |
| could've | would've | should've | might've | wouldn't |
| who've | shouldn't | who'd | this'll | couldn't |

**Words in Context** Complete each sentence with a list word.

1. The students want to raise money, so **they're** selling fruit.

2. James had been to big cities, but he **hadn't** ever been to Chicago.

3. I had never met anyone **who'd** been to Africa.

4. The electricity is out, so **what'll** we do about dinner?

5. We have practiced for weeks, so **this'll** be the best school play ever.

6. We'll go to the zoo after lunch since it **doesn't** open until noon on Monday.

7. Several players **weren't** at the first soccer practice.

8. If there were a big storm, **there'd** be many people without food and water.

9. You may help chop vegetables, but you **mustn't** cut yourself.

10. It's raining; I knew I **should've** brought my umbrella.

11. I just realized I **might've** left my spelling book at home.

12. You need to bring a pillow to camp, but you **needn't** bring a sleeping bag.

13. **Wouldn't** you like to go swimming?

14. Sophia tried, but she **couldn't** open the jar.

15. The Scotts aren't home; **they've** gone to Florida for two weeks.

16. It may rain Saturday, but it **shouldn't** affect our plans.

17. Put the dressing on the salad after **you've** mixed it well.

18. If I **could've** found my cap, I would've worn it to the game.

19. I admire people **who've** climbed high mountains.

20. Our team **would've** won the game if we'd gotten one more goal.

**Home Activity** Your child learned to spell contractions. Ask your child to give examples of and spell contractions formed with the words *are, not, have,* and *will.*

# Common, Proper, and Collective Nouns

**Directions** Write the proper noun from the box that matches each common noun. Add capital letters where they are needed.

> empire state building     mount everest     aunt lucinda
> *the dark is rising*     ms. simpson

| Common Noun | Proper Noun |
|---|---|
| **1.** teacher | Ms. Simpson |
| **2.** building | Empire State Building |
| **3.** mountain | Mount Everest |
| **4.** book | The Dark Is Rising |
| **5.** relative | Aunt Lucinda |

**Directions** Rewrite each sentence. Capitalize all proper nouns.

**6.** Americans in new york had good train service.

Americans in New York had good train service.

**7.** People in san francisco and other parts of california needed better transportation.

People in San Francisco and other parts of California needed better transportation.

**8.** A group of workers from china was led by mr. charles crocker.

A group of workers from China was led by Mr. Charles Crocker.

**9.** The eastern and western tracks were joined in promontory, utah, on may 10, 1869.

The eastern and western tracks were joined in Promontory, Utah, on May 10, 1869.

**10.** The tracks met near aunt joan's house: 491 e. 1st st., ogden, ut 84404.

The tracks met near Aunt Joan's house: 491 E. 1st St., Ogden, UT 84404.

# Notes for a Personal Narrative

**Directions** Fill in the graphic organizer with information about the event or experience that you plan to write about.

## Summary

What happened? _____ **Answers should include details**

When? _____ **about each part of student's**

Where? _____ **personal narrative.**

Who was there? _____

## Details

**Beginning**

**Middle**

**End**

# Words That Tell About *You*

**Directions** How did you feel about the challenge facing you at the beginning, middle, and end of your experience? Choose one or two words from the word bank to describe each part of your experience. Then add details that *show* readers each feeling.

| | | | |
|---|---|---|---|
| anxious | thrilled | proud | inspired |
| disappointed | excited | contented | determined |
| dismayed | fearful | delighted | upset |

**Beginning** **Answers should be based on adjectives from the word bank and expand with details that show the feelings the adjectives suggest.**

_____

_____

_____

**Middle** _____

_____

_____

_____

_____

**End** _____

_____

_____

_____

_____

# Combining Sentences

You can improve your writing by combining short simple sentences to make compound or complex sentences. This will create a smoother flow of ideas in your writing. The two sentences you combine must make sense together. You can create compound sentences by combining short sentences using the words *and*, *but*, or *or*. You can create complex sentences by combining short sentences with *if*, *because*, *before*, *after*, *since*, or *when*.

**Directions** Use the word in ( ) to combine the two sentences. Remember to capitalize the first word of the new sentence and to replace the first period with a comma.

1. (but) My big sister could climb the pine tree in the pasture. I had not tried.

   **My big sister could climb the pine tree in the pasture, but I had not tried.**

2. (because) The first limbs were so high. I thought it was too hard.

   **Because the first limbs were so high, I thought it was too hard.**

3. (when) She boosted me up. I could just reach the lowest limb.

   **When she boosted me up, I could just reach the lowest limb.**

4. (and) The rough bark scratched my skin. Sticky pine resin oozed onto my hands.

   **The rough bark scratched my skin, and sticky pine resin oozed onto my hands.**

5. (but) I was scared. I climbed to the very top of that pine.

   **I was scared, but I climbed to the very top of that pine.**

# Editing 1

**Directions** Edit these sentences. Look for errors in spelling, grammar, and mechanics. Use proofreading marks to show the corrections.

| Proofreading Marks | |
|---|---|
| Delete (Take out) | ⸺ |
| Add | ∧ |
| Spelling | ⬭ |
| Uppercase letter | ≡ |
| Lowercase letter | / |

1. A person who is born deaf **generally** ~~generaly~~ does not speak, but ~~they have~~ **he or she has** ∧ ways to communicate.

2. Like many deaf people, I use sign language, which includes hand signs, **gestures** ~~jestures~~, facial expressions∧ and body movements.

3. Did you know the first school for the deaf was started in Hartford, **C** connecticut, in 1817 **?**

4. Laurent Clerc∧ a founder of the school∧ ~~who~~ knew a **F** french form of sign language.

5. Users added to and adapted Clerc's sign language **until** ~~untill~~ it **became** ~~becom~~∧ the sign language that we use today.

6. Hearing parents often learn sign language⊙ **T** ~~they~~ **teach** ~~taught~~ it to their deaf children.

7. I tell everyone that time and effort **are** ~~is~~ **necessary** ~~neccesary~~ to learn sign language.

8. Sign language helps people who can**'**t **hear** ~~here~~ deal with communication challenges.

Now you'll edit the draft of your personal narrative. Then you'll use your revised and edited draft to make a final copy of your narrative. Finally, you'll share your written work with your audience.

# Compare and Contrast

- To **compare** and **contrast** two or more things is to show how things are alike and different.
- Some clue words are: *as, like, but,* and *however.*
- Sometimes writers do not use clue words when they compare and contrast things.

**Directions**  Read the following passage. Fill in the columns below based on Alex's observations about the differences between the ocean and the lake back home.

Alex had never been to the ocean before, so he was excited when Joel invited him to go with Joel's family to Rhode Island. As they walked across the sand, Joel asked Alex if he knew anything about a "riptide," a strong flow of water near the shore. Afraid to admit he knew nothing about the sea, Alex told Joel he knew all about riptides. As he swam, Alex noticed several differences between lakes and oceans.  Both were cold. Salty ocean water, however, seemed to allow him to float more easily. Ocean waves were also much larger than freshwater ones.

In the lake Alex remembered that small fish swam around his feet. In the ocean, crabs crawled over them. Suddenly, Alex and Joel heard a whistle blow. A lifeguard was ordering swimmers out of the water. Alex heard the lifeguard explain to a man that the riptides had become too strong and had pulled a young girl hundreds of feet from shore. She had almost drowned. Alex gulped. He knew he had put himself in danger by not being honest about his ignorance.

| Lake | Ocean |
|------|-------|
| fresh water | 1. **salt water** |
| 2. **fish** | 3. **crabs** |
| 4. **small waves** | 5. **large waves** |

© Pearson Education, Inc., 5

**School + Home**  **Home Activity** Your child compared and contrasted details from a short passage. Discuss with your child two places that you have gone for enjoyment. Ask your child to make a list of the similarities and differences.

# Writing · Description

**Key Features of a Description**

- vivid language helps readers visualize a scene

- can be part of a longer story

- often provides details that tell what something smelled, felt, or tasted like, as well as how something looked or sounded

## Remembering Grandpa

When my grandfather died, I learned that I could keep his memory alive through objects he left behind. I went to his house after the funeral and looked through the shelves and closets. They were filled with items from my past.

His coat still smelled like his cologne. I felt the soft material and inhaled the musky, sweet scent. I looked through stacks of photographs to remember his smile. We used to drink root beer together, so I looked in the refrigerator. He still had root beer! I took one and carried it around with me. It tasted so good. It made me happy to remember sharing root beer with Grandpa.

It started to rain outside. As I listened to the sound of the soft rain and my parents talking in the living room, I realized that Grandpa can still be alive in my heart. I can be sad and happy at the same time. I took his coat and some photographs home with me. When I wear his coat, I remember him with pride.

1. List three sensory words from the selection.

**soft; musky; sweet**

2. What is the writer like? How do you know?

**The writer seems to be a positive person. The writer is remembering all the good times instead of focusing on Grandpa's death.**

# Vocabulary

**Directions** Choose the word from the box that best matches each definition. Write the word on the line.

<u>**tweezers**</u>_____ 1. handheld, usually small tool used for pinching or grasping

<u>**concealed**</u>_____ 2. put out of sight; hidden

<u>**sternly**</u>_____ 3. harsh, firm, or strict

<u>**driftwood**</u>_____ 4. wood floating in a body of water or washed upon the shore of one

<u>**algae**</u>_____ 5. any of a group of aquatic organisms ranging in size from microscopic to hundreds of feet

> **Check the Words You Know**
>
> ___algae
> ___concealed
> ___driftwood
> ___hammocks
> ___lamented
> ___sea urchins
> ___sternly
> ___tweezers

**Directions** Choose the word from the box that best completes each sentence. Write the word on the line to the left of the sentence.

**sea urchins**_____ 6. The underwater divers harvested dozens of the spiny _____ at the ocean floor to sell to a local restaurant featuring Japanese specialties.

**hammocks**_____ 7. The brother and sister swung lazily in _____, side by side under a tree, discussing how to spend the last summer day before school started.

**concealed**_____ 8. He hid, or _____, his glee at winning the match, trying at least to appear to have a sense of good sportsmanship.

**sternly**_____ 9. The puppy's ears drooped and her tail stopped wagging as I _____ lectured her about not chewing on the furniture.

**lamented**_____ 10. The pop music star _____, or complained about, the loss of his youth and fame, sadly wondering if another fan letter would ever arrive in the mail.

## Write a Description

On a separate sheet of paper, write a description of what life might be like as a dolphin, living in the ocean. Use as many of the vocabulary words as you can.

**Home Activity** Your child identified and used vocabulary words from *At the Beach*. With your child, write a story about making the choice to be honest with someone.

# Regular and Irregular Plural Nouns

**Plural nouns** name more than one person, animal, place, or thing.

- Add -*s* to form the plural of most nouns.
  swing/swings    animal/animals
- Add -*es* to nouns ending in *ch, sh, x, z, s,* and *ss*.
  fox/foxes    bush/bushes    church/churches
- If a noun ends in a vowel and *y*, add -*s*.
  monkey/monkeys    toy/toys
- If a noun ends in a consonant and *y*, change *y* to *i* and add -*es*.
  blueberry/blueberries    pony/ponies    penny/pennies
- Some nouns have **irregular plural** forms. They change spelling.
  woman/women    tooth/teeth    ox/oxen
- For most nouns that end in *f* or *fe*, change *f* to *v* and add -*es*.
  wife/wives    wolf/wolves    thief/thieves
- Some nouns have the same singular and plural forms.
  salmon    trout    sheep

**Directions** Underline the plural nouns in each sentence.

1. Some <u>seals</u> live on those <u>beaches</u>.

2. The <u>fishermen</u> in <u>boats</u> near shore caught many <u>salmon</u>.

3. You will see <u>crabs</u>, <u>shells</u>, and <u>driftwood</u> near the water.

4. Don't burn your <u>feet</u> on the hot sand.

5. <u>Clumps</u> of seaweed float on the <u>waves</u>.

**Directions** Cross out each incorrectly spelled plural noun. Write the correct spelling above the word you crossed out.

6. You can find ~~blueberrys~~ **blueberries** on the ~~bushs~~ **bushes** near those beaches.

7. The ~~skys~~ **skies** over the shore were clear, but we saw ~~cloudes~~ **clouds** in the distance.

8. The four ~~woman~~ **women** prepared the picnic, and the children played with beach ~~toys~~ **toys**.

 **School + Home** **Home Activity** Your child learned about regular and irregular plural nouns. Take a walk and have your child identify people, places, animals, and things in groups. Ask him or her to spell these plural nouns correctly.

# Digraphs *th*, *sh*, *ch*, *ph*

| Spelling Words | | | | |
|---|---|---|---|---|
| shovel | southern | northern | chapter | hyphen |
| chosen | establish | although | challenge | approach |
| astonish | python | shatter | ethnic | shiver |
| pharmacy | charity | china | attach | ostrich |

**Word Meanings** Write the list word that has the same or nearly the meaning as the underlined words.

1. We are raising money for a <u>worthy cause</u>.

2. The <u>drugstore</u> filled the prescription for the medicine.

3. The United States is made up of many people from different <u>cultural</u> groups.

4. The restaurant chain wants to <u>set up</u> a diner in the community.

5. We set the table with our best <u>glass dishes</u>.

6. The best way to succeed is to constantly <u>test</u> yourself.

7. The cool breeze sent a <u>quiver</u> down my back.

8. I never would have <u>selected</u> those blue jackets.

9. The plane was on its final <u>move</u> toward the runway.

10. The magic trick was crafted to <u>amaze</u> the unsuspecting audience.

1. __charity__
2. __pharmacy__
3. __ethnic__
4. __establish__
5. __china__
6. __challenge__
7. __shiver__
8. __chosen__
9. __approach__
10. __astonish__

**Classifying** Write the list word that belongs in each group.

11. even if, while, ___

12. cobra, rattler, ___

13. fasten, join, ___

14. spade, scoop, ___

15. episode, part, ___

16. smash, break, ___

17. peacock, swan, ___

18. dash, line, ___

11. __although__
12. __python__
13. __attach__
14. __shovel__
15. __chapter__
16. __shatter__
17. __ostrich__
18. __hyphen__

© Pearson Education, Inc., 5

**Home Activity** Your child matched list words with synonyms. Name two list words and see if your child can give a synonym for each.

Web A

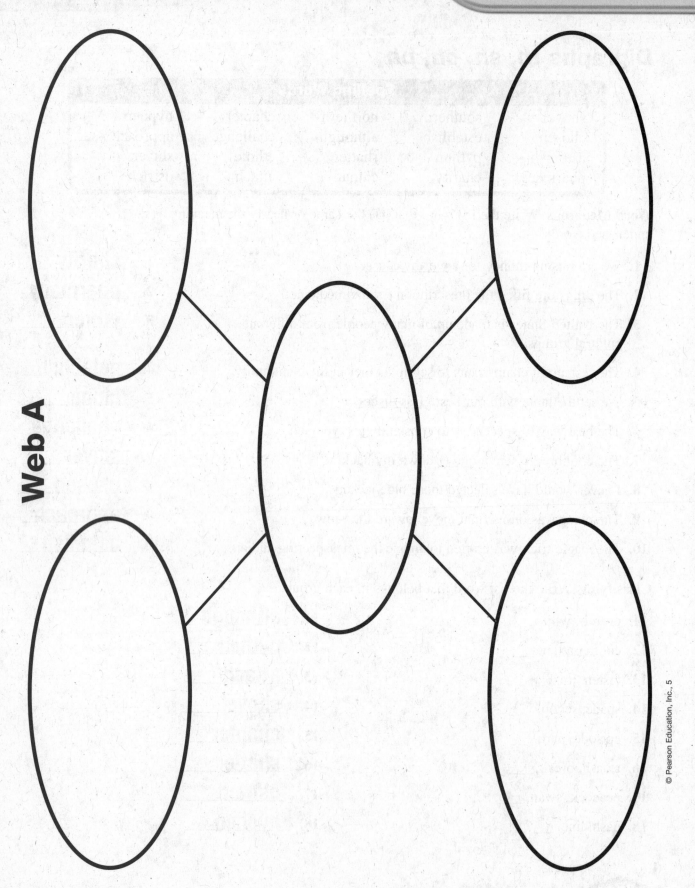

# Vocabulary • Unfamiliar Words

- **Dictionaries** provide alphabetical lists of words and their meanings.
- Sometimes looking at the words around an unfamiliar word can't help you figure out the word's meaning. If this happens, use a dictionary to find the meaning.

**Directions** Read the following passage. Look for unfamiliar words and nearby clues as to their meaning. Use a dictionary to look up words you do not know. Then answer the questions below.

The smell of brine was heavy in the air as Dr. Jansen dipped the glass vial into the brackish water of the salt marsh. She was collecting the samples from the grassy place by the shoreline to test for pollution. Many species of animals depended on the ecosystem of the marsh to remain healthy.

She held up the last vial and peered through the grass as she screwed the plastic cap on the top. She smiled, knowing that even though the water seemed to be absent of life, tiny organisms swam through the cloudy, muddy water. Glancing out over the waves in the distance, Dr. Jansen smiled. The seagulls whirling above the sand, swooping and diving in circles, always seemed to act as if there might be bread crumbs in Dr. Jansen's laboratory bag.

## Possible answers given.

1. Smell can travel a long way in the air. What does *brine* smell like? How do you know?

   **Salt, the ocean; The words salt, marsh, and shoreline are near "brine."**

2. Find a word in the passage whose meaning cannot be guessed by context clues nearby. Look up the word in a dictionary and provide the definition.

   **"brackish"; having a slightly salty taste or scent**

3. What might the word *vial* mean, based on the context clues in the paragraph? Use a dictionary to check your answer.

   **A vial might be some type of small glass container.**

4. What might the word *whirling* mean, based on the context clues in the paragraph? Use a dictionary to check your answer.

   **"Whirling" might mean "to move or spin quickly in a circle"**

5. The word *organism* is not easily guessed by context clues in the passage. Look the word up in a dictionary and provide its definition.

   **any life form, such as a plant or animal**

**Home Activity** Your child identified unfamiliar words that could be defined using a dictionary or glossary. Work with your child to identify unfamiliar words in a newspaper or magazine article. Ask your child if he or she needs to use a dictionary to find the meaning of the words. If so, ask your child to look up at least one definition in a dictionary or glossary.

# Reference Book

A **reference book** is a type of **manual.** Manuals usually contain instructions, either for immediate use or for reference. A grammar reference book is a manual for using language. Like other manuals, it usually has a table of contents, an index, sections, illustrations, and explanations. Be sure to consult a grammar reference book whenever you have questions about grammar.

**Directions** Use the following chart from a grammar book to answer the questions below.

---

**Quick Reference Chart for Using Apostrophes**

Use an apostrophe

1. to show possession

   *John's dad collects bottle caps.*

2. with *s* to show the plural of letters

   *b's      j's      t's*

3. to show the omission of a letter, letters, or numbers

   *We'll      class of '05      won't*

Study the following contractions and notice the letter or letters that have been omitted to form the contraction.

| | |
|---|---|
| *they're — they are* | *she'll — she will* |
| *we've — we have* | *let's — let us* |
| *o'clock — of the clock* | *aren't — are not* |

---

1. What is the title of the chart?

   **Quick Reference Chart for Using Apostrophes**

2. Which of the ways the apostrophe is used would apply if you were describing ownership of something?

   **The apostrophe in that case shows possession.**

3. How would you use an apostrophe to contract the words *must* and *not*?

   **mustn't**

4. How many different uses does the chart show for an apostrophe?

   **three**

5. Insert apostrophes where needed in the following sentence: *Ill take my moms casserole over to the neighbors house at 6 oclock.*

   **I'll take my mom's casserole over to the neighbor's house at 6 o'clock.**

**Directions** Use the following table of contents from a grammar book to answer the questions below.

## Possible answers given for 7, 8, 10.

**6.** Which chapter would you look in for a usage question about the word *theirs*?

## Chapter 3

**7.** Why do you think grammar books are organized by individual parts of speech?

## Organizing them by individual parts of speech helps make them easier to use and makes the content easier to absorb.

**8.** What kind of words might you find in the section on "Personal Pronouns"?

## I, me, mine, you, yours

**9.** If you were having trouble writing a word that showed ownership, in which section of the grammar book would you look?

## Possessive Forms of Nouns

**10.** Why might the short essays at the end of each chapter be included in a grammar book?

## The essays may provide helpful tips on how to use particular parts of the language.

**Home Activity** Your child answered questions about grammar reference books and manuals. With your child, find a manual to an item in your house (computer, refrigerator, television, phone, etc.) and read through the table of contents to see how it is organized. Does it make sense? Could you easily find an answer to a question or a problem by using the manual?

# Digraphs *th, sh, ch, ph*

**Proofread a Poster** Circle five spelling errors. Find one sentence with a punctuation error. Write the corrections on the lines.

Come to the (charaty) auction for the
new recreation center.

Help dig the building site. Buy a chance to
(shovle) some earth.

Bid on and buy ‸a wonderful prizes from around the world!

(Challange) yourself in contests and games.

Bid on lovely china figures and platters.

Sample delicious (northurn) and southern cooking!

Time: Saturday, from 9 A.M. to 6 P.M.

Place: The old (pharmecy) building

shovel
southern
northern
chapter
hyphen
chosen
establish
although
challenge
approach

astonish
python
shatter
ethnic
shiver
pharmacy
charity
china
attach
ostrich

1. **charity**
2. **shovel**
3. **Challenge**
4. **northern**
5. **pharmacy**
6. **Bid on and buy wonderful prizes from around the world!**

**Proofread Words** Circle the correct spelling of the word.

7. The ending of the book will ____ you.
   (astonish)   astonesh   astonash

8. I need a stapler to ____ the poster to the bulletin board.
   attatch   (attach)   atach

9. Music is my ____ field of study.
   (chosen)   chozen   choicen

10. I want to read a ____ a day.
    chaptar   shapter   (chapter)

11. Numbers, such as sixty-five, are written with a ____.
    hiphen   (hyphen)   hipfen

12. The ____ in the zoo was 12 feet long.
    pythn   (python)   pithon

**Frequently Misspelled Words**

which
they
thought

© Pearson Education, Inc., 5

**Home Activity** Your child identified misspelled list words. Select words with two different digraph sounds and ask your child to spell them.

Name _____

# Regular and Irregular Plural Nouns

**Directions** Read the passage. Then read each question. Circle the letter of the correct answer.

# Ocean Life

(1) There are interesting creatures at the beach. (2) Many bunchs of tiny fish swim near shore. (3) Seashells once covered the bodies of some animals. (4) Some loud geese fly overhead in autumn. (5) Many varieties of animals live in the ocean. (6) You might see sharks with sharp teeth. (7) Whales enjoy long lives in the deep sea's.

1 In sentence 1, *creatures* is which type of noun?
  **A** Regular plural
  **B** Irregular plural
  **C** Proper
  **D** Collective

2 What change, if any, should be made in sentence 2?
  **A** Change the period to an exclamation mark
  **B** Change *bunchs* to **bunches**
  **C** Change *shore* to **shore,**
  **D** Make no change

3 How many plural nouns are in sentence 3?
  **A** 1
  **B** 2
  **C** 3
  **D** 4

4 What are the irregular plural nouns in this paragraph?
  **A** geese, seashells, bunches
  **B** bodies, animals, varieties
  **C** bodies, geese, varieties
  **D** geese, teeth, lives

5 What change, if any, should be made in sentence 7?
  **A** Insert a comma after *lives*
  **B** Change *sea's* to **seas**
  **C** Capitalize *deep sea's*
  **D** Make no change

**School + Home** **Home Activity** Your child prepared for taking tests on regular and irregular plural nouns. Have your child make flash cards with singular and plural forms of nouns on opposite sides. Use the cards to help him or her learn plural forms.

# Sequence

- The **sequence** of events is the order in which they take place, from first to last.
- Clue words such as *first, next,* and *then* may show sequence in a story or article, but not always. Other clues are dates and times of day.
- Sometimes two events happen at the same time. Clue words that show this are *meanwhile* and *in that same year.*

**Directions** Read the passage and complete the time line below.

On July 1, 1863, a small group of Union cavalry troops fought off a larger force of Confederate soldiers near Gettysburg, Pennsylvania. By the next day, most of both armies had arrived. That day, the Confederates attacked both sides of the Union forces. However, the Union troops held them off. The third day, the Confederates attacked the middle of the Union forces with more than 12,000 soldiers. The attack was called Pickett's Charge. Again, the Union forces held. The Confederates had to retreat.

The Battle of Gettysburg was the turning point of the Civil War. After it, the Union victories began to mount. In November, President Lincoln visited the battle site and delivered a speech to honor those who fought there. The speech was called the *Gettysburg Address.*

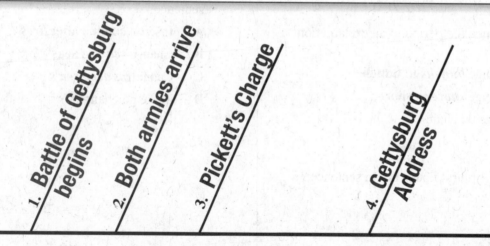

1. **July 1, 1863**   2. **July 2**   3. **July 3**   4. **November 1863**

5. Was Pickett's charge a success? Explain.

**No, the Confederates were forced to retreat.**

_____

**School + Home**   **Home Activity** Your child read a short passage and answered questions about the sequence of events described in it. Read a newspaper or magazine article with your child and discuss the sequence of events it describes.

# Writing • Informal Letter

**Key Features of an Informal Letter**

- contains a heading, salutation, and closing

- has a casual tone

- usually written to someone you know well

- contains a body, or the paragraphs that make up the main part of the letter

(April 12, 2011) **date**

(Dear Patrick,) **greeting**

  Has the news hit Texas yet? It turns out that I'm a big hero! I fearlessly braved dazzling heights in order to save a precious member of the Scales family. Okay, so I'm exaggerating a little, but let me tell you the story.

  I was on my way home from soccer practice when I found Melissa crying in front of her house. You remember Melissa, right? She is in the grade below us, and her family lives two houses down from mine. I asked why she was upset, and she said the family's pet rat had escaped. It was on the outer ledge that surrounds the second-story windows.

  "Good riddance," I thought. "Who wants a pet rat?" But Melissa was so upset that I knew I had to help. I told her to get a ladder, and I would see what I could do.

  Now you know how I feel about heights. I'm not going to say I'm a wimp, but heights are personally terrifying to me. Nevertheless, I asked Melissa to hold the base of the ladder steady, and I boldly faced my fear.

  My foot was shaking as I placed it on the first step. I tightly gripped the rung above me with each new step I took. When I got to the top, all I could think about was the sound my body would make as it hit the ground. I saw the rat shivering near the corner of the ledge. I grabbed it quickly and stuck it in my pocket. I don't think anybody in the history of the world has ever come down a ladder as fast as I did that day!

  Melissa was overjoyed. Her family invited me to dinner to thank me for saving their favorite pet. I sure wish you could have been there to see it! Things haven't been the same since you moved away. Even a big rat adventure is not as fun without my best pal. Hope you can visit soon.

(Your friend,) **closing**

Eric

**1.** Read the letter. Circle and label the date, greeting, and closing.

**2.** What is the relationship between Eric and Patrick? Underline clue words that help you know. **They are best friends; they used to be neighbors;**

**Students may underline:** *since you moved away; best pal; your friend*

# Vocabulary

**Directions** Choose the word from the box that best matches each definition. Write the word on the line.

<u>**glory**</u>_____ 1. great praise and honor

<u>**stallion**</u>_____ 2. a male horse

<u>**canteen**</u>_____ 3. a small container for carrying water or other drinks

<u>**union**</u>_____ 4. a joining of two or more people or things into one

<u>**quarrel**</u>_____ 5. a fight with words

<u>**confederacy**</u>_____ 6. a group of countries or states working together

<u>**rebellion**</u>_____ 7. a fight against your own government

**Directions** Choose the word from the box that best matches the underlined words in the sentences.

**8.** Some soldiers earn <u>valor</u> on the field of battle.

<u>**glory**</u>_____

**9.** A soldier or a scout might carry a <u>water bottle</u>.

<u>**canteen**</u>_____

**10.** A cavalry trooper would ride a <u>horse</u> into battle.

<u>**stallion**</u>_____

## Write a Newspaper Article

On a separate sheet of paper, write a newspaper article announcing that the United States has gone to civil war. Use as many vocabulary words as you can.

**Articles should include details about what a civil war might be like.**

**Home Activity** Your child identified and used vocabulary words from *Hold the Flag High*. With your child, discuss the meaning of each word from the vocabulary list. Help your child use each word in a sentence.

© Pearson Education, Inc., 5

Name _____

# Possessive Nouns

A **possessive noun** shows ownership. A **singular possessive noun** shows that one person, animal, place, or thing has or owns something. A **plural possessive noun** shows that more than one person, animal, place, or thing has or owns something.

- To make a singular noun show possession, add an apostrophe (') and -s.
  a bird's song
- To make a plural noun that ends in -s show possession, add an apostrophe (').
  several weeks' work
- To make a plural noun that does not end in -s show possession, add an apostrophe (') and -s.
  the women's papers

**Directions** Write each noun as a possessive noun. Write *S* if the possessive noun is singular. Write *P* if the possessive noun is plural.

1. friends    **friends'**    **P**
2. story    **story's**    **S**
3. freedom    **freedom's**    **S**
4. mornings    **mornings'**    **P**
5. children    **children's**    **P**
6. milk    **milk's**    **S**

**Directions** Add an apostrophe (') or an apostrophe (') and -s to make each underlined word possessive. Write the sentence on the line.

7. A soldier life can be difficult.

   **A soldier's life can be difficult.**

8. Would the Union flag fly in the South?

   **Would the Union's flag fly in the South?**

**Home Activity** Your child learned about possessive nouns. Have your child look at some sale ads and make up sentences about them using possessive nouns.

Name _____

# Irregular Plurals

| Spelling Words | | | | |
|---|---|---|---|---|
| staffs | ourselves | pants | scissors | loaves |
| volcanoes | chiefs | buffaloes | flamingos | beliefs |
| echoes | shelves | quizzes | sheriffs | dominoes |
| thieves | measles | avocados | chefs | pianos |

**Words in Context** Write a list word to complete each sentence.

1. When people get sick with ____, they get red spots all over their bodies.
2. The ____ of many people's voices bounced around the canyon walls.
3. At the assembly today, two people played ____ for the students.
4. Do you like fresh ____ in your salad?
5. The ____ were caught red-handed with the loot.
6. The old ____ were sagging under the weight of the books.
7. It took eight different ____ to prepare the huge banquet.
8. When ____ erupt, clouds of ash can travel many miles.
9. These ____ are made with waterproof material.
10. We have ____ for everyone who needs to cut ribbons.

1. __measles__
2. __echoes__
3. __pianos__
4. __avocados__
5. __thieves__
6. __shelves__
7. __chefs__
8. __volcanoes__
9. __pants__
10. __scissors__

**Classifying** Write the list word that belongs in each group.

11. deputies, detectives, ____
12. checkers, chess, ____
13. values, opinions, ____
14. cranes, herons, ____
15. deer, cattle, ____
16. employees, workers, ____
17. breads, buns, ____
18. us, we, ____
19. leaders, bosses, ____
20. tests, examinations, ____

11. __sheriffs__
12. __dominoes__
13. __beliefs__
14. __flamingos__
15. __buffaloes__
16. __staffs__
17. __loaves__
18. __ourselves__
19. __chiefs__
20. __quizzes__

**Home Activity** Your child wrote list words that are irregular plurals to complete sentences and word groups. Name two list words and ask your child to use each in a sentence.

© Pearson Education, Inc., 5

# Story Sequence A

Title _____

**Beginning**

**Middle**

**End**

# Vocabulary • Dictionary/Glossary

- As you read, you may find unknown words, or words you do not understand. You can use a **dictionary** or a **glossary** to look up the word.
- Dictionaries and glossaries provide alphabetical lists of words and their meanings.
- A dictionary is a book of words and their meanings, and a glossary is a short dictionary at the back of some books.
- An **entry** shows the spelling of a word and comes before the definition.

**Directions** Read the passage. Then answer the questions below using a dictionary or your glossary.

> John Sharp took a drink from the canteen as he looked over his army's campsite. It seemed to stretch for miles. Campfires, canvas tents, and blue uniforms were everywhere. This was the Army of the Potomac, the army of General Grant and President Lincoln. Most of the soldiers John knew were not here for glory. Most did not have a quarrel with individual Southerners, either. No, most of the men he knew were there to save that most precious union—the United States of America. For that reason, all of them knew they must give everything to stop the Southern rebellion.

1. What is the definition of *quarrel*? Put it in your own words.

   **A quarrel is a fight with words. I would call it a disagreement or an argument.**

2. What is a canteen? What part of speech is it?

   **A canteen is a small container for carrying water or other drinks. The word *canteen* is a noun.**

3. What is the meaning of *union*? Use it in a sentence.

   **A union is a joining of two or more people or things into one. Possible answer: The union of the Outdoor Club and the Hiking Club made the biggest club in the whole school.**

4. Look for the word *glory* in a dictionary. What other words could you use to replace *glory* in the passage?

   **fame, prestige, popularity**

5. Explain why a dictionary would give more complete information for an entry than a glossary.

   **A dictionary may include more parts of speech.**

**Home Activity** Your child used a dictionary to find out the meanings of unknown words. Choose a few words that your child does not know. Have your child use a dictionary to find their meanings.

# Parts of a Book

The **parts of a book** include its **cover, title page, copyright page, table of contents, chapter titles, captions, section heads, glossary,** and **index.** Examining the parts of a book can give you clues about a book and help you to learn as much as you can from it.

**Directions** Read the following copyright page and answer the questions below.

*A Three-Minute Speech: Lincoln's Remarks at Gettysburg*

Text copyright © 2003  Jennifer Armstrong
Illustration copyright © 2003 Albert Lorenz

First Aladdin Paperbacks
An imprint of Simon and Schuster Children's Publishing Division
1230 Avenue of the Americas
New York, NY 10020
All rights reserved, including the right of reproduction, in whole or in part in any form.

Library of Congress Control Number 2002107413
ISBN: 0-689-85622-9

1. What is the purpose of a copyright page in a book?

**It gives all of the publishing information.**

2. The owner of the copyright is listed after the symbol © and the year of publication. Who owns the copyright for the text of this book?

**Jennifer Armstrong**

3. What do you think it means to own the copyright to a book?

**It means you and only you have the rights to the book. It can't be published or used in any way without your permission.**

4. Who published this book? When was the book published?

**The book was published by First Aladdin Paperbacks in 2003.**

5. How might numbers such as the Library of Congress number or ISBN number be used?

**Numbers might make it easier to find the book in a library or a bookstore.**

**Directions** Study the following table of contents page. Then answer the questions below.

# CONTENTS

### Forming a Government
### for the United States of America

**6.** What does the title tell you this book will be about?

## It is about how the United States government was formed.

**7.** What do the numbers on the right side of the page represent? Where would you find a chapter about checks and balances?

## They are page numbers; page 48.

**8.** What can you learn about a book by studying its table of contents before you read?

## You can learn how the book is organized.

**9.** How many chapters are in the book? What is the purpose of chapter titles?

## There are 10 chapters in the book. Chapter titles tell you what
## each chapter is about.

**10.** What other sections can you find in this book besides chapters?

## There is a glossary, an appendix, and an index.

**Home Activity** Your child learned about the parts of a book. Pick out several kinds of books around your home (nonfiction, a reference book, a work of fiction) and examine the parts of the different books together.

# Irregular Plurals

**Proofread a List** Circle six spelling errors and one capitalization error.
Write the corrections on the lines.

six (scissors)
three sets of metal (shelfes)
twenty sets of (dominos)
ten waterproof pants
one dozen (avacadoes)
three toy pianos
twenty-five (loavs) of bread
three pink (Lawn) (flamingoes)

**Spelling Words**

staffs
ourselves
pants
scissors
loaves
volcanoes
chiefs
buffaloes
flamingos
beliefs

echoes
shelves
quizzes
sheriffs
dominoes
thieves
measles
avocados
chefs
pianos

1. **scissors**
2. **shelves**
3. **dominoes**
4. **avocados**
5. **loaves**
6. **flamingos**
7. **lawn**

**Proofread Words** Circle the correct spelling of the word.

8. Almost everyone used to get _____ as a child.

   meesles        measels        (measles)

9. We had pop _____ in math and science today.

   quizes        (quizzes)        quizzez

10. People are entitled to their own _____.

    (beliefs)        believes        beleifs

11. We have no one to blame except _____.

    ourselfs        hourselves        (ourselves)

12. The music school has three _____ for students to use.

    (pianos)        pianoes        painos

**Frequently Misspelled Words**

know
knew

**Home Activity** Your child identified misspelled list words. Select three words from the list and ask your child to spell them to you.

## Possessive Nouns

**Directions** Read the passage. Then read each question. Circle the letter of the correct answer.

# In the Officers' Tent

(1) Ending the battle, the generals men fled from the Southern soldiers. (2) Back at camp, the men ate, rested, and inspected the gear. (3) A soldier's shoes wore out quickly, and his rifle needed daily care. (4) Success often depended on an army's supplies. (5) In the officers' tent, we talked about these little details that were so important. (6) Later, I took out my children's letters. (7) I read them quietly while the enlisted men wrote letters home.

1  What change, if any, should be made in sentence 1?

   A  Change the period to an exclamation mark

   **B**  Change *generals* to **general's**

   C  Change *soldiers* to **soldier's**

   D  Make no change

2  What is the possessive noun in sentence 2?

   A  camp

   B  gear

   C  men

   **D**  None of the above

3  In sentence 3, what type of noun is *soldier's*?

   **A**  Singular possessive

   B  Plural possessive

   C  Irregular plural

   D  none of the above

4  What are the plural possessive nouns in this paragraph?

   **A**  officers', children's

   B  soldier's, officers', children's

   C  army's, officers', children's

   D  officers', children's, his

5  What change, if any, should be made in sentence 7?

   A  Insert a comma after *them*

   B  Change *letters* to **letter's**

   C  Change *enlisted men* to **enlisted men's**

   **D**  Make no change

© Pearson Education, Inc., 5

**Home Activity** Your child prepared for taking tests on possessive nouns. Have your child write several sentences describing a favorite toy or game using possessive nouns (such as *the bear's nose* or *the pieces' shapes*).

# Compare and Contrast

- When you **compare and contrast** things you tell how they are similar and how they are different.
- Sometimes clue words point out comparisons and contrasts, but not always.
- You can compare and contrast different things you read about with one another and also with what you already know.

**Directions** Read the following passage.

In Japan during the Middle Ages, samurai warriors followed a code of honor called bushido. Following the code meant being a fierce fighter, an athlete, a kind and honest person, and living a simple life. During the same time in Europe, knights were expected to follow the code of chivalry. Chivalry meant you were loyal to a lord (the landowner who hired the knight), brave in battle, and honorable in all deeds. They wore different armor. Samurai primarily wore protective leather gear, and knights wore heavy metal armor.

## Possible answers given.

**Directions** Complete the following graphic organizer. List similarities and differences between *chivalry* and *bushido*. Then compare them with a code with which you are familiar.

| Similarities in Text | Differences in Text | Compared with What I Know |
|---|---|---|
| 1. **Both had to be honorable.** | 3. **Samurai lived in Asia; knights lived in Europe.** | 4. **Our school honor code forbids cheating.** |
| 2. **Both were fierce fighters.** | Samurai wore leather gear, and knights wore metal armor. | 5. **Our school has school colors.** |

 **Home Activity** Your child read a short passage and made comparisons and contrasts. Read two of your child's favorite stories and compare and contrast the main characters.

# Writing • Poem

### Key Features of a Poem
- uses verse to communicate ideas
- may use poetic techniques, rhyme, or sound patterns
- often includes sensory details or vivid language

## The Day I Learned to Fish

I learned how to fish last (May)
My sister wanted me to (play)
She took a look at my thick (book)
And made me trade it for a (hook)

We took our poles and bags of (bait)
To the pond beyond the (gate)
We flung our lines, sat really (still)
And leaned back flat against the (hill)

Splash splash went my (fish)
I caught a big one for my (dish)
But I put mine back (anyway)
To catch again another (day)

1. Circle the rhymes in each stanza.

2. Underline the words that show the use of onomatopoeia.

3. List one example of assonance.
   **back, flat**

# Vocabulary

**Directions** Draw a line to connect each word on the left with its definition on the right.

1. astonished     thankfulness
2. procession     to suggest favorably
3. behavior     surprised greatly
4. gratitude     way of acting
5. recommend     something that moves forward

**Directions** Choose a word from the box that best completes each sentence. Write the word on the line to the left.

**distribution**     6. The unequal ____ of food caused some people to be hungry.

**benefactor**     7. Without the generosity of his supporter, or _____, Guillermo would not be able to afford to go to art school.

**sacred**     8. In some cultures, animals are highly valued and considered ____, or holy.

**traditions**     9. Our family's holiday____ are passed from generation to generation.

**astonished**     10. I was surprised by the contest results, but the winner was truly ____.

> **Check the Words You Know**
>
> ___astonished
> ___behavior
> ___benefactor
> ___distribution
> ___gratitude
> ___procession
> ___recommend
> ___sacred
> ___traditions

## Write a Thank-You Note

On a separate sheet of paper, write a thank-you note to someone who has helped you in some way. Use as many vocabulary words as you can.

**Thank-you notes should include words from the vocabulary list and specify the helpful gesture that was done.**

**Home Activity** Your child identified and used vocabulary words from the story *The Ch'i-lin Purse*. With your child, read a story about someone who performed an act of kindness. Look for words in the story that describe that person.

# Action and Linking Verbs

A complete sentence has a subject and a predicate. The main word in the predicate is a **verb**. An **action verb** tells what the subject does.

The little boy *cried* often.

A **linking verb** links, or joins, the subject to a word or words in the predicate. It tells what the subject is or is like.

He *seemed* very quiet. He *was* a good sport.

- Action verbs show actions that are physical (*hike, build*) or mental (*remember, approve*).
- Common linking verbs are forms of the verb *be* (*am, is, are, was, were*).
- These verbs can be linking verbs: *become, seem, appear, feel, taste, smell,* and *look*. (*The cake appears fresh. It looks tasty.*) However, some of them can also be used as action verbs. (*A boy appeared suddenly. He looked at the food.*)

**Directions** Write the verb in each sentence of the paragraph. Then write *A* if the verb is an action verb. Write *L* if it is a linking verb.

**1.** Are you a spoiled child? **2.** A spoiled child always gets his or her way. **3.** He or she seems selfish. **4.** Parents pamper the child too much. **5.** This treatment often leads to misery. **6.** The world responds better to a kind, unselfish person. **7.** Compassion is good for the giver and the receiver. **8.** The most unselfish people appear happiest.

1. **Are**    **L**
2. **gets**    **A**
3. **seems**    **L**
4. **pamper**    **A**

5. **leads**    **A**
6. **responds**    **A**
7. **is**    **L**
8. **appear**    **L**

**Directions** Write a verb from the box to complete each sentence. On the line after the sentence, write *A* if the verb is an action verb. Write *L* if it is a linking verb.

| combine | is | showed | are |

9. The dragon ___**is**___ popular in Chinese culture. **L**

10. In ancient China, people ___**showed**___ great respect for dragons. **A**

11. Dragons ___**are**___ not real animals. **L**

12. They ___**combine**___ traits of many animals. **A**

**Home Activity** Your child learned about action and linking verbs. Read a story together. Have your child point out several action verbs and linking verbs.

# Vowel Sounds with *r*

| Spelling Words | | | | |
|---|---|---|---|---|
| snore | tornado | spare | appear | career |
| square | report | prepare | pioneer | chair |
| beware | smear | repair | sword | ignore |
| order | engineer | resort | volunteer | declare |

**Words in Context** Write the list word to complete each sentence.

1. I _____ loudly when I sleep.

2. Have you heard the saying "The pen is mightier than the _____"?

3. The _____ fixed the machine.

4. It was hard to _____ the loud sirens outside.

5. The mayor will _____ a holiday.

6. I have to bring my worn shoes to the shop for _____.

7. We have guests staying in our _____ bedroom.

8. A triangle has three sides; a _____ has four sides.

9. The father told his small child to _____ of traffic.

10. Did the weather _____ forecast rain?

1. __snore__
2. __sword__
3. __engineer__
4. __ignore__
5. __declare__
6. __repair__
7. __spare__
8. __square__
9. __beware__
10. __report__

**Word Groups** Write the list word that best completes the group.

11. cyclone, twister, ___

12. show up, materialize, ___

13. job, employment, ___

14. lead the way, be the first, ___

15. get ready, make, ___

16. offer, give aid, ___

17. ask for, send for, ___

18. blur, spread, ___

19. vacation spot, dude ranch, ___

20. seat, bench, ___

11. __tornado__
12. __appear__
13. __career__
14. __pioneer__
15. __prepare__
16. __volunteer__
17. __order__
18. __smear__
19. __resort__
20. __chair__

**Home Activity** Your child wrote list words that have vowel sounds with *r*. Select three words and ask your child what they mean.

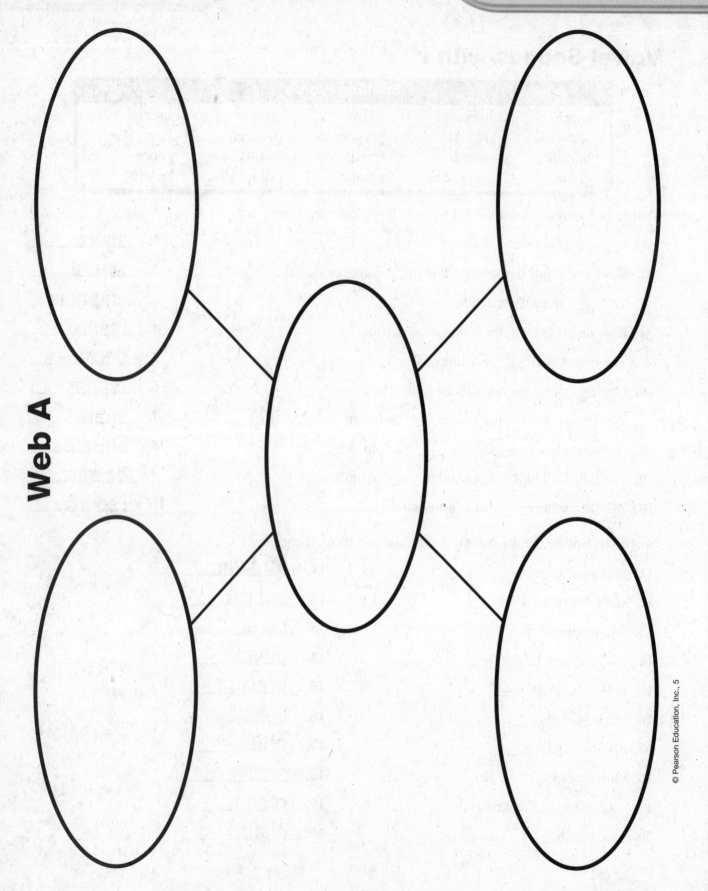

Web A

# Vocabulary · Greek and Latin Roots

- **Greek and Latin roots** are used in many English words.
- When you find a word you don't know, recognizing the root can help you figure out its meaning.
- The Latin word *bene* means "well" or "good," as in *beneficial, benefit,* and *benefactor*. The Latin word *gratus* means "pleasing," as in *gratitude* and *grateful*.

**Directions** Read the following passage. Then answer the questions below.

I always wanted to be a singer, and I worked very hard. I was grateful to be able to do something that I loved. However, it was difficult to make enough money to pay for lessons. One day, I was singing in a procession to celebrate the holidays. Afterward, my mother found me and she was very excited.

"This is Mrs. Kazarian. She is a benefactor for young artists and wants to pay for your lessons at the school of music," my astonished mother said.

"I'd like to recommend a teacher who works with young singers," Mrs. Kazarian told us. A month later, I was practicing with my new teacher. Each day, I am filled with gratitude that I am the beneficiary of Mrs. Kazarian's generosity. Without her support, I would not have had this chance.

## Possible answers given.

1. What is the Latin root in *grateful*? How does the root help you understand its meaning?

**_gratus; The root lets you know that the word has to do with something that is pleasing._**

2. What is the Latin root in *benefactor*? How does the root help you understand its meaning?

**_bene; The root lets you know that the word has to do with something that is good._**

3. What do you think *beneficiary* means? How does the root help you understand its meaning?

**_It probably means someone who receives something good, because bene means "good."_**

4. How does the root in *gratitude* help you understand its meaning?

**_The root means "pleasing," so it means being pleased._**

5. Write a sentence using a new word with either the root *bene* or *gratus*.

**_Exercising every day benefits your health._**

**Home Activity** Your child read a short passage and used Latin roots to identify the meanings of unfamiliar words. Look in a dictionary with your child to find other words that use the Latin roots *bene* and *gratus*.

# Textbook/Trade Book

A **textbook** usually teaches one subject, such as social studies or math. Textbooks contain **chapter titles, headings, subheadings,** and **vocabulary words.** A **trade book** is any book that is not a textbook, a periodical, or a reference book.

**Directions** Study the following table of contents from a textbook. Then answer the questions below.

**1.** What subject do you think this textbook is for? Why?

**The textbook is about social studies because the chapters are about events in history.**

**2.** Based on the table of contents, how are the sections of this textbook organized?

**The book is organized into chapters and subsections.**

**3.** In what chapter and section can you learn about the city of Tokyo?

**You can find out about Tokyo in Chapter 19, Section 1.**

**4.** In what section would you find a summary of the whole chapter?

**You can find summaries in the sections called *Chapter in Review.***

**5.** What do you think is included in the sections in italics? How can you tell?

**The sections in italics include graphic sources because they have words like *Map* and *Art* in their title.**

**Directions** Read the back cover of this trade book. Then answer the questions below.

---

# The Chinatown Dragon
### *The Day My Little Sister Was Eaten by a Paper Dragon*

THE UPDATED AND EXPANDED TENTH ANNIVERSARY EDITION

It has been ten years since Lori Liu first gave us her collection of stories about her childhood growing up in San Francisco's Chinatown. That edition let people from all over the world get a close-up glimpse of a Chinatown few outsiders are able to see. Readers eagerly immersed themselves in sights and sounds, like the time her little sister ran straight into the mouth of a block-long paper dragon during a parade!

Since then, Ms. Liu has captured new tales full of music, action, humor, and good food to add to the original collection. This edition celebrates the original collection and expands it in a way that will delight her long-time readers.

"Lori Liu's stories are full of the laughter and tears common to everyone's childhood."
—Mario Michelin, *San Jose Post*

"If you have ever enjoyed an afternoon's visit to Chinatown, you will love Lori Liu's collection of stories, *The Chinatown Dragon.* You will feel like a resident rather than a visitor."
—Beatrice Kelly, *San Francisco News*

---

**6.** What kind of book is this?

**It is a collection of stories.**

**7.** What is the book's title? What do you think the subtitle, which is in italics, means?

***The Chinatown Dragon;* It is the name of one of the stories.**

**8.** What is special about this edition of the book?

**This is the tenth anniversary edition and contains new stories.**

**9.** Why are quotes included on the back cover?

**The quotes are meant to convince people to buy the book.**

**10.** If you wanted to look up information about the history of Chinese New Year, would you look in a textbook or a trade book? Why?

**I'd look in a textbook because they tend to focus on facts.**

© Pearson Education, Inc., 5

**Home Activity** Your child read a short passage and then answered questions about textbooks and trade books. With your child, look at a trade book and a textbook. Ask your child to explain the difference between the two types of books.

# Vowel Sounds with *r*

**Proofread a Story** Ramon wrote this story about sharing a room with his brother. Circle six spelling errors. Find one sentence with a punctuation error. Write the corrections on the lines.

### My Brother

Mom asked my brother and me to (voluntier) to give up our rooms for our visiting grandparents. So, we're sharing the (spair) attic room, but it's no fun. My brother snores, and it's hard to (ignoure) it. Just as I was falling asleep, he snored like a (tornadoe.) That was it! I threw my pillow at him. It knocked over the lamp, which hit the (chare) with a loud pop. This did not (apear) to disturb him at all. I gave up and slept in the hallway as a last resort.

1. **volunteer**        2. **spare**
3. **ignore**           4. **tornado**
5. **chair**            6. **appear**
7. **That was it!**

**Proofread Words** Circle the correct spelling of the word.

8. A ____ is someone who leads the way for others.

   (pioneer)        pioner        pieneer

9. The knight wore a brightly polished ____ on his hip.

   swoard        (sword)        sworde

10. The ____ is a wind funnel.

    (tornado)        tornardo        tornadoe

11. Be careful or you'll ____ the fresh paint.

    (smear)        smere        smeer

12. I asked the bike shop to ____ my flat tire.

    ripare        (repair)        repare

**Home Activity** Your child identified misspelled list words in a paragraph. Ask your child to tell you the six patterns used in the list words to spell vowel sounds with *r*.

## Action and Linking Verbs

**Directions** Read the passage. Then read each question. Circle the letter of the correct answer.

# The Three Letters

(1) In ancient China, the Three Letters were important to a marriage. (2) The Betrothal Letter formally announced the engagement. (3) After that, a Gift Letter was <u>necessary</u>. (4) The letter listed gifts for the wedding. (5) The Wedding Letter _____ the third formal document. (6) The groom's family <u>presented</u> it to the bride's family. (7) This letter formally accepted the bride into the groom's family.

**1** What kind of verb is *were* in sentence 1?

  **A**  Action verb (physical)

  **B**  Action verb (mental)

  **(C)**  Linking verb

  **D**  Not a verb

**2** What kind of verb is *announced* in sentence 2?

  **(A)**  Action verb (physical)

  **B**  Action verb (mental)

  **C**  Linking verb

  **D**  Not a verb

**3** In sentence 3, what type of verb is the underlined word?

  **A**  Action verb (physical)

  **B**  Action verb (mental)

  **C**  Linking verb

  **(D)**  Not a verb

**4** In sentence 6, what type of verb is the underlined word?

  **(A)**  Action verb (physical)

  **B**  Action verb (mental)

  **C**  Linking verb

  **D**  Not a verb

**5** Which linking verb best completes sentence 5?

  **A**  were

  **(B)**  was

  **C**  are

  **D**  become

**School + Home** **Home Activity** Your child prepared for taking tests on action and linking verbs. Read a newspaper article with your child. Have your child circle action verbs and underline linking verbs in the article.

# Author's Purpose

- The **author's purpose** is the reason or reasons the author has for writing.
- An author may write to persuade, to inform, to entertain, or to express himself or herself.

**Directions** Read the passage. Then answer the questions below.

Dirty beaches are disgusting. I hate to see the shore of a lake or ocean dotted with candy wrappers, soda bottles, or other bits of garbage. Garbage on beaches is more than an eyesore. It also kills wildlife. Animals such as fish and turtles may eat drifting garbage they find in the water. If they do, they may choke. The plastic six-pack yokes from soda cans are dangerous to birds. Birds often become tangled in the plastic and die. To help keep beaches clean, you can volunteer on clean-up days. People who clean beaches help protect the environment and are definitely doing the right thing!

**Directions** Fill in the diagram below based on the passage.

1. **Detail:** Dirty beaches are **disgusting and can kill wildlife.**

2. **Detail:** If animals eat drifting garbage **they could die.**

3. **Detail:** Birds can become tangled **in six-pack yokes from soda cans and die.**

4. **Author's Purpose:** **to persuade readers to help keep beaches clean**

5. How do the details provided help support the author's purpose?

**The details illustrate problems created by dirty beaches and make people want to help keep beaches clean.**

**Home Activity** Your child analyzed the author's purpose in a passage about beaches. Challenge him or her to read an editorial from a newspaper and explain the author's purpose for writing the editorial. Ask your child to explain who the author is trying to persuade or convince.

# Writing · Personal Narrative

**Key Features of Personal Narratives**

- uses the first-person point of view (*I, me*)
- tells a story about a real event in your life
- shares thoughts and feelings about an event or time

## Mom or Me

I knew it was going to be the best birthday party I'd ever been to. Maria's parents really wanted to celebrate her turning ten years old. They planned out an entire day of fun for her and her friends, including me!

We were going to begin the day with breakfast at a great restaurant called Good Morning. After that, we would go to a water park to ride the water slides and swim in the wave pool. Then, we would go back to Maria's house for a cookout, including hot dogs and hamburgers. Later that night we would roast marshmallows and make s'mores while we sat by the campfire. It was a day full of my favorite things!

The party was still a month away when I found out the date—August 2, my mom's birthday! Every year, my mom asked for only one gift from her family for her birthday. She asked that we all be there

with her to celebrate. We usually had dinner together and either went to see a movie or rented movies to watch at home. How could I go to Maria's all-day birthday party and still be there for my mom's birthday dinner?

When I revealed my problem to my mom, she smiled and told me that it was okay for me to miss her birthday this year. But she looked sad. I know how she liked having her whole family together. I knew what I had to do.

Everyone had a great time at Maria's birthday party except for me—but that's because I wasn't there! I surprised my mom by staying home to celebrate her birthday with her and our family. She was so happy that she cried. She told me that I gave her the best present she had ever gotten. I showed her just how important she is to me.

1. Reread the selection. What difficult decision does the writer face? How does he or she solve the problem?

   **The writer has to choose between attending Maria's party or celebrating his or her mom's birthday. The writer decides to celebrate his or her mom's birthday.**

2. What are the writer's thoughts and feelings about the friend's birthday party?

   **The writer reveals how fun the birthday would be and how much he or she wanted to go.**

# Vocabulary

**Directions** Choose a word from the box that best matches each clue. Write the word on the line.

__jostled__ _____

1. shoved or pushed against someone roughly

__Navajo__ _____

2. a member of a group of Native Americans living mainly in New Mexico, Arizona, and Utah

__bracelet__ _____

3. a band or chain worn for ornament around the wrist or arm

__mesa__ _____

4. a high, steep hill that has a flat top and stands by itself

__turquoise__ _____

5. a clear blue or greenish blue precious stone, used in jewelry

__hogan__ _____

6. a dwelling used by the Navajo Indians of North America

> ### Check the Words You Know
>
> ___Navajo
> ___mesa
> ___jostled
> ___turquoise
> ___bandana
> ___hogan
> ___bracelet

**Directions** Choose the word from the box that best completes each sentence. Write the word on the line.

The southwestern United States is home to Native Americans such as the

7. ____Navajo____. A typical member might have lived in a 8. ____hogan____. He or

she may have worn a head scarf, such as a 9. ____bandana____. Navajos also wore jewelry

made of 10. ____turquoise____.

## Write About a Character

On a separate sheet of paper, write a description of one character from the story. Describe the character's appearance and personality. Use as many vocabulary words as you can.

**Descriptions should include details about Tony, Grandmother, or other characters.**

**Home Activity** Your child identified and used vocabulary words from *A Summer's Trade*. With your child, find out information on Native Americans in Texas. Use the vocabulary words to discuss them.

Name _____

# Main and Helping Verbs

Verbs that are made up of more than one word are **verb phrases.** In a verb phrase, the **main verb** names the action. The **helping verb** helps tell the time of the action. Some common helping verbs are *has, have, had, am, is, are, was, were, do, does, did, can, could, will, would,* and *should.*

- The main verb is always the last word in a verb phrase. (The horse is *looking* at me.)
- There may be more than one helping verb in a verb phrase. (She *has been riding* horses a long time.)
- Helping verbs such as *is* and *are* show that action is happening in the present. (Annamae *is reading* about the Navajo.) *Was* and *were* tell that the action happened in the past. (The class *was reading* about the Navajo last month.) *Will* tells that the action is going to happen in the future. (We *will study* the Anasazi next week.)

**Directions** Underline the verb phrase in each sentence. Put one line under each helping verb and two lines under the main verb.

1. I have ridden horses for years.

2. Right now I am mending my old saddle.

3. Some friends will visit the ranch tomorrow.

4. They have come to the ranch many times.

5. The wind is blowing gently on the range.

6. Within two days, we will have reached the mountains.

7. You can see everything from the mountain.

8. My chores will be waiting for me.

9. My sister is reminding me to take pictures.

10. People from the city should visit the ranch often.

**Home Activity** Your child learned about main and helping verbs. Have your child model an activity such as making a sandwich. Ask him or her to explain the job using sentences with verb phrases.

# Final Syllables *-en, -an, -el, -le, -il*

| Spelling Words | | | | |
|---|---|---|---|---|
| example | level | slogan | quarrel | scramble |
| evil | oxygen | wooden | double | travel |
| cancel | chuckle | fossil | toboggan | veteran |
| chisel | suburban | single | sudden | beagle |

**Word Clues** Write the list word that matches each clue.

1. a kind of laugh
2. not urban or rural
3. a kind of sled
4. a gas we breathe
5. something made of oak or maple
6. something that has been preserved in stone
7. a small argument
8. two of something
9. only one
10. a kind of hound dog

1. __chuckle__
2. __suburban__
3. __toboggan__
4. __oxygen__
5. __wooden__
6. __fossil__
7. __quarrel__
8. __double__
9. __single__
10. __beagle__

**Synonyms** Write a list word that has the same meaning as the underlined word.

11. I found a perfect <u>model</u> of my favorite color.
12. Did you <u>mix</u> the eggs for me?
13. The sculptor had to carefully <u>carve</u> the marble bit by bit.
14. One of my goals is to <u>journey</u> around the world.
15. The ground was <u>flat</u> and then it dropped down steeply.
16. The <u>wicked</u> queen tried to poison her enemy.
17. The company's <u>motto</u> was "Right every time!"
18. The politician was <u>an old hand</u> at running elections.
19. I had to <u>call off</u> my dentist appointment today.
20. The storm was <u>swift</u> and unexpected.

11. __example__
12. __scramble__
13. __chisel__
14. __travel__
15. __level__
16. __evil__
17. __slogan__
18. __veteran__
19. __cancel__
20. __sudden__

© Pearson Education, Inc., 5

**Home Activity** Your child matched list words to meanings. Ask your child to tell you the meanings of three list words.

# Story Sequence C

Title _____

**Characters**

**Setting**

**Problem**

**Events**

_____
_____
_____
_____
_____
_____
_____
_____
_____

**Solution**

# Vocabulary · Context Clues

As you read, you will find unfamiliar words. You can use context clues to figure out the meaning of a new word. **Context clues** are found in the words and sentences around an unfamiliar word.

**Directions** Read the following passage. Then answer the questions below. Look for context clues around unknown words to determine their meanings.

Centuries ago, high on a mesa in the heart of the Great Basin Desert, a man jostled his heavy pack into place on the back of his horse. Nearby, a woman dipped a canteen into a creek. On her arm she wore a bracelet of turquoise, the same color as the sky above. These people were members of the Navajo tribe.

They traveled across the desert to gather with other Navajos. From Arizona to New Mexico, they looked for a peaceful home, free from the aggressive Spaniards who had settled in what is now the southwestern United States. Today, most of northeastern Arizona is home to the Navajo Nation.

1. What does the word *mesa* mean?

**a high, flat desert hill**

2. What context clues can help you understand the meaning of the word *turquoise?*

**same color as the sky**

3. Look at the sentences after the word *Navajo*. How do these sentences give clues to the meaning of *Navajo?*

**We know the Navajos were Native Americans. These sentences tell where they live.**

4. What does *jostled* mean as it is used in this passage?

**pushed something into position**

5. What is the meaning of *bracelet?* How do you know?

**A bracelet is a piece of jewelry worn on the wrist or arm. In the passage, the woman is wearing a bracelet on her arm.**

© Pearson Education, Inc., 5

**Home Activity** Your child answered questions about unfamiliar words in a reading passage by using context clues. Explain a process to your child, such as making a complicated meal, using unfamiliar words, and help your child figure out what the new words mean by their context.

# Electronic Media

- There are two types of **electronic media**—computer and non-computer. Computer sources include computer software, CD-ROMs, DVDs, and the Internet. Non-computer sources include audiotapes, videotapes, films, filmstrips, television, and radio.
- To find information on the Internet, use a search engine and type in your keywords. Be specific. It's a good idea to use two or more keywords as well as typing "AND" between keywords. To go to a Web site that's listed in your search results, click on the underlined link.

**Directions** Use the following list of electronic media to answer the questions below.

- *From the Pueblo to the Shoshonean* (Public Television documentary about Native Americans of the Southwest)
- The Navajo Nation (Internet site about the Navajo people)
- *Our Native Tongue* (Podcast of authentic Native American music)
- *The Story of New Mexico* (Documentary about the history of the state of New Mexico)
- *North American Tribes and Nations* (CD-ROM showing the existing Native American tribes in the United States)
- The Sun and the Moon (Internet site showing Native American art, jewelry, and ceramics)

1. Which source would be the most helpful in writing a report on the Navajo?

   **The Navajo Nation would be the most helpful.**

2. How would you get information from *North American Tribes and Nations?*

   **You would have to use the CD-ROM at a computer.**

3. If you were doing an Internet search, what keywords would you type into the search engine to find the Web site The Sun and the Moon?

   **Use keywords *Native American* and *art* and *jewelry* and ceramics.**

4. Which source would be most useful if you wanted to learn about Navajo songs and chants?

   **The *Our Native Tongue* podcast would be the most useful.**

5. Which source would you start with if you wanted to learn about the Native Americans of Florida?

   **You would start with *North American Tribes and Nations.***

**Directions**  Use the following Internet search results found on a search engine to answer the questions below.

---

**Search Results**

Navajo Nation
     Official site of the Navajo Nation. Describes Navajo history, culture, and traditions.

Native American Indian Heritage Month
     United States Department of the Interior, Bureau of Indian Affairs. Discusses the importance of preserving Native American culture. Lists events across the country, highlighting Native American traditions. Describes Native American customs.

Box of Memories
     One man's effort to record the stories and traditions of Navajo Native Americans in the hope of preserving Navajo culture.

Navajo Traditions
     University of Arizona's study of Navajo traditions and how they have developed over time.

---

6. What does the information below the underlined links tell you?

**It tells you more specific information about each Web site.**

7. What keywords might have been used to get these search results?

**Possible answers: Navajo, traditions, culture**

8. Which site is a United States government source?

***Native American Indian Heritage Month***

9. Which site would be least reliable if you were doing a report for school?

***Box of Memories* would be the least reliable.**

10. In what ways might the Navajo Traditions site be valuable if you were doing a report?

**Possible answer: It might have more detailed information or be less biased than the others because it was created by a university.**

© Pearson Education, Inc., 5

**School + Home**  **Home Activity**  Your child answered questions about electronic media. With your child, look around your house and see how many different types of electronic media you have on hand. Talk with your son or daughter about how each of the various electronic media sources could be valuable in his or her studies.

# Final Syllables -*en*, -*an*, -*el*, -*le*, -*il*

**Proofread a Story** Sally wrote this story. There are seven spelling errors and one punctuation error. Circle the errors and write the corrections on the lines.

### The Old Woodcarver

We decided to (travle) to see a (veteren) woodcarver. My dad wanted him to make a (tobaggan) like the one Dad owned when he was a child. We drove down a long (suburben) road. When we got out of the car, a (beagel) ran from behind the house, followed by the woodcarver. He carried an example of a tiny sled made of metal. "Don't worry," he said with a chuckle, "your sled will be wooden." He pulled a (chisle) out of his pocket. "Would you like to learn how to carve?" he asked. "I may seem like an old (fossel) to you," he said. "I'm probably double your father's age, but I'm pretty handy with a chisel."

"Sure," I said, "that's a great idea!"

**Spelling Words**

example
level
slogan
quarrel
scramble
evil
oxygen
wooden
double
travel

cancel
chuckle
fossil
toboggan
veteran
chisel
suburban
single
sudden
beagle

1. **travel**          2. **veteran**

3. **toboggan**        4. **suburban**

5. **beagle**          6. **chisel**

7. **fossil**

8. **"Sure," I said, "that's a great idea!"**

**Proofread Words** Circle the correct spelling of the word.

9. oxygin          oxygan          (oxygen)

10. (cancel)        cancle          cancil

11. quarril        (quarrel)        quarele

12. evile          eval            (evil)

13. (slogan)        slogen          slogin

14. chukle         (chuckle)        chuckel

15. suddin         suddan          (sudden)

16. egsample       (example)        exsampel

**Frequently Misspelled Words**

Mom
Dad's
heard

**Home Activity** Your child identified misspelled words with the final syllables -*en*, -*an*, -*el*, -*le*, and -*il*. Ask your child which words are the most difficult for him or her to spell. Have your child spell them.

## Main and Helping Verbs

**Directions** Read the passage. Then read each question. Circle the letter of the correct answer.

# Tempe Wick

(1) Tempe Wick was a spirited girl and have often rode alone. (2) While she <u>was riding</u> one day, Tempe and her horse _____ captured by stray soldiers. (3) The soldiers knew the Wicks were a wealthy family and wanted to take Tempe's horse. (4) Tempe managed to escape the soldiers but knew they <u>would</u> come looking for the horse in the barn. (5) Tempe decided to hide the horse in her bedroom. (6) Who would think to look in a bedroom for a horse? (7) The soldiers never discovered where she <u>had been hiding</u> the horse.

1  What change, if any, should be made in sentence 1?

   A   Change *was* to **were**

   **(B)**  Remove helping verb *have*

   C   Change *have* to **has**

   D   Make no change

2  Which describes the underlined words in sentence 2?

   **(A)**  Verb phrase

   B   Main verb

   C   Helping verb

   D   None of the above

3  Which helping verb best completes sentence 2?

   A   did

   B   are

   C   was

   **(D)**  were

4  Which best describes the underlined word in sentence 4?

   A   Verb phrase

   B   Main verb

   **(C)**  Helping verb

   D   None of the above

5  How many helping verbs are in the underlined verb phrase in sentence 7?

   A   0

   B   1

   **(C)**  2

   D   3

© Pearson Education, Inc., 5

**School + Home**   **Home Activity** Your child prepared for taking tests on main and helping verbs and verb phrases. Have your child write sentences about his or her day's activities using verb phrases and point out main and helping verbs.

# Author's Purpose

- The **author's purpose** is the reason or reasons the author has for writing.
- An author may write to persuade, to inform, to entertain, or to express himself or herself.

**Directions** Read the following passage and look at the time line to answer the questions below.

The Reverend Martin Luther King Jr. was an important leader of the civil rights movement. In 1948, at the age of 19, King became a minister. During his lifetime, he organized many civil rights protests, including the Montgomery Bus Boycott and the Freedom March on Washington, D.C. Because of his frequent participation in civil rights protests, he was arrested 30 times. King received the Nobel Peace Prize for his work. Dr. King is a truly a hero of freedom in America.

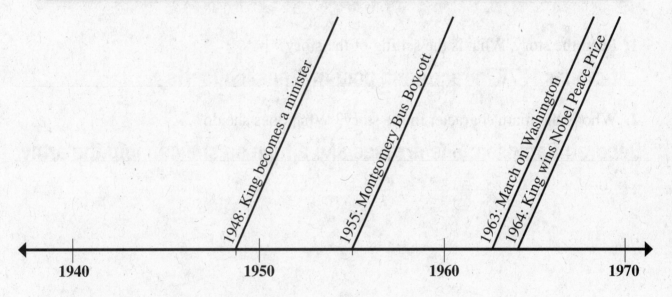

1948: King becomes a minister

1955: Montgomery Bus Boycott

1963: March on Washington

1964: King wins Nobel Peace Prize

1940    1950    1960    1970

1. For what purpose did the author write this passage?

**Information about the Reverend Martin Luther King Jr.'s life**

2. How does the time line support the author's purpose? **It shows visually when**

**important events in Dr. King's life took place.**

3. How many years passed between Dr. King becoming a minister and the March on Washington?

**15 years**

4. What happened first, the Montgomery Bus Boycott or the Freedom March on Washington?

**the Montgomery Bus Boycott**

**School + Home** **Home Activity** Your child analyzed the author's purpose in a nonfiction passage. Look at an article in a newspaper or magazine. Read the article with your child and discuss what you think is the author's purpose.

# Writing • Writing for Tests

## In the Army Now

On a cool October day in seventeen hundred and seventy eight, young Deborah Sampson packs her knapsack and walks to the recruiting post in Billingham, Massachusetts. She finds herself standing in front of a captain, a tired, wiry man with a scruffy red beard.

She hears herself say, "I want to join, I want to fight!" Her voice sounds high and weak. Deborah stands straight and bravely meets the captain's stare. She is wearing pants, a coarse wool vest, and a coat, and a man's hat covers her hair.

"You're but a boy, yet I reckon you'll do," the captain sighs. "The soldiers are waiting. Now, what is your name?"

"Call me Robert," Deborah replies.

"Welcome to the army," says the captain Deborah has just enlisted in the American army as a soldier. Now, she has to keep her true identity a secret.

1. Read the story. What is the setting of the story?

   **October 1778, a recruiting post in Massachusetts**

2. Who is the main character in the story? What does she do?

   **Deborah Sampson; She dresses like a man so she can join the army.**

Name_____

# Vocabulary

**Directions** Choose the word from the box that best completes each sentence. Write the word on the line.

**steed**      1. a high-spirited horse

**magnified**      2. made something look larger

**fearless**      3. not afraid

**glimmer**      4. a faint, unsteady light

**somber**      5. dark or gloomy

**Directions** Choose a word from the box that best matches each clue. Write the word on the line.

Some have fought for freedom in a **6. fearless** and inspiring way.

The founding fathers **7. magnified** this kind of commitment when they fought against the British and, some would say, **8. fate** itself.

The **9. glimmer** of hope they felt eventually became reality when they defeated the English king's forces. That dedication to the fight for freedom

**10. lingers** , remaining in all Americans to this day.

## Write a Conversation

On a separate sheet of paper, write a short conversation between two members of the colonial army in 1775. Use as many vocabulary words as you can.

**Conversations should include words from the vocabulary list and details about colonial life around the time of the Revolutionary War.**

**Home Activity** Your child identified and used vocabulary words from the poem *The Midnight Ride of Paul Revere*. With your child, look up information about Paul Revere and his activities as a colonist in the 1700s. Discuss the information, using as many vocabulary words as possible.

Name _____

# Subject-Verb Agreement

The subject and verb in a sentence must **agree,** or work together. A singular subject needs a singular verb. A plural subject needs a plural verb.
  Use the following rules for verbs that tell about the present time.

- If the subject is a singular noun or *he, she,* or *it,* add *-s* or *-es* to most verbs.
    The wagon *creaks*. It *lurches* along.

- If the subject is a plural noun or *I, you, we,* or *they,* do not add *-s* or *-es* to the verb.
    The oxen *pull* the wagon. They *strain* uphill.

- For the verb *be,* use *am* and *is* to agree with singular subjects and *are* to agree with plural subjects.
    I *am* hot. Thomas *is* happy. The patriots *are* loyal. We *are* late.

- A **collective noun** names a group, such as *family, team,* and *class.* A collective noun is singular if it refers to a group acting as one: The family *rides* in the wagon. A collective noun is plural if it refers to members of the group acting individually: The family *are arguing* about the tax.

**Directions**  Match each subject with a verb that agrees. Write the letter of the correct verb on the line.

**A or C** 1. The colonists        **A.** are training.

___**D**___ 2. The British king        **B.** is beginning.

___**B**___ 3. A war        **C.** rebel.

___**A**___ 4. Troops        **D.** sends his army.

**Directions**  Underline the verb in ( ) that agrees with the subject of each sentence.

5. The American colonies (<u>trade</u>, trades) with England.

6. Two of the colonies' exports (is, <u>are</u>) cotton and indigo.

7. England (tax, <u>taxes</u>) the items imported into the colonies.

8. Tea (<u>is</u>, are) a popular drink in the colonies.

9. The Boston Tea Party (show, <u>shows</u>) the colonists' anger about taxes.

10. Today, Americans (<u>drink</u>, drinks) more coffee than tea.

11. Earlier conflicts (is, <u>are</u>) forgotten.

12. The two countries (<u>consider</u>, considers) themselves close allies.

**Home Activity**  Your child learned about subject-verb agreement. Have your child make up sentences about clothes he or she wears, using both singular subjects (shirt, belt) and plural subjects (socks, shoes) and making sure verbs agree.

© Pearson Education, Inc., 5

# Final Syllables -er, -ar, -or

| Spelling Words |
| --- |

| danger | wander | tractor | dollar | harbor |
| eager | eraser | surrender | solar | sticker |
| locker | helicopter | pillar | refrigerator | caterpillar |
| rumor | glimmer | linger | sensor | alligator |

**Definitions** Write a list word that means the same or almost the same as the word or phrase.

1. spark          1. **glimmer**
2. port           2. **harbor**
3. sun            3. **solar**
4. gossip         4. **rumor**
5. post           5. **pillar**
6. peril          6. **danger**
7. cooler         7. **refrigerator**
8. excited        8. **eager**
9. 100 cents      9. **dollar**
10. roam          10. **wander**

**Missing Words** Write the list word that completes the sentence.

11. I have a habit of chewing on my pencil ____.          11. **eraser**
12. Smart criminals ____ when spotted.                    12. **surrender**
13. The farmer drove the ____ across the field.           13. **tractor**
14. I store my schoolbooks in my ____.                    14. **locker**
15. The ____ floated silently across the swampy water.    15. **alligator**
16. The ____ became a beautiful butterfly.                16. **caterpillar**
17. She pulled the price ____ off the package.            17. **sticker**
18. The news ____ flew over the accident scene.           18. **helicopter**
19. I like to ____ in my room instead of watching television downstairs.   19. **linger**
20. The motion ____ turns on the light when anyone is near.   20. **sensor**

© Pearson Education, Inc., 5

**Home Activity** Your child wrote words with the final syllables -er, -ar, and -or. Select three list words and ask your child to define them.

**Spelling** Final Syllables -er, -ar, -or   **157**

# Scoring Rubric: Historical Fiction

| | 4 | 3 | 2 | 1 |
|---|---|---|---|---|
| **Focus/Ideas** | Excellent, focused historical fiction; interesting and realistic characters and events | Somewhat focused historical fiction; characters and events are believable but not fully described | Some unclear or off focus details; characters and events are not described well | Historical fiction does not have a clear focus; characters and events have not been described |
| **Organization** | Plot events follow a clear order | Order of plot events is generally clear | Order of plot events isn't always clear | Unorganized and no clear order of events |
| **Voice** | Strongly engages reader | Somewhat engages reader | Not fully engaged | Writer is not engaged |
| **Word Choice** | Uses many sensory details to create strong imagery | Uses some sensory details to create imagery | Few or no sensory details to create imagery | No sensory details or imagery |
| **Sentences** | Uses simple and compound sentences | Some varied sentence structures | Sentences are not varied | Fragments or run-on sentences |
| **Conventions** | Excellent control, few or no errors; correct subject-verb agreement | Good control, few errors; subject-verb agreement generally correct | Errors that hamper understanding; subjects and verbs rarely agree | Many serious errors; subjects and verbs do not agree |

# Vocabulary • Inflected Endings -s, -ed, -ing

**Inflected endings -s, -ed, and -ing** are attached to the end of a word to create a new word with a new meaning. If you are unsure about the meaning of a word with an inflected ending, check the dictionary.

**Directions** Read the following passage about the colonists. Then write the words from the passage that have the inflected ending.

Sometimes your life may seem complicated, but in fact it may be simple compared to a colonist's life. For example, in the 1700s the car had not been invented. Instead of depending on cars for swift travel, people rode horses to get where they needed to go—a very slow method of transportation. The pace was more leisurely than driving a car, but it was still faster than walking.

Walking outside the settlement left a person open to such dangers as wild animals. Since there were no sidewalks or streetlights outside of town, it was best not to linger but to come home quickly. Horses gave colonists an extra measure of safety.

1. -s __cars, horses, dangers, animals, sidewalks, streetlights, colonists__

2. -ed __complicated, compared, invented, needed__

3. -ing __depending, driving, walking__

**Directions** Write the following words with inflected endings -s, -ed, and -ing. Then write a sentence using one of the three new words.

4. depend __depends, depended, depending__

__Possible sentence: My family depends on me to do my chores.__

5. compare __compares, compared, comparing__
__Possible answer: Traveling from place to place is easy today compared to what it was like during colonial times.__

**School + Home** **Home Activity** Your child reviewed the inflected endings -s, -ed, and -ing. Together, make a list of words from a book or a magazine article that contain these endings. Then help your child write new sentences using those words.

© Pearson Education, Inc., 5

# Illustration/Caption

- **Illustrations** or **pictures** can convey information about characters and events in a story. They can help establish mood, dramatize action, reinforce the author's imagery or symbolism, or help explain the text.
- A **caption** is the text explaining the illustration or picture. It usually appears below or to the side of the image.

**Directions** This illustration appears in a text about Ben Franklin. Look at the illustration and read the caption. Then answer the questions below.

This illustration shows Benjamin Franklin flying a kite in an experiment to relate lightning and electricity.

**Possible answers given.**

1. Based on the illustration, in what kind of weather did Franklin fly his kite?

**The weather is cloudy.**

2. Look at the picture. How did Franklin's experiment work?

**Franklin flew a kite in cloudy weather, which caused a key tied to the string to spark.**

3. What do the clothes of the people in the illustration tell you?

**Their clothing is old-fashioned, from over 200 years ago.**

4. Why do Ben Franklin and his companion look pleased?

**Their experiment is going well.**

5. Can you tell where the event took place by looking at the illustration?

**The experiment was carried out in a field.**

**Directions** This illustration gives additional information in a text about state coins. Look at the illustration and read the caption. Then answer the question below.

This illustration shows the Illinois state quarter, whose design was inspired by the artwork of Thom Cicchelli of Chicago.

6. Look at the illustration of the quarter. Who is pictured on the quarter?

**The quarter features Abraham Lincoln.**

7. Based on the illustration, in what year was Illinois admitted to the United States?

**1818**

8. What do the tall buildings show?

**Possible answer: Chicago, a major city in Illinois**

9. What does the caption tell you that is not reflected in the image?

**The design was inspired by Thom Cicchelli's artwork.**

10. How many stars appear on the coin? What do you think they signify?

**Possible answer: 21 stars. The state was the 21$^{st}$ state to join the United States.**

**Home Activity** Your child learned how illustrations and captions can help convey information about a story. Look at one of your child's favorite books and discuss how the illustrations in it help your child learn more about the story.

# Final Syllables -*er*, -*ar*, -*or*

**Proofread a Sign** There are seven spelling errors and one capitalization error. Circle the errors and write the corrections on the lines.

> (welcome) to the Wildlife and (Alligater) Preserve
> - Admission is one dollar for an all-day parking pass.
> - You can rent an all-day locker for your convenience.
> - (Helicoptor) rides are available to see the (harber) from the air.
> - To preserve the ecology, stay on the path. Do not (wandar) off.
> - There is no (dangor.) Animals stay behind a motion (senser) fence.
> - Linger over lunch on our beautiful terrace.
> - Do not forget to (surrendar) your parking pass at the gate when leaving.

1. **Welcome**
2. **Alligator**
3. **Helicopter**
4. **harbor**
5. **wander**
6. **danger**
7. **sensor**
8. **surrender**

**Proofread Words** Circle the word that is spelled correctly.

9. doller       (dollar)       dollor
10. erasor       (eraser)       erasar
11. stickar       (sticker)       stickor
12. soler       (solar)       solor
13. helicoptor       helicoptar       (helicopter)
14. tracter       tractar       (tractor)
15. rumer       (rumor)       rumar

**Home Activity** Your child identified misspelled words with the final syllables -*er*, -*ar*, and -*or*. Select three list words and ask your child to spell them.

# Subject-Verb Agreement

**Directions** Read the passage. Then read each question. Circle the letter of the correct answer.

# Like Longfellow

(1) My grandmother enjoy the poems of Longfellow. (2) Longfellow's poems uses both rhyme and rhythm. (3) "The Midnight Ride of Paul Revere" is called a narrative poem. (4) These poems tell a story. (5) My grandmother write poems too. (6) She entered a narrative poem in a poetry contest and won first prize. (7) Sometimes we recites the poem in a soft voice.

1 What change, if any, should be made in sentence 1?

(A) Add -s to *enjoy*

B Add -s to *grandmother*

C Change *poems* to **poem**

D Make no change

2 What change, if any, should be made in sentence 2?

A Change *poems* to **poem**

(B) Change *uses* to **use**

C Change *Longfellow's* to **Longfellows**

D Make no change

3 In sentence 3, how would you describe the subject?

A Collective noun

B Plural subject

(C) Singular subject

D None of the above

4 What change, if any, should be made in sentence 5?

A Change *My* to **The**

(B) Change *write* to **writes**

C Change *poems* to **poem**

D Make no change

5 What is true about sentence 7?

A The subject is plural.

B The verb is a linking verb.

C The subject is a collective noun.

(D) The subject and verb do not agree.

**School + Home** **Home Activity** Your child prepared for taking tests on subject-verb agreement. Have your child copy some subject and verb pairs from a favorite book and explain why the subjects and verbs agree.

# Digraphs *th*, *sh*, *ch*, *ph*

| Spelling Words | | | | |
|---|---|---|---|---|
| shovel | hyphen | challenge | shatter | charity |
| southern | chosen | approach | ethnic | china |
| northern | establish | astonish | shiver | attach |
| chapter | although | python | pharmacy | ostrich |

**Alphabetize** Write the ten list words below in alphabetical order.

| | |
|---|---|
| ethnic | python |
| ostrich | charity |
| hyphen | although |
| chapter | establish |
| northern | southern |

1. **although**
2. **chapter**
3. **charity**
4. **establish**
5. **ethnic**

6. **hyphen**
7. **northern**
8. **ostrich**
9. **python**
10. **southern**

**Synonyms** Write the list word that has the same or nearly the same meaning.

11. surprise    **astonish**
12. dare    **challenge**
13. shake    **shiver**
14. pottery    **china**
15. picked    **chosen**

16. drugstore    **pharmacy**
17. break    **shatter**
18. fasten    **attach**
19. dig    **shovel**
20. near    **approach**

© Pearson Education, Inc., 5

**Home Activity** Your child learned to spell words with the digraphs *th*, *sh*, *ch*, and *ph*. Ask your child to give an example of a word with each digraph and spell it.

# Regular and Irregular Plural Nouns

**Directions** Write the plural form of each noun.

1. guess  **guesses**
2. cocoon  **cocoons**
3. ax  **axes**
4. branch  **branches**
5. boy  **boys**
6. story  **stories**
7. life  **lives**
8. mouse  **mice**
9. foot  **feet**
10. jacket  **jackets**

**Directions** Underline the plural nouns in each sentence.

11. There are many <u>kinds</u> of <u>beaches</u> in our fifty <u>states</u>.

12. Some <u>shores</u> are packed with <u>shops</u>, <u>restaurants</u>, and <u>hotels</u>.

13. Some are friendly <u>spaces</u>, popular among <u>families</u> with <u>children</u>.

14. In other <u>areas</u>, <u>fishermen</u> catch <u>trout</u>, <u>salmon</u>, and other <u>fish</u>.

15. <u>People</u> can swim in the <u>waves</u> or collect <u>seashells</u> at the beach.

**Directions** Cross out each incorrectly spelled plural noun. Write the correct spelling above the word you crossed out.

16. In autumn, bushes with red <u>leafs</u> **leaves** and berrys **berries** grow near the sand dunes.

17. <u>Foxs</u> **Foxes**, <u>deers</u> **deer**, and wolves are spotted on the sand.

18. Several men and <u>woman</u> **women** relax on benchs **benches** near the water.

# Irregular Plurals

| Spelling Words | | | | |
|---|---|---|---|---|
| staffs | ourselves | pants | scissors | loaves |
| volcanoes | chiefs | buffaloes | flamingos | beliefs |
| echoes | shelves | quizzes | sheriffs | dominoes |
| thieves | measles | avocados | chefs | pianos |

**Analogies** Write the word that completes each comparison.

1. Doctors are to hospitals as **chefs** are to restaurants.

2. Arms are to shirts as legs are to **pants**.

3. Drawers are to chests as **shelves** are to closets.

4. Articles are to essays as tests are to **quizzes**.

5. Storm is to tornado as disease is to **measles**.

6. Knives are to meat as **scissors** are to paper.

7. Ants are to insects as **flamingos** are to birds.

8. Strings are to violins as keys are to **pianos**.

9. Potatoes are to stews as **avocados** are to salads.

10. Ice is to cubes as bread is to **loaves**.

**Word Clues** Write the list word that fits each clue.

11. These animals roamed all over the West.   **buffaloes**

12. These are often black rectangles with white dots.   **dominoes**

13. You might hear these in a huge canyon.   **echoes**

14. These people enforce the law.   **sheriffs**

15. These people may steal from you.   **thieves**

16. You don't want to be close when these erupt.   **volcanoes**

17. These are in charge of tribes or companies.   **chiefs**

18. People have these about topics such as politics.   **beliefs**

19. Organizations such as schools have these.   **staffs**

20. We use this word to describe us.   **ourselves**

© Pearson Education, Inc., 5

**Home Activity** Your child learned to spell words that are irregular plurals. Locate three irregular plurals in a newspaper. Say the singular forms of the words and ask your child to spell the plurals.

# Possessive Nouns

**Directions** Write the possessive form of each underlined noun.

1. <u>mother</u> advice — **mother's**
2. <u>survivor</u> story — **survivor's**
3. <u>child</u> toy — **child's**
4. <u>man</u> overcoat — **man's**
5. <u>monument</u> history — **monument's**
6. <u>mothers</u> lessons — **mothers'**
7. <u>survivors</u> groups — **survivors'**
8. <u>children</u> books — **children's**
9. <u>men</u> clothing — **men's**
10. <u>monuments</u> construction — **monuments'**

**Directions** Rewrite each sentence. Write the possessive form of the underlined noun.

11. A box is tucked away in my <u>grandfather</u> closet.

    **A box is tucked away in my grandfather's closet.**

12. It contains a <u>soldier</u> memories of service.

    **It contains a soldier's memories of service.**

13. Several <u>pictures</u> edges are worn and crumpled.

    **Several pictures' edges are worn and crumpled.**

14. In those pictures, the young <u>men</u> faces are handsome and smiling.

    **In those pictures, the young men's faces are handsome and smiling.**

15. Grandpa treasures his war <u>friends</u> letters and visits.

    **Grandpa treasures his war friends' letters and visits.**

# Vowel Sounds with *r*

| Spelling Words | | | | |
|---|---|---|---|---|
| snore | tornado | spare | appear | career |
| square | report | prepare | pioneer | chair |
| beware | smear | repair | sword | ignore |
| order | engineer | resort | volunteer | declare |

**Word Search** Circle ten hidden list words. Words are down, across, and diagonal. Write the words on the lines.

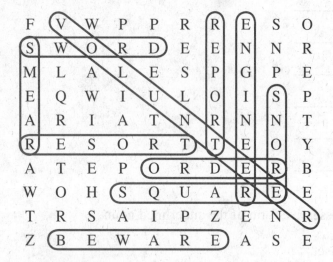

1. __volunteer__
2. __sword__
3. __resort__
4. __order__
5. __square__

6. __beware__
7. __smear__
8. __report__
9. __engineer__
10. __snore__

**Synonyms** Write the list word that has the same or nearly the same meaning.

11. twister __tornado__
12. ready __prepare__
13. occupation __career__
14. announce __declare__
15. seat __chair__

16. fix __repair__
17. overlook __ignore__
18. seem __appear__
19. extra __spare__
20. pathfinder __pioneer__

**School + Home**

**Home Activity** Your child learned to spell words that have vowel sounds with *r*. Select three words from your child's spelling list and make up a sentence with him or her. Ask your child to write the sentence.

# Action and Linking Verbs

**Directions** Underline the verb in each sentence. Write *A* if it is an action verb. Write *L* if it is a linking verb.

1. Myths and tales often <u>seem</u> true.    **L**

2. They <u>are</u> important to each civilization.    **L**

3. Myths <u>address</u> basic human questions.    **A**

4. Myths <u>are</u> part of every culture.    **L**

5. Animals often <u>play</u> a role in myths and tales.    **A**

6. These animals <u>speak</u> like people.    **A**

7. Their actions <u>are</u> clever.    **L**

8. Early civilizations <u>understood</u> the value of myths.    **A**

9. They <u>sought</u> answers around them.    **A**

10. Myths and tales <u>answered</u> questions about the world.    **A**

**Directions** Write a verb from the box to complete each sentence. On the line after the sentence, write *A* if the verb is an action verb. Write *L* if it is a linking verb.

> | brought | tells | was | cause |
> |---------|-------|-----|-------|
> | seems | honored | frightened | were |

11. Children ___**honored**___ the adults. ___**A**___

12. Children who ___**were**___ respectful received praise. ___**L**___

13. The guardian ___**brought**___ a gift for his niece. ___**A**___

14. The uncle's mask ___**frightened**___ his niece. ___**A**___

15. There ___**was**___ a big party for this special day. ___**L**___

16. It ___**seems**___ that many people attend this special party. ___**L**___

17. The Chinese New Year ___**was**___ the cause of the festivities. ___**L**___

18. The uncle ___**tells**___ a story about this special day. ___**A**___

# Final Syllables *-en*, *-an*, *-el*, *-le*, *-il*

| Spelling Words | | | | |
|---|---|---|---|---|
| example | level | slogan | quarrel | scramble |
| evil | oxygen | wooden | double | travel |
| cancel | chuckle | fossil | toboggan | veteran |
| chisel | suburban | single | sudden | beagle |

**Words in Context** Write the word to complete each sentence.

1. I __chuckle__ when I hear an amusing joke.

2. You must __cancel__ your appointment if you can't make it.

3. Breathe deeply to get plenty of __oxygen__.

4. Sailing is a(n) __example__ of a water sport.

5. Molly's __beagle__ is a friendly, cheerful dog.

6. The boys went down the snowy hill on a(n) __toboggan__.

7. A sculptor uses a(n) __chisel__ to shape marble.

8. The scientist found a(n) __fossil__ of a dinosaur in the ground.

9. People can __travel__ in cars, trains, and planes.

10. Baseball players use a(n) __wooden__ bat.

11. Shall we fry, poach, or __scramble__ the eggs?

12. The company's __slogan__ was easy to remember.

**Antonyms** Write the list word that has the opposite or nearly the opposite meaning.

13. newcomer __veteran__

14. agree __quarrel__

15. rural __suburban__

16. married __single__

17. good __evil__

18. uneven __level__

19. gradual __sudden__

20. single __double__

© Pearson Education, Inc., 5

**Home Activity** Your child learned to spell words with the final syllables *-en*, *-an*, *-el*, *-le*, and *-il*. To practice at home, dictate a word with each final syllable. Ask your child to spell the word and provide a synonym or antonym for it.

# Main and Helping Verbs

**Directions** Find the verb phrase in each sentence. Underline the helping verb. Circle the main verb.

1. I <u>am</u> (studying) the American Southwest.

2. The Navajo <u>have</u> (lived) there for generations.

3. Many <u>are</u> (living) on reservations.

4. The people <u>can</u> (farm) the land.

5. Rugs and jewelry <u>are</u> (taken) to market.

6. My parents <u>are</u> (traveling) to the Navajo market.

7. I <u>will</u> (go) with them next year.

8. Everyone <u>should</u> (learn) about native cultures.

9. My moccasins <u>were</u> (sewn) by a Navajo artist.

10. I <u>would</u> (like) a traditional painting.

**Directions** Underline the verb phrase in each sentence. Write *Present* or *Past* to tell the time of the action.

11. The boy <u>is working</u> at a trading post.          **Present**

12. He <u>has saved</u> some money for a saddle.          **Present**

13. People <u>can buy</u> baskets, jewelry, and rugs there.          **Present**

14 His grandmother <u>had sold</u> her bracelet.          **Past**

15. The boy <u>was worrying</u> about his grandmother.          **Past**

16. He <u>had spent</u> his money at the store.          **Past**

17. The boy <u>was giving</u> her back the bracelet.          **Past**

18. His grandmother <u>has gotten</u> the saddle for him.          **Present**

19. He <u>can see</u> the saddle in the truck.          **Present**

20. The boy <u>is smiling</u> at his grandmother.          **Present**

# Final Syllables -er, -ar, -or

| Spelling Words | | | | |
|---|---|---|---|---|
| danger | wander | tractor | dollar | harbor |
| eager | eraser | surrender | solar | sticker |
| locker | helicopter | pillar | refrigerator | caterpillar |
| rumor | glimmer | linger | sensor | alligator |

**Analogies** Write the word that completes each comparison.

1. Hot is to oven as cold is to **refrigerator** .

2. Page is to book as penny is to **dollar** .

3. Flower is to bud as butterfly is to **caterpillar** .

4. Moon is to lunar as sun is to **solar** .

5. Clothes are to closet as books are to **locker** .

6. Walk is to stroll as roam is to **wander** .

7. Patio is to yard as port is to **harbor** .

8. Fingernail is to finger as **eraser** is to pencil.

9. Fact is to fiction as truth is to **rumor** .

10. Sail is to ship as fly is to **helicopter** .

**Hidden Words** Each of these small words can be found inside one of the list words. Write the list word that contains the small word.

11. in **linger**

12. tick **sticker**

13. act **tractor**

14. me **glimmer**

15. all **alligator**

16. end **surrender**

17. ill **pillar or caterpillar**

18. so **sensor or solar**

19. an **danger or wander**

20. age **eager**

© Pearson Education, Inc., 5

**School + Home**

**Home Activity** Your child learned to spell words with the final syllables -er, -ar, and -or. Choose a word with each final syllable from your child's spelling list. Ask your child to spell the word and use it in a sentence.

# Subject-Verb Agreement

**Directions** Underline the verb in ( ) that agrees with the subject of each sentence.

1. Today horses (is, <u>are</u>) no longer needed for transportation.

2. We (<u>use</u>, uses) them to ride for pleasure.

3. Some horse lovers (<u>buy</u>, buys) horses of their own.

4. Food and equipment (<u>become</u>, becomes) expensive.

5. Martin (take, <u>takes</u>) riding lessons at a stable.

6. He (enjoy, <u>enjoys</u>) a horse without the responsibilities of ownership.

7. A saddle and bridle (<u>cost</u>, costs) quite a bit.

8. Our family (do, <u>does</u>) not have the land to keep a horse.

9. A dude ranch (offer, <u>offers</u>) accommodations with horse riding privileges.

10. Guests (<u>stay</u>, stays) in a bunkhouse.

**Directions** Add a verb to complete each sentence. Be sure the verb agrees with the subject.

Possible answers:

11. Paul Revere's horse __**stamps**__ the ground impatiently.

12. Redcoats __**cross**__ the river under cover of night.

13. Two lights __**shine**__ from the church tower.

14. The man and horse __**ride**__ away on their journey.

15. A little moonlight __**shows**__ through the clouds.

16. A warning cry __**rings**__ out in the night.

17. As the sun rises, farmers __**grab**__ their muskets.

18. They __**fight**__ for independence.

19. The fighting __**is**__ fierce.

20. The colonial militia __**defeats**__ the redcoats.

# Comic Book/Graphic Novel Chart

**Directions** Fill in the chart with the characters, problem, settings, and events for your comic book or graphic novel. Make notes about possible illustrations for the events.

---

### Characters

**Answers should include details about each element of a comic book/graphic novel.**

---

### Problem

---

### Settings

---

| Events | Illustrations |
|---|---|
|  |  |
|  |  |
|  |  |
|  |  |

# Create Dialogue

**Directions** Write one or two sentences of dialogue for each part of your comic book or graphic novel. Be sure to indicate which character is speaking each piece of dialogue.

**Beginning** **Answers should have a distinctive voice; use vivid, informal language; and advance the story's plot.**

_____

_____

_____

_____

**Middle** _____

_____

_____

_____

**End** _____

_____

_____

_____

# Adding, Deleting, or Rearranging Sentences

**Directions** Use the word in ( ) to combine the two sentences. Remember to capitalize the first word of the new sentence and to replace the first period with a comma.

(1) Rosa Parks was an African-American woman living in Montgomery, Alabama, in 1955. (2) At that time, African Americans were not allowed to sit in the front of public buses. (3) They also had to give up their seats to white people if the bus became overcrowded. (4) Parks knew these laws were unfair. (5) Rosa Parks later moved to Detroit. (6) One December day, Rosa Parks refused to give up her seat on a bus. (7) She was arrested and later found guilty of disorderly conduct. (8) The African-American community staged a boycott, refusing to ride on Montgomery buses for more than a year. (9) By taking one brave action, Rosa Parks did the right thing to help all African Americans achieve equal rights. (10) After this boycott, the unfair bus laws were changed.

1. Write the number of the sentence that should be deleted. Tell why you think it should be deleted.

## 5; The sentence does not stick to the main topic.

2. Underline the two sentences that need to be rearranged. Write the sentences in the correct order.

## After this boycott, the unfair bus laws were changed. By taking one brave action, Rosa Parks did the right thing to help all African Americans achieve equal rights.

3. Choose one fact below that could be added to improve the paragraph. Write the letter of the sentence. Tell where you would add the sentence. Explain why you think it would improve the paragraph.
   A. Rosa Parks worked as a seamstress.
   B. Rosa Parks had attended African-American political meetings.
   C. In the 1960s, Martin Luther King, Jr. led marches for racial equality.

## Sentence B could be added before or after sentence 4. It gives relevant information about Rosa Parks's background.

# Editing 2

**Directions** Edit these sentences. Look for errors in spelling, grammar, and mechanics. Use proofreading marks to show the corrections.

| Proofreading Marks | |
|---|---|
| Delete (Take out) | ✎ |
| Add | ∧ |
| Spelling | ⬭ |
| Uppercase letter | ≡ |
| Lowercase letter | / |

1. Lauren searched everywhere for Beth's book but she couldnt locate it.

2. Beth and ~~her~~ **she** both liked books by that **author** ~~auther~~, so Beth generously let Lauren read her copy.

3. Lauren looked under her bed, in her **closet** ~~closit~~ and in her backpack.

4. Lauren was **nervous** ~~nervos~~ about telling Beth about the book because everyone dislikes

   someone losing ~~their~~ **his or her** things.

5. Finally, Lauren said, "Beth, unfortunately i **I** have misplaced your book.

6. Beth was upset for a minute **s** ~~soon~~ she said she had a **great** ~~grate~~ idea.

7. Lauren and Beth agreed that Lauren would ~~purchased~~ **purchase** a new book by **their** ~~they're~~ favorite writer.

**This would give**

8. ~~Giving~~ both the opportunity to **read** ~~reed~~ a new book.

Now you'll edit the draft of your personal narrative. Then you'll use your revised and edited draft to make a final copy of your narrative. Finally, you'll share your written work with your audience.

# Sequence

- **Sequence** is the order in which events take place, from first to last.
- Clue words such as *first, next,* and *then* may show sequence in a story or article, but not always.
- Several events can occur at the same time. Words such as *meanwhile* and *during* give clues that two events are happening at the same time.

**Directions** Read the passage. Then use the diagram and the passage to answer the questions.

I went to an astronomy conference last week. Before attending any of the lectures I signed in and was given my free copy of *Earth: Its History and Future.* My favorite lecture was the very first one on the first day of the conference. The only speaker that I didn't enjoy was the person who spoke about Einstein's theories. It was great to be a part of the award ceremony at the close of the conference on the last day, but I have to admit that I was very tired at that point. Other than that, I learned a lot and would recommend the conference to anyone.

**Astronomy Conference Lecture Schedule**

|  | **Mon.** | **Tue.** | **Wed.** | **Thurs.** | **Fri.** |
|---|---|---|---|---|---|
| **9:00 A.M.** | Black Holes in our Galaxy | Einstein's Theories | Asteroids and the Earth | Jupiter's Moons | Supernovas |
| **12:00 NOON** | Lunch | Lunch | Lunch | Lunch | Lunch |
| **1:00 P.M.** | Life in Our Solar System | Space Travel in the 21st Century | Supernovas | The Expansion of the Universe | The Future of NASA |

1. What is the first thing the author did? **signed in and received a free book**

2. What was topic of the first lecture on Wednesday? **asteroids**

3. Which lecture was given right after lunch on Monday? **Life in Our Solar System**

4. On what day and time did the speaker discuss Einstein's Theories? **Tuesday at 9:00 A.M.**

5. What was the last part of the conference? **the awards ceremony**

**Home Activity** Your child read a passage including a schedule of lectures to determine sequence. Work with your child to have him or her produce a weekly schedule of extracurricular activities or chores. Then ask your child questions about the sequence of his or her activities.

# Writing • Short Play

**Key Features of a Short Play**

- includes a list of characters
- describes the setting, time, or place
- features characters who often think or act distinctly

## Summer Dreams

**CHARACTERS**
**SARAH,** an 11-year-old girl
**PATTY,** a 12-year-old girl

**SETTING AND TIME:** a park on a sunny summer day

*(Two girls sit on the grass eating ice cream cones.)*

**PATTY:**   *(Dreamily)* Wouldn't it be great if we could invent a 24-hour ice cream machine? All it would do is make ice cream all day, every day.

**SARAH:**   Yeah! We could make the machine out of melted down old aluminum cans or something. What kind of flavors would we have it make?

**PATTY:**   Everything. Chocolate, vanilla, strawberry, orange, raspberry—everything.

**SARAH:**   *(Excitedly)* And we could have a "sprinkles" option and "fudge" and "whipped cream" options, too!

**PATTY:**   And people could ask for whatever cone they wanted—sugar, waffle . . .

**SARAH:**   And we could have a machine on every corner in the summer!

**PATTY:**   And they'd be free for everyone!

**SARAH:**   *(looking down as ice cream cone drops into her lap)* Um . . . how soon are we inventing this thing?

1. Tell where and when the play is taking place.

   <u>**a park on a sunny summer day**</u>

2. Name two examples of stage directions included in the play.

   <u>**Two girls sit on the grass eating ice cream cones.**</u>

   <u>**Dreamily.**</u>

# Vocabulary

**Directions** Choose the word from the box that best matches each definition.
Write the word on the line.

inspecting _____ 1. examining closely

applauds _____ 2. claps hands in appreciation

fabulous _____ 3. especially good or unique

project _____ 4. tasks planned and performed
to achieve a specific goal

browsing _____ 5. viewing randomly or casually

**Directions** Choose the word from the box that best completes each sentence. Write the word on
the line.

project _____ 6. Building the scenery for the spring play was a _____, or plan,
that took us most of March to complete.

inspecting _____ 7. After carefully examining, or _____, the burned building, the
chief decided that the fire had been an accident.

Browsing _____ 8. _____ through the latest catalog, Shelly found just the right
hat to go with the jacket she'd bought last weekend.

applauds _____ 9. If Dr. Omachi _____ after a performance, you know that the
orchestra was excellent.

fabulous _____ 10. I can't remember a more _____ warm, sunny summer day.

## Write a Newspaper Article

On a separate piece of paper, write a newspaper article about an imaginary new invention. Describe
one or two failures the inventor experienced before he or she was successful. Use as many of the
vocabulary words as you can.

**Narratives should include words from the vocabulary list and details
about a new invention, real or imagined.**

**Home Activity** Your child identified and used vocabulary words from *The Fabulous Perpetual Motion
Machine*. Choose items in the room where you and your child are sitting. See if your child can guess what
you are describing based on the clues you offer.

© Pearson Education, Inc., 5

# Past, Present, and Future Tenses

The **tense** of a verb shows when something happens. Verbs in the **present tense** show action that happens now. Some present tense singular verbs end with *-s* or *-es*. Most present tense plural verbs do not end with *-s* or *-es*.

An inventor <u>creates</u> a new tool. Inventions <u>serve</u> us well.

Verbs in the **past tense** show action that has already happened. Most verbs in the past tense end in *-ed*.

Not long ago, electronics <u>changed</u> the world.

Verbs in the **future tense** show action that will happen. Add *will* (or *shall*) to most verbs to show the future tense.

Many more inventions <u>will appear</u>.

- Some regular verbs change spelling when *-ed* is added. For verbs ending in *e*, drop the *e* and add *-ed*: *used, celebrated*. For verbs ending in a consonant and *y*, change the *y* to *i* and add *-ed*: *spied, lied*.

- For most one-syllable verbs that end in one vowel followed by one consonant, double the consonant and add *-ed*: *wrapped, patted*.

- Irregular verbs change spelling to form the past tense: *are/were, bring/brought, eat/ate, find/found, fly/flew, go/went, have/had, is/was, make/made, see/saw, sit/sat, take/took, tell/told, think/thought, write/wrote.*

**Directions** Write the correct present, past, and future tense of each verb.

| Verb | Present | Past | Future |
|------|---------|------|--------|
| 1. jump | She **jumps**. | She **jumped**. | She **will jump**. |
| 2. sit | He **sits**. | He **sat**. | He **will sit**. |
| 3. worry | We **worry**. | We **worried**. | We **will worry**. |
| 4. stop | It **stops**. | It **stopped**. | It **will stop**. |

**Directions** Rewrite each sentence. Change the underlined verb to the tense in ( ).

5. The Perez twins <u>dream</u> about a new invention. (present)

**The Perez twins dream about a new invention.**

6. They <u>study</u> the laws of motion. (past)

**They studied the laws of motion.**

**School + Home**

**Home Activity** Your child learned about present, past, and future tenses. Have your child read a page in a story aloud, changing past tense verbs to present tense ones or present tense verbs to past tense ones.

Name _____

# Words with Schwa

| Spelling Words | | | | |
|---|---|---|---|---|
| .jewel | kingdom | gasoline | factory | garage |
| tropical | pajamas | estimate | tomorrow | humidity |
| Chicago | bulletin | carnival | illustrate | elegant |
| census | terrific | celebrate | operate | celery |

**Word Clues** Write the list word that fits each clue.

1. This may have rides, contests, costumes, and parades.      1. **carnival**

2. This type of place has palm trees and year-round warm weather.      2. **tropical**

3. This is a type of board for special announcements.      3. **bulletin**

4. This is what you do at birthdays, anniversaries, and holidays.      4. **celebrate**

5. This is a time that is not yesterday or today.      5. **tomorrow**

6. This is where royalty lives and rules.      6. **kingdom**

7. This green vegetable has long, crisp stalks.      7. **celery**

8. This is anything with fancy, classic style.      8. **elegant**

9. This is what you do when you draw pictures.      9. **illustrate**

10. This is a kind of nightwear.      10. **pajamas**

**Words in Context** Write the list word that best completes each sentence.

11. The national ____ is a counting of everyone who lives in the U.S.      11. **census**

12. Can you ____ the number of students in your school?      12. **estimate**

13. Our car needs to be put in the ____ for the night.      13. **garage**

14. We'll need to fill the tank with ____.      14. **gasoline**

15. That ____ makes parts for lawnmowers.      15. **factory**

16. Air conditioning is used in places with lots of heat and ____.      16. **humidity**

17. The doctor had to ____ on me to remove my appendix.      17. **operate**

18. A diamond is a valuable and precious ____.      18. **jewel**

19. The largest city in Illinois is ____.      19. **Chicago**

20. That was one ____ roller coaster ride!      20. **terrific**

© Pearson Education, Inc., 5

**Home Activity** Your child wrote words with the schwa sound. Ask your child to spell three list words, telling you where the schwa sound is in each word.

# Story Sequence B

| Title |
|---|
| |

| Characters |
|---|
| |

| Setting |
|---|
| |

| Events |
|---|
| |

# Vocabulary · Multiple-Meaning Words

- Some words have more than one meaning. They are called **multiple-meaning words.**
- When you see a word you don't know, you may find clues about the word's meaning in the words near the unknown word. These are called context clues.

**Directions** Read the following passage. Then answer the questions below. Use context clues to help you.

The two-wheeled vehicle known as the bicycle was invented in Europe in the nineteenth century. A French version, called a "boneshaker," ran on wooden wheels covered with iron. Its front wheel was slightly larger than the rear one. As indicated by its name, this was not a comfortable bike to ride.

In the 1880s, the English inventor John Kemp Starley took on the project of improving the bicycle. In 1885, he manufactured the Rover Safety Bicycle, a more stable bike. The air-filled tire and the "bicycle built for two," or tandem bicycle, contributed to the popularity of the bicycle in the 1890s.

Today, many cyclists still applaud the bicycle as a convenient and flexible way to get from place to place. Because bikes don't pollute, many people consider them a fabulous way to get around town.

## Possible answers given.

1. What context clues helped you figure out the meaning of *stable*?

**It must mean "safe" or "secure," because the bike is called the Rover Safety Bicycle.**

2. What is another meaning of *stable*?

**A place where horses live is also called a stable.**

3. What are two meanings of the word *tire*?

**Tire can be a verb, meaning "to lose energy," or a noun, meaning "an inflatable wheel for a vehicle."**

4. How do you know which meaning of *tire* is used here?

**The passage is about bicycles, so the "inflatable wheel" meaning makes sense; also, the adjective *air-filled* is a clue.**

© Pearson Education, Inc., 5

**Home Activity** Your child read a passage containing multiple-meaning words and determined their definitions using context clues. Read a newspaper or magazine article with your child, and see who can find and define more multiple-meaning words.

# Advertisement

- An **advertisement** is meant to sell a product or service. Written advertisements may appear in newspapers or on the Internet. Advertisers use many techniques to persuade the reader.
- **Loaded words** affect the reader by creating emotions or making value judgments.
- A **slogan** is a short phrase that is easily remembered.
- A **generality** is vague. It lacks specific details and supporting evidence and facts.
- **Getting on the bandwagon** is another way of saying "everyone else does it."
- A **sweeping generalization** has inadequate evidence and speaks for a large group.

**Directions** Read this advertisement for a car dealership and answer the questions.

---

**Best Deals Ever on Pre-Loved Cars!**

If you've ever wanted a luxury sports car with all the extras, now's the time to buy. **Carz-for-U Sales** is having its biggest sale ever on many of its top-of-the-line sports cars. Most cars come equipped with many of the latest luxury features! Choose from the exciting new fluorescent colors that everyone's buying. These are orange, white, green, or pink. Have you had credit card problems? Don't worry. We always find a way for you to buy your dream car with a just small down payment. **Carz-for-U Sales**—the best deals on wheels!

---

## Possible answers given for 1, 4, 5.

1. Which technique is the advertisement's headline an example of? Why do you think the advertiser calls the cars "pre-loved" instead of "pre-owned" or "used"?

   **loaded words; *Pre-loved* appeals to the buyer's emotion more than *used* does.**

2. Which technique is being used in the third sentence?

   **generality**

3. Which sentence in the ad uses the getting-on-the-bandwagon technique?

   **Choose from the exciting new fluorescent colors that everyone's buying.**

4. The advertiser says that at Carz-for-U Sales, "We always find a way for you to buy your dream car with just a small down payment." What kind of technique is being used? What doesn't the advertiser tell the reader?

   **sweeping generalization; The advertiser doesn't say how much the "small down payment" will be.**

5. How might this advertisement be different if it were made for TV?

   **It probably would show some cars; it would use sound which probably would be loud.**

**Directions**  Read this advertisement for a credit card and answer the questions.

---

# ACT NOW!

## Diamond Classic Plus

**New, Promotional 5.9% APR! ***

- No annual fee
- Online account and bill payment
- **FREE additional cards**
- Special **cardmember privileges**

**Your Credit Limit: Up to $15,000**

Reply within 10 days

Can you believe it? The holidays are just around the corner. Impress your friends with your new **Diamond Classic Plus Card** with no annual fee.

Save hundreds of dollars with free coupons to your favorite stores and restaurants—as part of your **cardmember privileges.** All you have to do is sign up before December 1. Pay your bill online and save with our special online **Shopping Mall.** Need cash? You can use your new card to receive cash within seconds.*

How can you benefit from this offer? It's easy. Just fill out the Application below and mail it today!

*See details on reverse.

---

**Possible answers given.**

**6.** List two statements the advertiser uses to convince the reader to take immediate action.

**act now, reply within 10 days**

**7.** Identify three examples of loaded words used in the advertisement.

**special, privileges, impress your friends**

**8.** The advertiser uses an asterisk twice to refer to the note at the bottom of the page. Why do you think the advertiser refers the reader to the other side of the letter?

**This may keep the reader from noticing any negative parts of the offer.**

**9.** List three services or extras the advertiser offers beyond being able to buy now and pay later.

**free additional cards, online payment, card member privileges**

**10.** Would this advertisement most likely appear on a billboard or in a letter mailed to a person's home? Why do you think so?

**Students should explain the reasoning behind their answers.**

**Home Activity**  Your child learned about advertisements. Write an advertisement for an imaginary product or service with your child using some of the advertising techniques your child has learned about. Discuss how the advertisement tries to persuade the reader.

Name _____

# Words with Schwa

**Proofread a Letter** Laura wrote this letter to her aunt. Circle six spelling errors. Write the words correctly. Find one punctuation error. Write the sentence correctly.

> Dear Aunt Betty,
>     Next week we will (celabrate) at the (carnaval) We've been decorating a float. Our theme will be the city of Chicago. The city has many (eligant) buildings. We want to (illestrate) this on our float. We were a little off on our (estamate) of how long it would take to complete it. It (probly) won't be easy(,) to get this beautiful, decorated platform out of the garage. Even so, we are looking forward to a terrific day!

1. **celebrate**
2. **carnival**
3. **elegant**
4. **illustrate**
5. **estimate**
6. **probably**
7. **It probably won't be easy to get this beautiful, decorated platform out of the garage.**

**Proofread Words** Circle the correct spelling of the list word.

8. We moved to a _____ climate this winter.

   tropecal        (tropical)        troppicle

9. The _____ made people feel sticky when they went outside.

   (humidity)        humiduty        humidety

10. My favorite _____ have feet in them.

   pajammas        pajamers        (pajamas)

11. The _____ shows that the population of our town has doubled.

   sensus        (census)        censis

12. The weather _____ says that snow is on the way!

   bullatin        bulliten        (bulletin)

**Spelling Words**

jewel
kingdom
gasoline
factory
garage
tropical
pajamas
estimate
tomorrow
humidity

Chicago
bulletin
carnival
illustrate
elegant
census
terrific
celebrate
operate
celery

**Frequently Misspelled Words**

Christmas
beautiful
probably

**School + Home  Home Activity** Your child identified misspelled words with schwa. Have your child tell you the three hardest words and then spell the words aloud.

## Past, Present, and Future Tenses

**Directions** Read the passage. Then read each question. Circle the letter of the correct answer.

# Science Fair

(1) Most schools in our county host an annual science fair. (2) In many cases, each grade hold its own competition. (3) Students from each grade compete against one another. (4) Students perform experiments and make displays to explain scientific ideas. (5) The most original projects will win the highest honors. (6) Winning projects _____ with winners from other schools. (7) Right now, avid competitors _____ daily on their projects for next year.

1  What is the verb tense in sentence 1?

  A   Past

  **B**   Present

  C   Future

  D   There is no verb.

2  What change, if any, should be made in sentence 2?

  **A**   Change *hold* to **holds**

  B   Change *cases* to **case**

  C   Change *its* to **it's**

  D   Make no change

3  In sentence 4, how would you change the underlined verb to future tense?

  A   has performed

  **B**   will perform

  C   performs

  D   performing

4  Choose the future tense form of *compete* to best complete sentence 6.

  A   were competing

  B   competed

  C   have competed

  **D**   will compete

5  Which form of *work* best completes sentence 7?

  A   worked

  B   works

  **C**   work

  D   working

© Pearson Education, Inc., 5

**School + Home**   **Home Activity** Your child prepared for taking tests on present, past, and future tenses. Have your child explain the present, past, and future tenses of verbs and give examples of each.

# Main Idea and Details

- The **main idea** is the most important idea about a paragraph, passage, or article.
- **Details** are small pieces of information that tell more about the main idea.

**Directions** Read the following passage and complete the diagram. State the main idea of the passage and three supporting details.

> Artist Wesley Dennis (1903–1966) was an expert at painting horses. He had the ability to capture each horse's personality in his paintings. In 1945, writer Marguerite Henry asked him to illustrate her first book, *Justin Morgan Had a Horse*. He illustrated fifteen of Henry's horse books, including *King of the Wind* and *Misty of Chincoteague*. All three of these books were very popular with children and won awards for children's literature. Dennis is also known for his paintings in Anna Sewell's powerful story *Black Beauty*.

## Possible answers given for 2–5.

**Main Idea**

1. **Wesley Dennis was an expert at painting horses.**

**Detail**

2. **Dennis could capture each horse's personality.**

**Detail**

3. **Marguerite Henry asked him to illustrate her books.**

**Detail**

4. **Dennis illustrated *Black Beauty*.**

5. Write a one-sentence summary of this passage.

**Wesley Dennis illustrated many children's books about horses.**

**Home Activity** Your child identified the main idea and details of a brief passage. Work with your child to identify the main idea and details for individual paragraphs in a magazine or newspaper article. Challenge your child to write a summary of it.

# Writing • Writing for Tests

## How Cell Phones Changed Lives

The cell phone is the modern invention that has changed people's lives the most. Before cell phones were invented, people were unable to contact one another without being inside a house where there was a landline telephone. Now you use a cell phone to call people when you are just about anywhere! You can also use cell phones for more than just phone calls.

Cell phones now come in all shapes and sizes. You can keep them in your purse, pocket, or even attached to your ear. Cell phones are used to send e-mail, surf the Internet, and play games. You can even take photos or make videos using your phone!

A cell phone can be a telephone, a computer, a camera, and a camcorder, a game player, and a music player all in one. Imagine if you had to carry around all of those things in your school bag at the same time. That would be too much! Don't you agree?

For these reasons, I think the cell phone is the most important invention of our times.

1. Underline the topic sentence.

2. List two examples of details or relevant evidence that support the writer's viewpoint.

   **Cell phones can send e-mail. You can call someone from almost anywhere.**

3. Circle where the writer tries to get support for the idea.

© Pearson Education, Inc., 5

Name_____

# Vocabulary

**Directions** Choose the word from the box that best matches each definition. Write the word on the line.

cannon _____

architect _____

fashioned _____

philosopher _____

rival _____

1. a big gun mounted on a base or wheels

2. a person who designs and makes plans for buildings

3. made, shaped, or done

4. a person who studies the basic nature of knowledge and reality

5. a person who wants and tries to get the same thing as another or tries to do better than another

**Directions** Choose the word from the box that best fits in each sentence. Write the word on the line shown to the left.

bronze _____

achieved _____

rival _____

midst _____

depressed _____

6. The horse's yellow-brown coat was so rich and shiny it looked like it was made from ____.

7. Working together on their books about horses, Wesley Dennis and Marguerite Henry ____ great success.

8. Amelia was known as the best artist in school, but her ____ Lily was trying to outdo her with a new painting.

9. The wild pony did not like being fenced in. It was happier in the ____ of the wide open fields.

10. Julia felt sad, or ____, when she had to leave the ranch at the end of the summer.

## Write a Journal Entry

On a separate sheet of paper write a journal entry describing an animal you have drawn. Use as many vocabulary words as you can. Include a drawing if possible.

**Journal entries should describe an animal the student has drawn and include words from the vocabulary list. It may also include a drawing.**

© Pearson Education, Inc., 5

**Home Activity** Your child identified and used vocabulary words from *Leonardo's Horse*. Read a story or nonfiction article with your child. Have your child point out unfamiliar words. Work together to figure out the meaning of each word by using other words that are near it.

# Principal Parts of Regular Verbs

A verb's tenses are made from four basic forms. These basic forms are called the verb's **principal parts.**

| Present | Present Participle | Past | Past Participle |
|---|---|---|---|
| watch | (am, is, are) watching | watched | (has, have, had) watched |
| study | (am, is, are) studying | studied | (has, have, had) studied |

A **regular verb** forms its past and past participle by adding *-ed* or *-d* to the present form.

- The present and the past forms can be used by themselves as verbs.
- The present participle and the past participle are always used with a helping verb.

**Directions** Write the form of the underlined verb indicated in ( ).

1. For centuries, people <u>admire</u> the works of Leonardo da Vinci. (past participle)

   **have admired**

2. Today he <u>enjoy</u> the title of greatest genius of the Renaissance. (present participle)

   **is enjoying**

3. He <u>observe</u> everyday activities as a scientist. (past) _____ **observed** _____

4. Leonardo <u>paint</u> with greater skill than any other artist of his time. (past)

   **painted**

5. He <u>fill</u> notebooks with his observations, illustrations, and original ideas. (past)

   **filled**

6. Scientists <u>create</u> working models from his instructions and drawings. (past participle)

   **have created**

7. Leonardo's life <u>inspire</u> me to be more observant. (past participle) _____ **has inspired** _____

**Directions** Underline the verb in each sentence. Write *present, present participle, past,* or *past participle* to identify the principal part used to form the verb.

8. Leonardo <u>lived</u> in Vinci, Italy, as a boy. _____ **past** _____

9. Soon he <u>had developed</u> a keen eye and an observant nature. _____ **past participle**

10. Most people <u>recognize</u> the name Leonardo da Vinci. _____ **present** _____

**Home Activity** Your child learned about principal parts of regular verbs. Ask your child to write the principal parts of *love, live,* and *dream* and then use each part in a sentence about himself or herself.

© Pearson Education, Inc., 5

Name _____

# Compound Words

© Pearson Education, Inc., 5

| Spelling Words | | | | |
|---|---|---|---|---|
| waterproof | teaspoon | grasshopper | homesick | barefoot |
| courthouse | earthquake | rowboat | scrapbook | countryside |
| lightweight | fishhook | spotlight | blindfold | whirlpool |
| tablespoon | greenhouse | postcard | hummingbird | thumbtack |

**Complete the Sentence** Write the list word that best completes the sentence.

1. Do you know that three teaspoons equal one _____?

2. The _____ is a place where justice is tested every day.

3. The ant stored food while the _____ played.

4. When you're away for a while, it is common to feel _____.

5. The hum from a _____ comes from its rapidly beating wings.

6. Some people wear a _____ to sleep on an airplane.

7. The _____ is full of exotic plants.

8. The circle of light on the stage was from the _____.

9. I like to walk _____ in the wet sand.

10. The _____ was full of old news clippings and photos.

1. __tablespoon__
2. __courthouse__
3. __grasshopper__
4. __homesick__
5. __hummingbird__
6. __blindfold__
7. __greenhouse__
8. __spotlight__
9. __barefoot__
10. __scrapbook__

**Definitions** Answer each clue with a list word. Write it on the line.

11. hills, trees, and lakes

12. not heavy at all

13. carries a message

14. hang something with it

15. stays dry

16. shaking ground

17. boat with oars

18. worm holder

19. one-third of a tablespoon

20. circling water

11. __countryside__
12. __lightweight__
13. __postcard__
14. __thumbtack__
15. __waterproof__
16. __earthquake__
17. __rowboat__
18. __fishhook__
19. __teaspoon__
20. __whirlpool__

**School + Home**

**Home Activity** Your child used the meanings of list words to write them in sentences and match them with synonyms. Ask your child to tell you what a compound word is and give three examples.

# Scoring Rubric: Persuasive Speech

|  | 4 | 3 | 2 | 1 |
|---|---|---|---|---|
| **Focus/Ideas** | Has a clear focus, idea, and position; uses sound reasoning | Has a mostly clear focus, idea, and position; uses some sound reasoning | Lacks a clear idea, focus, and position; lacks sound reasoning | Has no clear idea, focus, or position; has no sound reasoning |
| **Organization** | Has the argument stated in a topic sentence with strong supporting details | Includes an argument and some supporting details | Lacks an argument or supporting details | Has no argument or supporting details |
| **Voice** | Uses clear persuasive language and an active voice | Uses mostly persuasive language and an active voice | Uses very little persuasive language; very little active voice | Uses no persuasive language or active voice |
| **Word Choice** | Strong persuasive language | Language persuasive | Language sometimes unpersuasive | Language unpersuasive |
| **Sentences** | Smooth, varied, rhythmic sentences | Some variety in sentences | Many sentences lacking variety | Choppy or rambling sentences |
| **Conventions** | Correct use of principal parts of regular verbs | Mostly correct use of principal parts of regular verbs | Little correct use of principal parts of regular verbs | No correct use of principal parts of regular verbs |

# Vocabulary • Greek and Latin Roots

- Many English words are based on **Greek or Latin roots,** which are often included in their definitions in a dictionary. Greek and Latin roots may help you understand the meanings of unfamiliar words.
- The root *bio-* means "life," *arch-* means "chief or ruler," and *philo-* means "loving."

**Directions** Read the following passage. Then answer the questions below.

> The great Renaissance artist Raphael achieved fame during his lifetime. He was respected as an architect. He designed two churches in Rome, but he is known more for his painting than for his architecture. One of his most famous paintings is called *The School of Athens.* It shows the philosopher as a hero. The Greek philosophers Plato and Aristotle are at the center of the painting. They are standing in the midst of other great philosophers from ancient times.
>
> Raphael had many students in his studio. They helped him complete his larger works. Raphael was a well-loved teacher, and some of the students thought of others students as rivals. After Raphael's death, however, his students worked together to complete many important works started by their teacher. The biographer Giorgio Vasari called Raphael "the prince of painters."

1. The Greek root *arch–* means "chief or ruler." The Greek word *tekton* means "builder." What do these tell you about the meaning of *architect*?

   **An architect can be a chief builder.**

2. The Greek root *philo–* means "loving." The Greek word *sophia* means "knowledge, learning." What do these tell you about the meaning of *philosopher*?

   **A philosopher can be a person who loves knowledge.**

3. The Greek root *bio–* means "life." The Greek word *graphia* means "record." What do these tell you about the meaning of *biographer*?

   **It means "a person who makes a record of someone's life."**

4. The Latin word *studium* means "to study." What does this tell you about the meaning of *studio*?

   **A studio can be a place to study.**

5. Write as many words as you can think of that use the roots *arch–, philo–,* and *bio–.* If you cannot think of any words on your own, use the dictionary for help.

   **Check students' answers for accuracy.**

**Home Activity** Your child identified Greek and Latin roots to understand unfamiliar words in a passage. Read a passage with your child and see if you can find words with Greek and Latin roots. Use a dictionary for any words you are not sure of. Then think of other words with the same root to figure out their meanings.

# Skim and Scan

- To **scan** is to move one's eyes quickly down the page, seeking specific words and phrases. Scanning is used to find out if a resource will answer a reader's questions. Once a reader has scanned a document, he or she might go back and skim it.

- To **skim** a document is to read the first and last paragraphs, as well as to use headings, summaries, and other organizers as you move down the page. Skimming is used to quickly identify the main idea. You might also read the first sentence of each paragraph.

**Directions**  Scan the passage to answer the questions below.

---

**Albrecht Dürer (1471–1528)**

**Early Life and Career.** Dürer's training began as a draftsman in his father's workshop in Germany. By the age of thirteen, he had already made his first self-portrait. One year later, in 1485, he produced *Madonna with Musical Angels*. For four years, he studied painting and woodcutting with a master.

**Travel and Artistic Growth.** In 1490, Dürer began several years of travel and painting. His trips around Europe were very important to his artistic development.

His journeys to Italy, the Netherlands (Holland), France, and Switzerland especially influenced his art.

**Important Works.** By 1505, Dürer was famous. Eventually he became recognized as the greatest German Renaissance painter and printmaker. Some of Dürer's important works include *Self-Portrait* (1500), *Portrait of a Young Man* (1500), *The Feast of the Rose Garlands* (1506), *Adam and Eve* (1507), and *Four Apostles* (1526).

---

1. When you scan this passage, what helps you find specific information?

   **the title of the passage,  the headings of the paragraphs**

2. In which paragraph would you find the titles of Dürer's most famous paintings?

   **the last paragraph**

3. In which paragraph would you find out if Dürer painted as a youth?

   **the first paragraph**

4. In what part of the passage would you find when Dürer lived?

   **the title**

5. Can you find out about Dürer's printmaking methods by scanning this passage?

   **No, because none of the paragraph titles mentions Dürer's printmaking methods.**

**Directions** Skim the following passage to answer the questions below.

### The Printing Press

The inventor of the printing press was a goldsmith named **Johannes Gutenberg**. The invention of the press occurred around 1450 in Germany, and it marked an important advance for Renaissance culture.

The use of the printing press spread rapidly throughout Europe. By the year 1500, as many as twenty million books had been printed. The discovery changed life during the Renaissance. For one thing, there was an increase in the number of people who learned to read. Secondly, printing spread knowledge and ideas. Some scholars believe that the invention of the printing press was nearly as important as the invention of writing itself.

**Possible answers given for 6, 9, 10.**

**6.** What is a good way to skim this passage?

**Read the first sentence of each paragraph and the last sentence of the passage.**

**7.** What is the topic of this passage?

**The passage is about the invention of the printing press.**

**8.** Is the passage about silversmithing? How can you tell?

**No, the passage does not mention silver-smithing.**

**9.** Is the writer of this passage conveying facts or opinions? How can you tell?

**The writer is conveying facts; The sentences I skimmed contain no personal references or judgment words.**

**10.** How would you express the main idea of this passage?

**The printing press was an extremely important invention that changed human culture.**

© Pearson Education, Inc., 5

**Home Activity** Your child learned about skimming and scanning a text. Have your child quickly skim an encyclopedia entry and tell you what he or she learned.

# Compound Words

**Proofread a Letter** Halie wrote a letter home from camp. There are seven spelling errors and one capitalization error. Circle the errors and write the corrections on the lines.

Dear Mom and Dad,

I'm not crying or homsick This paper got a little wet because I'm in a rowboat. I have a fish hook on the line. The countryside around camp is awesome. We run around bearfoot most days. My Counselor is the nature teacher. Yesterday, everybody saw a hummbird The camp has a greenhouse where all the vegetables we eat are grown. Thanks for the waterproff slicker. It's litewait and will keep me dry. You sent a really beautiful postcard of the Grand Canyon. I used a thumtack to hang it on my bunk wall!

Write soon,
Halie

1. **homesick**          2. **fishhook**
3. **barefoot**          4. **hummingbird**
5. **waterproof**       6. **lightweight**
7. **thumbtack**
8. **My counselor is the nature teacher.**

**Proofread Words** Correct the spellings of the list words. Write the words correctly on the lines.

9. Meet me on the steps of the <u>corthouse</u>.

10. My <u>scapebook</u> is full of pictures and mementos.

11. Performers love to be in the <u>spotelite</u>.

12. The bathwater went down the drain in a little <u>wirlpool</u>.

13. Pictures fell off the wall during the <u>erthkwake</u>.

14. I folded my scarf into a <u>blindefold</u>.

15. A <u>grasshoper</u> has long, strong legs.

9. **courthouse**
10. **scrapbook**
11. **spotlight**
12. **whirlpool**
13. **earthquake**
14. **blindfold**
15. **grasshopper**

**Home Activity** Your child identified misspelled compound words. Ask your child to spell three of the compound words for you.

© Pearson Education, Inc., 5

## Principal Parts of Regular Verbs

**Directions** Read the passage. Then read each question. Circle the letter of the correct answer.

# Leonardo's Journals

(1) Leonardo da Vinci pursued a wide range of interests. (2) He had so many ideas that new ones distracted him from other projects. (3) Some have observed that he possessed too many abilities. (4) One lifetime contains too few hours for such a man. (5) Leonardo's journals (preserve) many of his plans and ideas. (6) In them, he recorded plans for many inventions. (7) This is how we learn of his great genius today.

**1** Which describes the principal part of the underlined verb in sentence 1?

- **A** Past
- **B** Present
- **C** Past participle
- **D** Present participle

**2** What is the present form of the underlined verb in sentence 2?

- **A** distract
- **B** am distracting
- **C** is distracting
- **D** are distracting

**3** Which describes the principal parts of the two underlined verbs in sentence 3?

- **A** Past/Past
- **B** Present participle/Past
- **C** Past participle/Past
- **D** Present participle/Past participle

**4** Which two present tense verbs are found in this passage?

- **A** preserved, learn
- **B** have, learn
- **C** recorded, learn
- **D** contains, learn

**5** Which form of the verb in parentheses best completes sentence 5?

- **A** has preserved
- **B** have preserved
- **C** are preserved
- **D** is preserving

© Pearson Education, Inc., 5

**School + Home** **Home Activity** Your child prepared for taking tests on principal parts of verbs. Ask your child to name the principal parts of the verbs *paint* and *invent* and then use each part in a sentence.

# Fact and Opinion

- You can prove a **statement of fact** true or false. You can do this by using your own knowledge, asking an expert, or checking a reference source such as an encyclopedia or a nonfiction text.
- A **statement of opinion** gives ideas or feelings, not facts. It cannot be proved true or false.
- A sentence may contain both a statement of fact and a statement of opinion.

**Directions** Read the following passage. Then complete the diagram below by following its instructions, and answer the questions.

In 1861, the fossil remains of an *Archaeopteryx* (Ahr-key-OP-ter-iks) were discovered in Germany. They are about 150 million years old. Many scientists believe *Archaeopteryx* is the earliest known bird. When I saw it in a museum, I thought it looked like it was part dinosaur and part bird. It had feathers and wings like birds. It also had teeth and three claws on each wing. According to many scientists, *Archaeopteryx* could fly, but I'm not so sure. I think it might have flapped its wings, but I can't imagine it ever got off the ground.

**Possible answers given.**

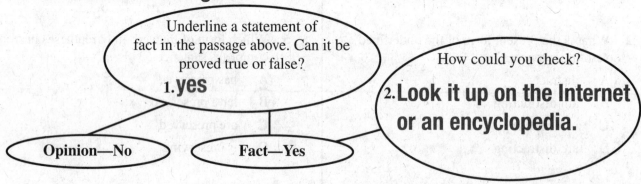

Underline a statement of fact in the passage above. Can it be proved true or false?
1. **yes**

Opinion—No          Fact—Yes

How could you check?
2. **Look it up on the Internet or an encyclopedia.**

3. Write a statement of opinion from the passage. How do you know it is a statement of opinion?

**"I thought it looked part dinosaur and part bird."; It cannot be proven.**

4. Which sentence contains both a fact and an opinion?

**"... many scientists ... could fly, but I'm not so sure."**

5. In the last sentence, the author expresses an opinion that *Archaeopteryx* couldn't have flown. What kind of details would support this opinion?
**The size of the fossil makes it look too heavy to fly.**

**School + Home**

**Home Activity** Your child read a short passage and identified facts and opinions. Read an article together. Ask your child to identify statements of fact and ask how they can be proven.

© Pearson Education, Inc., 5

# Writing • Advertising Brochure

**Key Features of an Advertising Brochure**

- persuades readers to do something, such as buy a product or attend an event
- lists reasons why reader should do something
- may appeal to a specific audience, such as teens, women, fathers

## Come Visit the Oak Lake Music Festival!

The Oak Lake Music Festival offers pleasing sounds for the whole family. Come and hear something new!

**When and Where**
The Festival takes place at the Main Pavilion, Oak Lake Park.
It runs daily from Thursday, March 6 through Sunday, March 9.

**What is the Festival?**
The Oak Lake Music Festival began in 1973. It has brought a wide variety of musical performers to the Oak Lake region. Features of the festival include:

- National acts playing a variety of musical styles; lineup includes Shanita, the Stockton Boys, and Avery Taylor
- Workshops on playing both traditional and contemporary music
- A refreshment tent offering delicious and affordable food
- Fireworks on Saturday!

Mariana Ciwiec, who attended last year's festival, writes, "I'm definitely coming back to Oak Lake with my husband and kids. Last year we all had a blast!"

What better way to celebrate the beginning of spring than listening to music in the beautiful environs of the lake? Make your reservation today: you can call or e–mail us.

1. Why does the author include the quote by Mariana Ciwiec?

   **To support the claim that the festival is fun for the whole family.**

2. Put a box around the list of reasons for attending. How did the author decide to order the list?

   **Students should box bulleted list. The reasons are ordered from the most important to the least important.**

# Vocabulary

**Directions** Draw a line to connect each word on the left to the matching definition on the right.

1. proportion          a special event

2. foundations          put up; built

3. erected          space or building where work is done

4. workshop          a proper relation among parts

5. occasion          parts on which other parts rest for support

**Check the Words You Know**

___erected
___foundations
___mold
___occasion
___proportion
___tidy
___workshop

**Directions** Choose the word from the box that best completes each sentence. Write the word on the line to the left.

**mold**_____ 6. Julia poured plaster into a _____ shaped like a bird.

**occasion**_____ 7. She was creating a statue for a special event, or _____.

**erected**_____ 8. We _____, or built, a statue in front of the new library.

**workshop**_____ 9. When she finished making the bird, her _____ was a mess.

**tidy**_____ 10. She likes to wipe up the dust made by the plaster and _____ her workbench before she goes home.

## Write a News Report

On a separate sheet of paper, write a news report about an important discovery, like the discovery of the *Archaeopteryx* fossil remains. Use as many vocabulary words as you can.

**The news report should include words from the vocabulary list and details about a discovery.**

© Pearson Education, Inc., 5

**Home Activity** Your child identified and used vocabulary words from *The Dinosaurs of Waterhouse Hawkins*. Read a story or nonfiction article with your child about dinosaurs or animals. Have him or her describe the dinosaur or animal and then explain whether the description is a statement of fact or of opinion.

# Principal Parts of Irregular Verbs

Usually you add -ed to a verb to show past tense. **Irregular verbs** do not follow this rule. Instead of having -ed forms to show past tense, irregular verbs usually change to other words.

| | |
|---|---|
| **Present Tense** | The king sees the Crystal Palace. |
| **Present Participle** | The king is seeing the Crystal Palace. |
| **Past Tense** | The king saw the Crystal Palace. |
| **Past Participle** | The king has seen the Crystal Palace. |

| Present Tense | Present Participle | Past Tense | Past Participle |
|---|---|---|---|
| bring | (am, is, are) bringing | brought | (has, have, had) brought |
| build | (am, is, are) building | built | (has, have, had) built |
| choose | (am, is, are) choosing | chose | (has, have, had) chosen |
| come | (am, is, are) coming | came | (has, have, had) come |
| draw | (am, is, are) drawing | drew | (has, have, had) drawn |
| eat | (am, is, are) eating | ate | (has, have, had) eaten |
| find | (am, is, are) finding | found | (has, have, had) found |
| grow | (am, is, are) growing | grew | (has, have, had) grown |
| run | (am, is, are) running | ran | (has, have, had) run |
| set | (am, is, are) setting | set | (has, have, had) set |
| speak | (am, is, are) speaking | spoke | (has, have, had) spoken |
| tell | (am, is, are) telling | told | (has, have, had) told |

**Directions** Underline the verb in each sentence. Write *present, present participle, past,* or *past participle* to identify the principal part of the verb.

1. He built a studio in Manhattan. _____ past _____

2. Hawkins had chosen Central Park for his display._____ past participle _____

**Directions** Write the sentence using the principal part of the underlined verb indicated in ( ).

3. Archaeologists find many more dinosaur bones. (past participle) Archaeologists have found many more dinosaur bones.

4. Today dinosaur exhibits draw huge crowds. (present participle)
Today dinosaur exhibits are drawing huge crowds.

**Home Activity** Your child learned about principal parts of irregular verbs. Ask your child to write the principal parts of *tell* and *write* and then use each part in a sentence telling what he or she could communicate about dinosaurs.

# Consonant Sounds /j/, /ks/, /sk/, and /s/

| Spelling Words | | | | |
|---|---|---|---|---|
| excuse | scene | muscle | explore | pledge |
| journal | science | schedule | gigantic | scheme |
| Japan | excellent | exclaim | fascinate | ginger |
| scholar | scent | dodge | smudge | schooner |

**Classify** Write the list word that best completes the group.

1. plan, plot, _____

2. avoid, elude, sidestep, _____

3. diary, log, magazine, _____

4. setting, landscape, _____

5. aroma, perfume, odor, _____

6. captivate, interest, _____

7. bone, skin, _____

8. yacht, kayak, _____

9. outstanding, brilliant, _____

10. basil, oregano, _____

1. __scheme__

2. __dodge__

3. __journal__

4. __scene__

5. __scent__

6. __fascinate__

7. __muscle__

8. __schooner__

9. __excellent__

10. __ginger__

**Words in Context** Write the list word that completes each sentence.

11. Tokyo is the largest city in _____.

12. Cry out and _____ mean the same thing.

13. A _____ enjoys learning and studying.

14. The bad weather is my _____ for being late today.

15. Astronauts _____ outer space.

16. I'll add the meeting to my _____.

17. I made a donation _____ to the local charity.

18. My _____ book contains many experiments.

19. The _____ on the wall is from finger paint.

20. The redwood trees in California are _____.

11. __Japan__

12. __exclaim__

13. __scholar__

14. __excuse__

15. __explore__

16. __schedule__

17. __pledge__

18. __science__

19. __smudge__

20. __gigantic__

**Home Activity** Your child wrote words with special spellings for certain consonant sounds. Have your child pick the five most difficult words for him or her. Go over the spellings of these words with your child.

© Pearson Education, Inc., 5

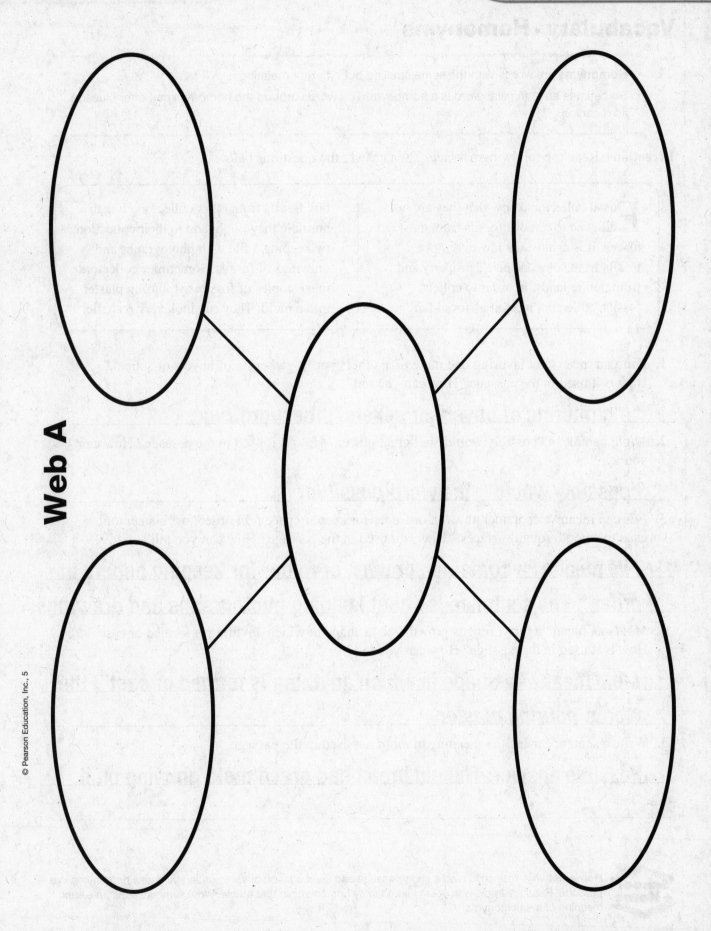

**Web A**

# Vocabulary • Homonyms

- **Homonyms** are words with the same spelling but different meanings.
- Sometimes an unfamiliar word is a homonym. The words around the homonym can offer clues to its meaning.

**Directions** Read the following passage. Then answer the questions below.

> Fossil collectors know that they are not allowed to remove fossils from most places. It is against the law to remove fossils from someone else's property and from public lands. In order to collect fossils, collectors meet at a "fossil fair" to buy fossils from other collectors. It's also possible they might add to their collection by keeping a file with photographs and drawings of fossils. Sometimes collectors make copies of fossils by pouring plaster into a mold. They can look very realistic.

1. *Fair* can mean "not favoring one more than others" or "a gathering of buyers or sellers." How is it used in the passage? How can you tell?

   **"a gathering of buyers or sellers"; the word *buy***

2. *Might* can mean "possibly would" or "great power." How is it used in the passage? How can you tell?

   **"possibly would"; the word *possible***

3. *File* can mean "a container, drawer, or folder for keeping papers in order" or "a steel tool used to smooth rough surfaces." How is it used in the passage? How can you tell?

   ***File* means "a container, drawer, or folder for keeping papers in order"; The sentence is about keeping photographs and drawings.**

4. *Mold* can mean "a furry, fungus growth" or "a shape in which anything is formed or cast." How is it used in the passage? How can you tell?

   ***Mold* means "a shape in which anything is formed or cast"; the words *pouring plaster***

5. Write a sentence using the meaning of *mold* not used in the passage.

   **Possible answer: The old bread had green mold growing on it.**

**Home Activity** Your child read a short passage and used context clues to understand new homonyms in a passage. Read an article with your child. Identify homonyms in that article. Write sentences that use each meaning of the homonyms.

# Schedule

A **schedule** is a kind of table with **rows** and **columns**. The rows and columns meet at boxes that are called **cells**. Schedules show times, dates, and locations for airplanes, trains, buses, activities, and sporting events.

**Directions** Use this train schedule to answer the questions.

**Departure Schedule for Trains to Chicago**

| | | A.M. | A.M. | A.M. | P.M. | P.M. | P.M. |
|---|---|---|---|---|---|---|---|
| **Waukekee** | | 5:01 | 7:30 | 11:30 | 1:00 | 3:30 | 5:00 |
| **Hampton** | | 5:45 | 8:15 | 12:15 | 1:45 | 4:15 | 5:45 |
| **Rainville** | * | 6:15 | 8:45 | 12:45 | 2:15 | 4:45 | 6:15 |
| **Harbor Park** | * | 7:00 | 9:30 | 1:30 | 3:00 | 5:00 | 7:00 |
| **Arrive in Chicago** | | 8:00 | 10:30 | 2:30 | 4:00 | 6:00 | 8:00 |

\* Indicates food service.

1. How many trains go to Chicago every day? Which train leaves Waukekee in the morning and arrives in Chicago in the afternoon?

   **Six trains go to Chicago every day; 11:30 A.M.**

2. Counting Waukekee, how many stops does the train make? What is the fourth stop?

   **The train makes five stops; Harbor Park.**

3. You live in Rainville. You want to meet your friends in Chicago at 10:30 A.M. What time do you have to catch the train in Rainville to be on time? How much extra time will you have when you arrive in Chicago?

   **You need the 8:45 A.M. train; There will be no extra time.**

4. You live in Harbor Park and have to take the train that leaves at 7:00 A.M. for Chicago. You don't have time to fix yourself breakfast. Will you be able to get something to eat on the train? How do you know?

   **yes; The asterisk in the column indicates food service.**

5. You live in Hampton. Every Monday at 5:00 P.M., you have violin lessons in Rainville. To be on time, which train do you have to catch? Will you have time to spare?

   **You need the 4:15 P.M. train; You will have 15 minutes to spare.**

© Pearson Education, Inc., 5

**Directions** Use this camp schedule to answer the questions.

### Camp Want-To-Get-Away Schedule

|  | Monday | Tuesday | Wednesday | Thursday | Friday | Saturday | Sunday |
|---|---|---|---|---|---|---|---|
| **8 A.M.** | Breakfast in Olson Hall | Breakfast in Olson Hall | Breakfast in Olson Hall | Breakfast in Olson Hall | Breakfast in Olson Hall | Breakfast in Olson Hall | Breakfast in Olson Hall |
| **10 A.M.** | Swimming at Lake Beluga | Play Rehearsal | Archery | Swimming at Lake Beluga | Band Practice | You Choose | Play Rehearsal |
| **1 P.M.** | Crafts | Crafts | Horseback Riding | Letters Home | Horseback Riding | You Choose | Parents Visit |
| **4 P.M.** | Group Games | Archery | Water Sports | Group Games | Hiking | Group Games | Swimming at Lake Beluga |
| **8 P.M.** | Lights Out | Lights Out | Lights Out | Lights Out | MOVIE | Campfire Stories | Lights Out |

6. How many time slots for each day are listed on this schedule? How many days are listed?

**There are five time slots listed each day; seven days.**

7. You want to sharpen your swimming skills. What days and times can you go swimming?

**You can swim on Mondays and Thursdays at 10 A.M. and Sundays at 4 P.M.**

8. You want your parents to come for a visit. What day and time is best?

**Sundays at 1 P.M. are the best time for parent visits.**

9. What time can you eat breakfast every day? Where is breakfast held?

**Breakfast is at 8 A.M.; Olson Hall**

10. You love to act. What is a good activity to take part in? When is this activity available?

**Play Rehearsal; It is held on Tuesday and Sunday at 10 A.M.**

© Pearson Education, Inc., 5

**Home Activity** Your child learned about reading schedules. Look at the schedule of a sports team your child likes. Find out when the next game is and whether or not it takes place during school hours.

# Consonant Sounds /j/, /ks/, /sk/, and /s/

**Proofread a Travel Poster** There are seven spelling errors and one
punctuation error. Circle the errors and write the corrections on the lines.

excuse
scene
muscle
explore
pledge
journal
science
schedule
gigantic
scheme

Japan
excellent
exclaim
fascinate
ginger
scholar
scent
dodge
smudge
schooner

(Exsplore) Japan

This trip will (facinate) the (scolar) or the casual traveler.

(Exsellent) first-class hotels are available.

Experience the exotic taste of ginger and other spices.

Visit a typical school full of excited children.

Enjoy the (sent) of lotus flower in your own private spa.

Enjoy the peaceful (cene) of a
Japanese garden and teahouse.

The (skedule) is made to meet your needs(.)

1. **Explore**
2. **fascinate**
3. **scholar**
4. **Excellent**
5. **scent**
6. **scene**
7. **schedule**
8. **The schedule is made to meet your needs.**

**Proofread Words** Circle the correct spelling of the list word.

| | | |
|---|---|---|
| 9. plege | pleje | (pledge) |
| 10. sceme | (scheme) | skeme |
| 11. (smudge) | smuge | smuje |
| 12. mussle | muscel | (muscle) |
| 13. dodje | (dodge) | dogde |
| 14. (journal) | journle | jurnal |
| 15. jigantic | gidgantic | (gigantic) |
| 16. skooner | (schooner) | scooner |

**Frequently
Misspelled
Words**

except
excited
school

**Home Activity** Your child identified misspelled list words. Review the *sch* and *sc* words and their
pronunciations with your child.

## Principal Parts of Irregular Verbs

**Directions** Read the passage. Then read each question. Circle the letter of the correct answer.

# If These Bones Could Talk

(1) Scientists have sought dinosaur skeletons for many years. (2) They study the bones to learn about the behavior and appearance of prehistoric animals. (3) The dinosaur's skull has been especially important to scientists. (4) The skull helps the scientist tell what type of animal it was. (5) Also, it (speak) volumes about the dinosaur's vision, hearing, and sense of smell. (6) We (build) many skeletons from skulls and bones. (7) There is a lot to learn from these ancient bones!

**1** Which describes the principal part of the underlined verb in sentence 1?

   **A** Past

   **B** Present

   **(C)** Past participle

   **D** Present participle

**2** What is the present form of the underlined verb in sentence 1?

   **(A)** seek

   **B** is seeking

   **C** am seeking

   **D** sought

**3** Which describes the principal part of the underlined verb in sentence 3?

   **A** Past

   **B** Present

   **(C)** Past participle

   **D** Present participle

**4** Which form of the verb in parentheses best completes sentence 5?

   **(A)** has spoken

   **B** have spoken

   **C** is speaking

   **D** speak

**5** Which form of the verb in parentheses best completes sentence 6?

   **A** are building

   **B** is building

   **C** has built

   **(D)** have built

© Pearson Education, Inc., 5

**Home Activity** Your child prepared for taking tests on principal parts of irregular verbs. Ask your child to name the principal parts of the verbs *choose* and *find* and then use each part in a sentence.

# Main Idea and Details

- The **main idea** is the most important idea about the topic.
- **Details** are small pieces of information that tell more about the main idea.

**Directions** Read the following passage. Then complete the diagram below.

Who earned the title *Mother of the Blues*? That would be Ma Rainey (1886–1939), the first great African American blues singer. Her career began when she was fourteen years old in a local talent show in Georgia. Just four years later, she married "Pa" Rainey, and they formed a song-and-dance act that included blues songs. They traveled and performed throughout the South.

In 1923, she made her first recording. She recorded about 100 songs. She performed with many notable jazz musicians during her career, which lasted until the 1930s. Her singing influenced many younger blues singers.

## Possible answers given.

**Main Idea 1.** Ma Rainey was the first great blues singer.

**Details**

| | | | |
|---|---|---|---|
| **2. career began when she was 14** | **3. performed with her husband** | **4. made her first recording in 1923** | **5. influenced younger singers** |

© Pearson Education, Inc., 5

**Home Activity** Your child read a short passage and used a graphic organizer to identify the main idea and details. Work with your child to identify the main idea and details of individual paragraphs in a magazine article about music.

**Comprehension 211**

# Writing • Description

**Key Features of a Description**

- creates a vivid mental picture
- imagery may appeal to the five senses
- uses precise words and vivid adjectives

---

## Swing Music

Swing grew out of jazz music, and in the 1930s and 1940s it was as popular as could be. A top-flight swing band might have twenty or twenty-five musicians in it, playing trumpets, trombones, clarinets, saxophones, a piano, and drums. Just imagine the sound!

The name *swing* says it all. Swing music swings. It has a fast tempo and a syncopated rhythm. When you hear swing music, you just can't sit still—you have to get up and dance. In the 1940s swing dancers were called "jitterbugs" because they jumped and hopped and twisted all over the dance floor. A male swing dancer often picks up his partner and swings her over his head or across his shoulders.

Swing music is still around. Its popularity faded during World War II because most musicians were men, and most men joined the military. The types of popular music that came later, such as bebop and rock and roll, were made by smaller bands—often just three or four musicians.

But swing music never died. One of the greatest swing bandleaders, Glenn Miller, died in 1944, but the Glenn Miller Orchestra still performs across America and Europe. Modern dance competitions always feature swing. The 1990s saw a huge revival in swing music, with brand new swing bands forming and recording.

---

**1.** Read the description. What is this passage describing?

**swing music**

**2.** Underline two sentences that contain vivid details.

# Vocabulary

**Directions** Choose the word from the box that best matches each definition below.

appreciate _____

**1.** to think highly of

slavery _____

**2.** the condition of being owned by another person and being made to work without wages

religious _____

**3.** devoted to religion

choir _____

**4.** a group of singers who sing together often in a church service

teenager _____

**5.** a person in his or her teens

**Directions** Match each word on the left with the word that has a similar meaning on the right. Write the correct letter on the line.

_____ **d** _____     **6.** released     **a.** spiritual

_____ **c** _____     **7.** barber     **b.** singers

_____ **e** _____     **8.** appreciate     **c.** haircutter

_____ **b** _____     **9.** choir     **d.** published

_____ **a** _____     **10.** religious     **e.** value

## Write a Journal Entry

On a separate sheet of paper, write a journal entry describing your favorite kind of music and why you like it. Use as many vocabulary words as you can.

**Journal entries should include words from the vocabulary list and details about a certain kind of music.**

© Pearson Education, Inc., 5

**Home Activity** Your child identified and used vocabulary words from *Mahalia Jackson*. Make up a song using the vocabulary words from the story to help your child remember their meanings.

# Troublesome Verbs

Some pairs of verbs are confusing because they have similar meanings or because they look alike.

|  | **Present** | **Past** | **Past Participle** |
|---|---|---|---|
| *Lay* means "put" or "place." | lay | laid | (*has, have, had*) laid |
| *Lie* means "rest" or "recline." | lie | lay | (*has, have, had*) lain |
| *Set* means "put something somewhere." | set | set | (*has, have, had*) set |
| *Sit* means "sit down." | sit | sat | (*has, have, had*) sat |
| *Let* means "allow." | let | let | (*has, have, had*) let |
| *Leave* means "go away." | leave | left | (*has, have, had*) left |

**Directions** Write the form of the underlined verb indicated in ( ).

1. A teenage girl <u>sit</u> with the choir. (past) _____**sat**_____

2. She has <u>lay</u> her hand over her heart. (past participle) _____**laid**_____

3. The choir director <u>let</u> her join. (past) _____**let**_____

4. The music never <u>leave</u> her head. (past) _____**left**_____

5. When she <u>set</u> her suitcases down in Chicago, Mahalia knew she was home. (past) _____**set**_____

6. Mahalia's father had <u>let</u> her follow her dream. (past participle) _____**let**_____

**Directions** Use context to help you decide which verb is needed. Then find the principal part needed on the chart. Underline the verb that correctly completes the sentence.

7. I (<u>set</u>, sit) a CD on the counter.

8. Will you (leave, <u>let</u>) me pay for it?

9. My parents have already (<u>left</u>, let) the store.

10. After dinner we (<u>sat</u>, set) down and listened to the CD.

11. Tom has (laid, <u>lain</u>) down on the floor.

12. Fiona (<u>laid</u>, lied) a log on the fire.

**Home Activity** Your child learned about troublesome verbs. Ask your child to explain the difference in meaning between *sit/set, lie/lay,* and *leave/let* and then act out the meanings of the verbs in each pair to demonstrate the difference.

# One Consonant or Two

| Spelling Words | | | | |
|---|---|---|---|---|
| address | collar | mirror | recess | committee |
| collect | Mississippi | immediate | command | appreciate |
| announce | possess | Tennessee | gallop | opponent |
| barricade | broccoli | accomplish | allowance | zucchini |

**Words in Context** Write the list word that best completes the sentence.

1. The vegetable _____ looks like little trees.

2. It was hard to cross the street because of the police _____.

3. The capital of _____ is Nashville.

4. Don't forget to button your _____.

5. "Faster, faster," he urged the horse as it began to _____.

6. He looked in the _____ to comb his hair.

7. The _____ River is the second-longest river in the United States.

8. Our class has _____ after lunch.

9. Do you get a weekly _____ for doing chores?

10. I need your telephone number and _____ for our records.

1. __broccoli__
2. __barricade__
3. __Tennessee__
4. __collar__
5. __gallop__
6. __mirror__
7. __Mississippi__
8. __recess__
9. __allowance__
10. __address__

**Antonyms** Write the list word that has the opposite or nearly the opposite meaning.

11. scatter

12. delayed

13. obey

14. disregard

15. remove

11. __collect__
12. __immediate__
13. __command__
14. __appreciate__
15. __possess__

**Synonyms** Write the list word that has the same or almost the same meaning.

16. declare

17. group

18. foe

19. summer squash

20. succeed

16. __announce__
17. __committee__
18. __opponent__
19. __zucchini__
20. __accomplish__

© Pearson Education, Inc., 5

**School + Home**

**Home Activity** Your child wrote words with double consonants. Take turns saying and spelling the list words aloud.

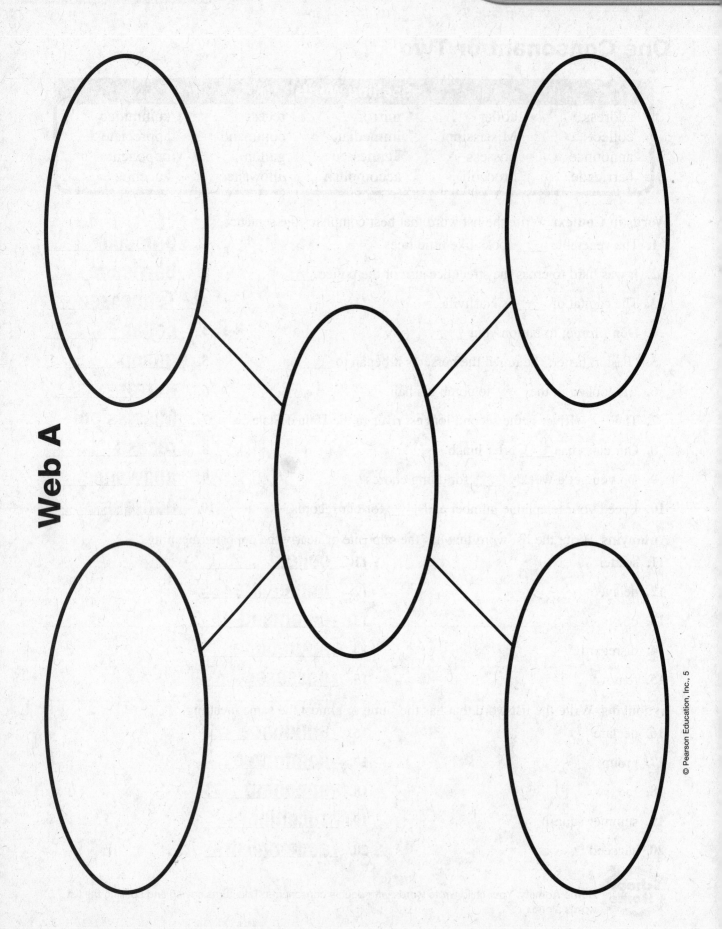

**Web A**

# Vocabulary · Antonyms

- An **antonym** is a word that means the opposite of another word.
- Words such as *unlike, but,* and *instead* may indicate the presence of antonyms.
- A **thesaurus** is a book that lists words and their antonyms and synonyms.

**Directions** Read the following passage. Then answer the questions below. You may use a thesaurus.

> The songs called spirituals were inspired by the lives of the people who wrote them: slaves living in the southern United States. By singing spirituals, slaves expressed their hope of being released and not enslaved, either in this life or the next. After slavery ended, spirituals were neglected because they reminded people of something they wanted to forget. But time passed, and spirituals came to be appreciated for their message and music. Spirituals are closely related to the gospel music, blues, and jazz that we hear today.

## Possible answers given.

1. Find the antonym in the passage for *released*. How does this antonym help to define *released*?

**enslaved; *Released* means the opposite of *enslaved*.**

2. Find the antonym for *appreciated*. How does this antonym help to define *appreciated*?

**neglected; *Appreciated* means the opposite of *neglected*.**

3. In this passage, the word *spiritual* means "a religious song." *Spiritual* also means "interested in the belief and worship of God or gods." What is an antonym for the second meaning?

**Unbelieving is an antonym for *spiritual*.**

4. In this passage, the word *slavery* means "the condition of being owned by another person and being made to work without wages." What is an antonym for *slavery*?

**Freedom is an antonym for *slavery*.**

5. Write down a word from the passage and its antonym. Write a sentence or sentences using the original word and its antonym.

**hope, despair; I hope to get a new radio, but I despair of ever saving enough money to buy one.**

**Home Activity** Your child read a short passage and identified words and their antonyms. Read an article with your child and identify unfamiliar words. Try to find their meanings by identifying their antonyms in the article.

# Card Catalog/Library Database

- You can use a **card catalog** or **library database** to find books, magazines, audiotapes, videotapes, CD-ROMS, and other materials in the library. You can search for materials by author, title, or subject. A card catalog is a box of drawers filled with cards containing detailed information about books and other library materials. A library database is an electronic version of a card catalog.

- If you don't know exactly what you are searching for in the library database, you can use "keywords." Be sure to type and spell words carefully. If you use more than one keyword in your search, put the word "AND" between the keywords.

- Both card catalog and library databases contain certain types of basic information. For instance, call numbers are used by libraries to identify and organize the items in their collections. Nonfiction books, videos, and recordings are arranged on library shelves by call number. Fiction books are arranged in alphabetical order by the author's last name.

**Directions** Look at the starting search screen for a library database below. For each of the numbered items, tell which of the six categories you would choose for each search. Then write the information you would enter into the library database.

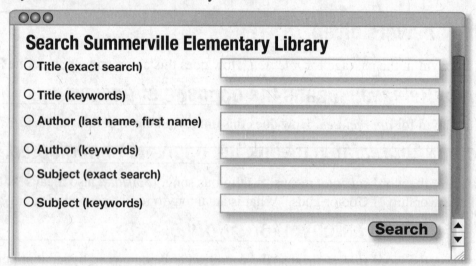

**Search Summerville Elementary Library**

- ○ Title (exact search)
- ○ Title (keywords)
- ○ Author (last name, first name)
- ○ Author (keywords)
- ○ Subject (exact search)
- ○ Subject (keywords)

[ Search ]

1. Ray Charles's autobiography

   __Author (last name, first name); Charles, Ray__

2. a Louis Armstrong recording on CD, audiotape, or vinyl LP

   __Author (last name, first name); Armstrong, Louis__

3. a biography of Louis Armstrong

   __Subject (key words); Louis Armstrong__

4. *Mahalia: A Life in Gospel Music*

   __Title (exact search); *Mahalia: A Life in Gospel Music*__

5. a critical history of Motown Records

   __Subject (key words); Motown Records__

**Directions** Use the following sample card from a library card catalog to answer the questions below.

L424.7 RE

**Roots of Blues Music**

Parker, Mark, 1959-

Blues has influenced many different types of music today. It changed the way many people felt about music, as well. Blues emerged after slavery was abolished and changed the way singers approached music. Blues is still a popular form of music played today.

Publisher: Wilson Musical Reference

Pub date: c2001.

Pages: 313 p.

ISBN: 0534212311

**6.** Who is the author of this reference book?

**Mark Parker**

**7.** What is the book's call number?

**L424.7 RE**

**8.** What is the title of the book?

**Roots of Blues Music**

**9.** How many pages does this book have? When was it published, and by whom?

**313 pages; published in 2001 by Wilson Musical Reference**

**10.** What do you learn about the book from the card's summary?

**Possible answer: The book gives information on the history of blues music, and explains how it relates to different types of music today.**

 © Pearson Education, Inc., 5

 **School + Home**

**Home Activity** Your child learned about using a library database and a card catalog. Visit the library with your child. Take turns searching for subjects that interest one or both of you.

# One Consonant or Two

**Proofread a Newspaper Article** Circle six misspelled words. Write the words correctly. Find one capitalization error. Write the sentence correctly.

> Something odd (hapenned) in the students' dining room. Some students wanted (brocoli) at every meal. Their (oponents) wanted (zuchinni). A (commitee) was formed. They decided to take a vote. No one expected an (immediat) result. The committee had something surprising to announce. (most) of the students preferred carrots!

| | | | |
|---|---|---|---|
| 1. | **happened** | 2. | **broccoli** |
| 3. | **opponents** | 4. | **zucchini** |
| 5. | **committee** | 6. | **immediate** |

7. **Most of the students preferred carrots!**

**Proofread Words** Circle the correct spelling of the list words.

8. Memphis and Nashville are cities in _____.

   Tenessee          Tennese          (Tennessee)

9. Most students love _____ after being inside.

   (recess)          reccess          recces

10. I _____ a collection of old comic books.

   posess          (possess)          posses

11. The settlers used a wooden plank to _____ the door.

   (barricade)          barricad          bariccade

12. I am hoping to _____ a lot this school year.

   acomplish          (accomplish)          accommplish

13. The bathroom _____ was foggy because of the steam from the shower.

   mirrer          miror          (mirror)

14. I will _____ the winner at the end of the game.

   (announce)          anounce          anounnce

**Spelling Words**

address
collar
mirror
recess
committee
collect
Mississippi
immediate
command
appreciate

announce
possess
Tennessee
gallop
opponent
barricade
broccoli
accomplish
allowance
zucchini

**Frequently Misspelled Words**

different
happened

© Pearson Education, Inc., 5

**Home Activity** Your child identified misspelled list words. Have your child tell you the three most difficult list words and then spell them to you.

## Troublesome Verbs

**Directions** Read the passage. Then read each question. Circle the letter of the correct answer.

# The Missing Book

(1) My father had let me borrow his book about Bessie Smith, the great blues singer. (2) Last night, I (lay) on my bed, reading. (3) My mother called for dinner, so I (set) my book on the bed. (4) After dinner, I went back to my room to lie down with my book. (5) To my surprise, my book was not where I leaved it! (6) How would I learn what happened to Bessie when she left Chattanooga? (7) I (sit) down to consider where the book might have gone. (8) Later, I learned that my father had picked up the book and had set it down on the bookshelf.

**1** Which form of the verb in parentheses best completes sentence 2?

**(A)** lay

**B** laid

**C** lie

**D** lain

**2** Which form of the verb in parentheses best completes sentence 3?

**A** sit

**B** sat

**C** have set

**(D)** set

**3** What change, if any, should be made in sentence 4?

**A** Change *lie* to **laid**

**B** Change *lie* to **let**

**C** Change *lie* to **lay**

**(D)** Make no change

**4** What change, if any, should be made in sentence 5?

**A** Change *leaved* to **leave**

**(B)** Change *leaved* to **left**

**C** Change *leaved* to **have left**

**D** Make no change

**5** Which form of the verb in parentheses best completes sentence 7?

**(A)** sat

**B** sit

**C** set

**D** have sat

**School + Home** **Home Activity** Your child prepared for taking tests on principal parts of troublesome verbs. Ask your child to name the principal parts of the verbs *lie, lay, sit, set, leave,* and *let* and then use each part in a sentence.

# Graphic Sources

- Some graphic sources are maps, time lines, charts, diagrams, and pictures with captions.
- A graphic source makes information easy to see and understand.

**Directions** Study the circle graph below. Then answer the following questions.

**Small Films Company Annual Budget for Special Effects**

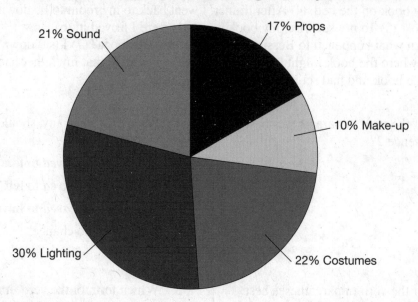

21% Sound

17% Props

10% Make-up

30% Lighting

22% Costumes

1. What do the percentages show?

   **They show how much of the budget was spent in each area.**

2. On what special effect did the company spend the most money?

   **The company spent the most money on lighting.**

3. How much more of the budget went toward costumes than make-up?

   **twelve percent**

4. In what kind of article might you see a circle graph?

   **Possible answers: An article about the costs of special effects, making a movie, or budgets in general.**

5. What prior knowledge did you use to help you understand the graphic source?

   **Possible answer: I saw a play once and noticed all the different elements that go into putting it together.**

© Pearson Education, Inc., 5

**School + Home**

**Home Activity** Your child learned how to interpret a graphic source. Together, imagine you are both writing an article about a favorite subject. Draw a graphic source that could be included in the article.

# Writing • Expository Text

**Key Features of Expository Text**

- gives information about a topic
- is often written in the present tense
- includes main ideas and supporting details
- has an introduction, body, and conclusion

## Movies vs. Television: The Showdown

I enjoy watching movies and television. I love exciting stories, interesting characters, and crazy plot twists. But I prefer watching movies to watching television. Let me tell you why.

First of all, movies are on a bigger screen (if you watch them in the theater, of course). Big screens make things a lot more exciting. Television screens, even big ones, are a lot smaller than theater screens. Nothing is as big or as fancy on television screens.

Second, the special effects are better in movies. Television shows have better effects than they did a long time ago. But they're nothing compared to what you see in movies like *Transformers* and *Spider-Man*.

Finally, movies have better actors than television shows do. I like movies that star people like Brad Pitt, Shia LaBeouf, and Harrison Ford. Actors like these bring a story to life. Television actors are good, but they don't seem as realistic as movie actors.

In conclusion, I definitely like watching movies more than television. But I still enjoy television. After all, who doesn't love *Hannah Montana*?

1. What is the main idea in each paragraph?

   **Paragraph 1: Movies are better because they're on a big screen.**

   **Paragraph 2: Special effects are better in movies.**

   **Paragraph 3: Movies have better actors.**

2. Transitional words are words that link ideas, details, or paragraphs together. What transitional words does the author use in the text?

   ***First of all, Second, Finally, In conclusion.***

# Vocabulary

**Directions** Choose the word from the box that best matches each definition. Write the word on the line.

**prehistoric**_____

1. of or belonging to periods before recorded history

**reassembled**_____

2. put back together again

**landscape**_____

3. view of scenery on land

**miniature**_____

4. done or made on an extremely small scale

**background**_____

5. the part of a picture or scene toward the back

**Check the Words You Know**

____background
____landscape
____miniature
____prehistoric
____reassembled

**Directions** Choose the word from the box that best completes the sentence. Write the word on the line shown to the left.

**reassembled**_____

6. Three hours after the storm, the set for the movie had already been put together again, or_____.

**miniature**_____

7. In preparing for the movie, the crew created a _____ village.

**background**_____

8. The film crew built a ruined temple to appear in the _____ of the scene.

**prehistoric**_____

9. The dinosaur film used models of huge, _____ creatures to show what some animals may have looked like before history was recorded.

**landscape**_____

10. The park provided a perfect _____ for the film.

## Write a Movie Review

On a separate sheet of paper write a review of a movie that had lots of special effects. Describe the special effects and how they worked. Use as many vocabulary words as you can.

## Movie reviews should include words from the vocabulary list and details about special effects used in the movies.

**Home Activity** Your child identified and used vocabulary words from *Special Effects in Film and Television*. Read the review of a movie with your child. Have him or her point out unfamiliar words. Work together to try to figure out the meaning of each word.

© Pearson Education, Inc., 5

# Prepositions and Prepositional Phrases

A **preposition** begins a group of words called a **prepositional phrase**. The noun or pronoun that follows the preposition is called the **object of the preposition**. Prepositional phrases convey location, time, or direction or provide details.

People have watched animated movies <u>for</u> a long time. (preposition)
People have watched animated movies <u>for a long time</u>. (prepositional phrase)
People have watched animated movies for a long <u>time</u>. (object of the preposition)

**Common Prepositions**

| | | | | | |
|---|---|---|---|---|---|
| about | around | by | into | over | until |
| above | at | down | near | through | up |
| across | before | for | of | to | with |
| after | below | from | on | toward | |
| against | between | in | onto | under | |

**Directions** Underline the prepositional phrase in each sentence. Write *P* above the preposition. Write *O* above the object of the preposition.

1. The characters <u>in animated films</u> often seem quite real.
               P     O

2. Young viewers may identify <u>with the superheroes</u>.
                     P      O

3. Ariel was a mermaid who lived <u>under the sea</u>.
                       P   O

4. She wanted a life <u>on dry land</u>.
         P    O

**Directions** Underline the prepositional phrases. The number in ( ) tells how many prepositional phrases are in that sentence.

5. Many fairy tales have been made <u>into animated movies</u> <u>for children</u>. (2)

6. Their stories take youngsters <u>from childhood</u> <u>into adulthood</u>. (2)

7. The hero <u>of the tale</u> must pass <u>through trials and adventures</u>. (2)

8. <u>At the end</u>, he or she has shown great strength <u>of character</u>. (2)

**Home Activity** Your child learned about prepositions and prepositional phrases. Read a favorite story with your child. Ask him or her to point out prepositional phrases and identify the preposition and object of the preposition in each.

Name _____

# Prefixes *un-*, *de-*, *dis-*

| Spelling Words | | | | |
|---|---|---|---|---|
| uncover | defrost | uncomfortable | discourage | disadvantage |
| unfortunate | unfamiliar | disability | discomfort | deodorant |
| unemployed | deflate | disbelief | unpredictable | disapprove |
| disappoint | unpleasant | dehydrated | disqualify | undecided |

**Definitions in Context** Write the list word that has the same or almost the same meaning as the underlined word or words.

1. Moisture is removed from <u>dried out</u> food.

2. I need to <u>melt</u> the turkey.

3. It was <u>unlucky</u> that I broke my leg.

4. My mother has been <u>out of work</u> since the factory closed.

5. The outcome of the contest was <u>in doubt</u> for months.

6. The player's tardiness was a <u>difficulty</u> for the team.

7. I took a route home from school that was <u>new</u> to me.

8. The roller coaster ride was <u>disagreeable</u> to me.

9. It was <u>painful</u> to sleep on the old, lumpy mattress.

10. The team decided to <u>ban</u> a player for cheating.

1. **dehydrated**

2. **defrost**

3. **unfortunate**

4. **unemployed**

5. **undecided**

6. **disadvantage**

7. **unfamiliar**

8. **unpleasant**

9. **uncomfortable**

10. **disqualify**

**Antonyms** Write the list word that has the opposite or nearly the opposite meaning.

11. ability

12. with odor

13. belief

14. expected

15. please

16. inflate

17. conceal

18. support

19. encourage

20. comfortable

11. **disability**

12. **deodorant**

13. **disbelief**

14. **unpredictable**

15. **disappoint**

16. **deflate**

17. **uncover**

18. **disapprove**

19. **discourage**

20. **discomfort**

**Home Activity** Your child wrote words with prefixes. Say a prefix and have your child respond with one word from the list that has that prefix.

© Pearson Education, Inc., 5

Name_____

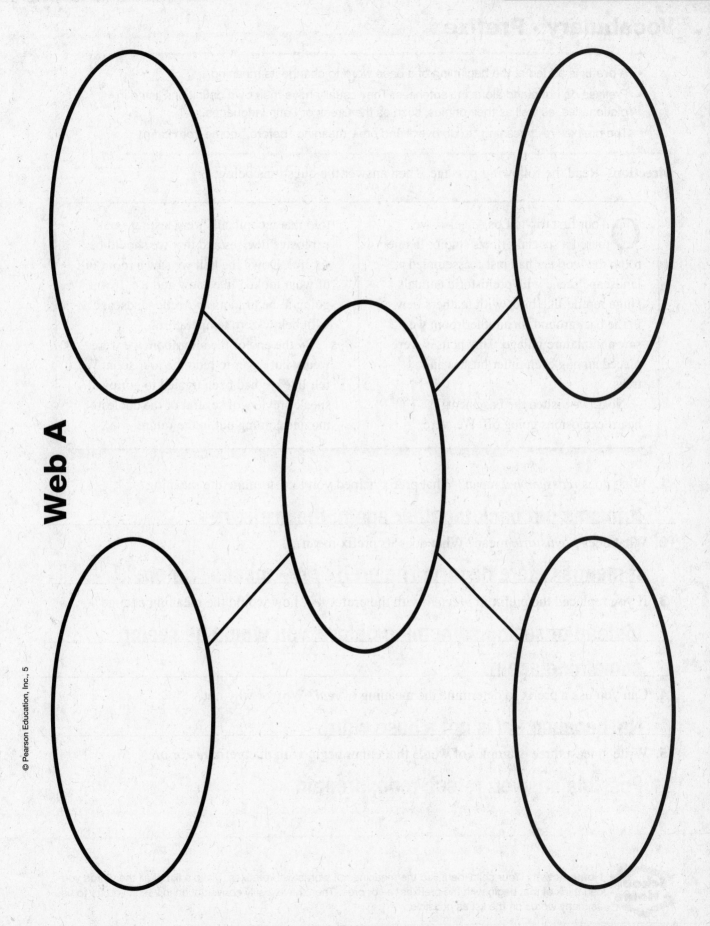

**Web A**

# Vocabulary • Prefixes

- A **prefix** is added at the beginning of a base word to change its meaning.
- Prefixes do not stand alone in sentences. They usually have their own definitions listed in dictionaries, as well as their origins, such as the Greek or Latin languages.
- The prefixes *re-,* meaning "to do over," and *pre-,* meaning "before," come from Latin.

**Directions** Read the following passage. Then answer the questions below.

On our first trip to Los Angeles, we toured a special-effects studio. In one room the workers had just reassembled a landscape scene with prehistoric animals. Huge reptile-like birds with feathers flew in the background. In another room we saw a miniature village. Tiny houses were placed among even tinier bushes and trees.

Next, we visited the basement. We heard explosions going off. We were told that technicians were testing small explosive devices and that we should be careful. Down the hall we saw a room full of what looked like snow and ice. It was going to be used as an Arctic landscape with below-zero temperatures.

By the end of the afternoon, we were weary but eager to redo the tour soon. We felt like we had been treated to our own sneak preview of several of the coolest movies coming out in the future.

1. What does *reassembled* mean? What prefix helped you to determine the meaning?

   **It means put back together again; the prefix *re–***

2. What does *prehistoric* mean? What does its prefix mean?

   **It means before history; The prefix *pre–* means "before".**

3. If you replaced the prefix in *preview* with the prefix *re–,* how would the meaning change?

   **Instead of seeing something before, you would be seeing something again.**

4. Can you use a prefix to determine the meaning of *real*? Why or why not?

   **No, because *–al* is not a base word.**

5. Write at least three examples of words that either begin with the prefix *re–* or *pre–.*

   **Possible answer: retest; redo; prepaid**

**Home Activity** Your child identified the meanings of words with prefixes. Make a list of all the words you can think of that begin with the prefixes re– or pre–. Then, have a silly conversation in which you try to use as many words on the list as possible.

© Pearson Education, Inc., 5

# Graphics/Symbols

- **Graphics** aid in the use of instructions and communication. They identify and summarize information.

- **Graphics** have an effect on the user's understanding of material and provide additional meaning to the text that they accompany.

- **Symbols** and icons can be used to represent ideas, concepts, and information.

**Directions** Study the Web page below.

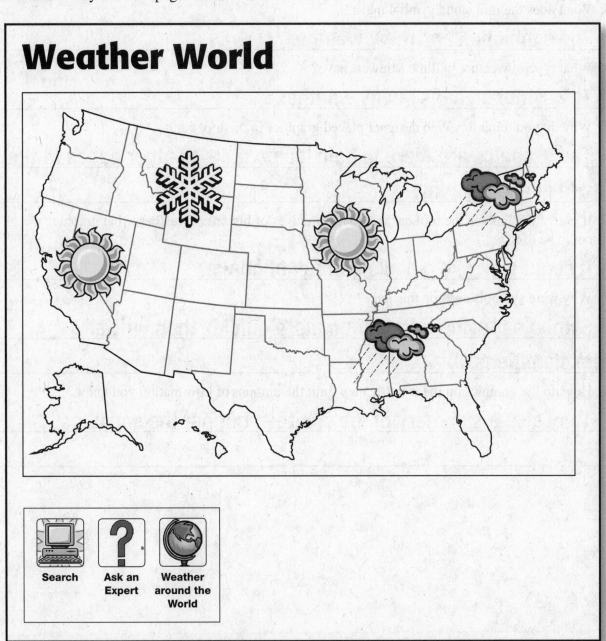

**Possible answers given for 6 and 7.**

1. What is the name of this Web page? How do you know?

   **The name of the page is Weather World. The name is at the top of the page.**

2. What do the symbols on the weather map tell you?

   **The symbols show the types of weather around the country.**

3. What does the rain cloud symbol mean?

   **The symbol means rainy weather.**

4. What type of weather will the Midwest have?

   **The symbol means sunny weather.**

5. Why do you think this Web designer placed graphics in the tool bar?

   **The graphics are there to help locate links to other pages in the site in a faster way.**

6. If one of the links in the tool bar was to the archives of historical weather, what graphic could be used?

   **It could look like a bookshelf full of books.**

7. Why were symbols used on this page?

   **Symbols provide information more quickly than written explanations.**

8. How do the graphics on the weather map limit the amount of information you know?

   **They give a summary of the weather, but not the specifics.**

© Pearson Education, Inc., 5

**Home Activity** Your child learned about the use of graphics and symbols as visual representations of information. Look at a Web page or book that uses graphics and symbols. Challenge your child to explain what the graphics and symbols mean.

Name _____

# Prefixes *un-*, *de-*, *dis-*

**Proofread an Article** There are seven spelling errors and one capitalization error. Circle the errors and write the corrections on the lines.

**Spelling Words**

uncover
defrost
uncomfortable
discourage
disadvantage
unfortunate
unfamiliar
disability
discomfort
deodorant

unemployed
deflate
disbelief
unpredictable
disapprove
disappoint
unpleasant
dehydrated
disqualify
undecided

---

### A Very Long Race

Many look upon marathon runners with (disbeleaf.) These athletes run 26 miles in (unfamilar) cities. They deal with (unpredictible) and sometimes (unplesant) weather. Many run with discomfort and some with a (disbility.) Many runners become (dehidrated.) Spectators do not (disapoint) the runners. They give cups of water to all (R)unners.

---

1. **disbelief**
2. **unfamiliar**
3. **unpredictable**
4. **unpleasant**
5. **disability**
6. **dehydrated**
7. **disappoint**
8. **They give cups of water to all runners.**

**Frequently Misspelled Words**

until
before

**Proofread Words** Circle the correct spelling of the list word.

| 9. | deordorent | (deodorant) | deoderant |
| 10. | (disqualify) | disqualyfie | dequalify |
| 11. | uncomfortible | unconfortable | (uncomfortable) |
| 12. | (deflate) | deflait | defleat |
| 13. | deapprove | (disapprove) | disaprove |
| 14. | disadvantadge | disadvantige | (disadvantage) |
| 15. | (undecided) | indecided | undecide |
| 16. | discomfrt | (discomfort) | discomefrt |

**Home Activity** Your child identified misspelled list words. Ask your child to name one word for each prefix studied and spell the word.

# Prepositions and Prepositional Phrases

**Directions** Read the passage. Then read each question. Circle the letter of the correct answer.

# Pinocchio's Journey

(1) The film *Pinocchio* is a tale _____ a puppet who wants to be a real boy.
(2) Pinocchio was carved _____ Gepetto and turned _____ a wooden boy.
(3) He is lured away by a con artist named Honest John and sold over a puppeteer.
(4) In time, Pinocchio winds up on Pleasure Island, where wild boys are turned
into donkeys! (5) Next, the poor puppet is swallowed _____ Monstro the whale.
(6) Finally, father and son are reunited. (7) Pinocchio becomes a real boy in the end.

1 Which preposition best completes
sentence 1?

  A   on

  B   from

  **C**   about

  D   for

2 Which pair of prepositions best completes
sentence 2?

  **A**   by/into

  B   by/about

  C   for/from

  D   with/into

3 What change, if any, should be made in
sentence 3?

  A   Change *by* to **until**

  **B**   Change *over* to **to**

  C   Change *over* to **into**

  D   Remove both prepositions

4 How many prepositional phrases does
sentence 4 have?

  A   0

  B   1

  C   2

  **D**   3

5 Which preposition best completes
sentence 5?

  **A**   by

  B   down

  C   up

  D   through

**Home Activity** Your child prepared for taking tests on prepositions and prepositional phrases. Ask your child to make flash cards for prepositions he or she has learned. Show each card and have your child use the preposition in a sentence.

# Words with Schwa

| Spelling Words | | | | |
|---|---|---|---|---|
| jewel | kingdom | gasoline | factory | garage |
| tropical | pajamas | estimate | tomorrow | humidity |
| Chicago | bulletin | carnival | illustrate | elegant |
| census | terrific | celebrate | operate | celery |

**Synonyms** Write the list word that has the same or nearly the same meaning.

1. great __**terrific**__
2. festival __**carnival**__
3. count __**census**__
4. carport __**garage**__
5. tasteful __**elegant**__

6. gem __**jewel**__
7. rejoice __**celebrate**__
8. nightclothes __**pajamas**__
9. moisture __**humidity**__
10. guess __**estimate**__

**Scramble** Unscramble the list words and write them on the lines.

11. seloaing __**gasoline**__
12. slurtileat __**illustrate**__
13. tublelin __**bulletin**__
14. wormorto __**tomorrow**__
15. plorcita __**tropical**__

16. troycaf __**factory**__
17. torapee __**operate**__
18. coaCgih __**Chicago**__
19. midkong __**kingdom**__
20. rylcee __**celery**__

© Pearson Education, Inc., 5

**School + Home** **Home Activity** Your child learned to spell words with the schwa sound. Ask your child to name three words with this sound and spell them.

# Past, Present, and Future Tenses

**Directions** Write the correct present, past, and future tense of each verb.

| Verb | Present | Past | Future |
|---|---|---|---|
| 1. spy | He **spies** | He **spied** | He **will spy** |
| 2. have | I **have** | I **had** | I **will have** |
| 3. trap | You **trap** | You **trapped** | You **will trap** |
| 4. think | She **thinks** | She **thought** | She **will think** |
| 5. eat | They **eat** | They **ate** | They **will eat** |

**Directions** Identify the tense of each underlined verb. Write *present, past,* or *future.*

6. Many people <u>dreamed</u> of a perpetual motion machine.   **past**

7. This machine <u>runs</u> forever.   **present**

8. It <u>will make</u> its own energy.   **future**

9. The machine <u>will save</u> tons of money!   **future**

10. The Perez twins <u>created</u> a version of the machine.   **past**

11. But the machine <u>borrows</u> energy from other machines.   **present**

12. Sadly, the perpetual motion machine <u>will remain</u> a dream.   **future**

**Directions** Rewrite each sentence. Change the underlined verb to the tense in ( ).

13. Once, the idea of a computer <u>seems</u> impossible. (past)

**Once, the idea of a computer seemed impossible.**

14. Now, people constantly <u>use</u> computers for work and enjoyment. (present)

**Now, people constantly use computers for work and enjoyment.**

15. Someday, perhaps a perpetual motion machine <u>is</u> a reality. (future)

**Someday, perhaps a perpetual motion machine will be a reality.**

# Compound Words

### Spelling Words

| | | | | |
|---|---|---|---|---|
| waterproof | teaspoon | grasshopper | homesick | barefoot |
| courthouse | earthquake | rowboat | scrapbook | countryside |
| lightweight | fishhook | spotlight | blindfold | whirlpool |
| tablespoon | greenhouse | postcard | hummingbird | thumbtack |

**Analogies** Write the word that completes each comparison.

1. Urban is to city as rural is to **countryside**.
2. Short is to tall as heavy is to **lightweight**.
3. Librarian is to library as judge is to **courthouse**.
4. Animal is to zoo as plant is to **greenhouse**.
5. Snake is to reptile as **grasshopper** is to insect.
6. Glue is to tape as nail is to **thumbtack**.
7. Pedal is to bicycle as oar is to **rowboat**.
8. Scarf is to neck as **blindfold** is to eyes.
9. Cup is to china as **teaspoon or tablespoon** is to silverware.
10. E-mail is to computer as **postcard** is to mailbox.

**Word Clues** Write the list word that fits each clue.

11. This might describe a raincoat and boots. **waterproof**
12. Cooks use this to measure ingredients. **tablespoon or teaspoon**
13. Make this to remember a special trip. **scrapbook**
14. Don't become an actor if you don't like this. **spotlight**
15. You can feed this in your backyard. **hummingbird**
16. A big one might cause buildings to fall. **earthquake**
17. Beware of this when swimming in a big lake or river. **whirlpool**
18. Going away to summer camp might make you feel like this. **homesick**
19. Walk this way at the beach if you like sand between your toes. **barefoot**
20. Put this on the end of your line. **fishhook**

 **Home Activity** Your child learned to spell compound words. Find four compound words in a magazine. Write all the words in the compounds in random order. Ask your child to put the correct words together to make the compound words.

© Pearson Education, Inc., 5

# Principal Parts of Regular Verbs

**Directions** Write *present, present participle, past,* or *past participle* to identity the principal part of the underlined verb.

1. What <u>defines</u> genius? **present**

2. A genius <u>offers</u> a fresh view. **present**

3. Often, the public <u>has rejected</u> ideas of genius at first. **past participle**

4. After time <u>has passed</u>, we understand what was offered. **past participle**

5. People <u>recognized</u> Leonardo's genius at once. **past**

6. He <u>concealed</u> many of his ideas in journals. **past**

7. Today we <u>are studying</u> them. **present participle**

8. Many of his ideas <u>have appeared</u> as inventions. **past participle**

9. His ideas <u>waited</u> for the right time and place. **past**

10. We <u>acknowledge</u> his genius gratefully. **present**

**Directions** Write the sentence using the principal part of the underlined verb indicated in ( ).

11. Brilliant ideas <u>change</u> the world. (present participle)

**Brilliant ideas are changing the world.**

12. Sir Isaac Newton <u>discover</u> universal laws of motion. (past)

**Sir Isaac Newton discovered universal laws of motion.**

13. An object in motion <u>tend</u> to stay in motion. (present)

**An object in motion tends to stay in motion.**

14. This concept <u>form</u> the basis for the first of his laws of motion. (present)

**This concept forms the basis for the first of his laws of motion.**

15. Newton's laws <u>help</u> us understand how the world works. (past participle)

**Newton's laws have helped us understand how the world works.**

# Consonant Sounds /j/, /ks/, /sk/, and /s/

| Spelling Words | | | | |
|---|---|---|---|---|
| excuse | scene | muscle | explore | pledge |
| journal | science | schedule | gigantic | scheme |
| Japan | excellent | exclaim | fascinate | ginger |
| scholar | scent | dodge | smudge | schooner |

**Word Search** Circle ten hidden list words. Words are down, across, and diagonal.
Write the words on the lines.

```
F  V  S  C  H  E  D  U  L  E
E  X  C  L  A  I  M  N  N  R
C  D  H  M  G  I  N  G  E  R
K  Q  O  I  U  L  O  I  S  S
E  R  L  D  T  S  S  N  M  C
D  E  A  O  G  T  C  E  U  I
U  X  R  P  O  E  E  L  R  E
L  C  H  E  O  U  N  R  E  N
S  C  H  O  O  N  E  R  N  C
Z  F  A  S  C  I  N  A  T  E
```

1. schedule
2. exclaim
3. ginger
4. schooner
5. fascinate

6. scholar
7. scene
8. science
9. dodge
10. muscle

**Hidden Words** Each of these small words can be found inside one of the list words.
Write the list word that contains the small word.

11. ant    gigantic
12. cell   excellent
13. mud    smudge
14. use    excuse
15. pan    Japan

16. our    journal
17. aim    exclaim
18. edge   pledge
19. hem    scheme
20. cent   scent

**Home Activity** Your child learned to spell words with various consonant sounds. Ask your child to write two words in which the *sk* sound is spelled in different ways.

© Pearson Education, Inc., 5

# Principal Parts of Irregular Verbs

**Directions** Write *present*, *present participle*, *past*, or *past participle* to identify the principal part used to form the underlined verb.

1. Dinosaurs <u>have been</u> extinct for millions of years.  **past participle**

2. The iguanodon <u>was</u> a plant eater.  **past**

3. An iguanodon <u>stood</u> about 16 feet tall.  **past**

4. It <u>ran</u> on two legs or walked on four.  **past**

5. Gideon Mantell <u>had found</u> a few bones in 1822.  **past participle**

6. He <u>had seen</u> the similarity to an iguana.  **past participle**

7. Mantell <u>gave</u> the dinosaur its name.  **past**

8. Even today, archaeologists <u>are finding</u> dinosaur bones.  **present participle**

9. Bones and fossils <u>tell</u> us much about extinct animals.  **present**

10. We <u>draw</u> conclusions about their size and shape.  **present**

**Directions** Write the sentence using the principal part of the underlined verb indicated in ( ).

11. Once all of Earth's land <u>be</u> one big mass. (past)

**Once all of Earth's land was one big mass.**

12. Over time, it <u>break</u> into pieces. (past)

**Over time, it broke into pieces.**

13. We now <u>know</u> these pieces moved. (present)

**We now know these pieces moved.**

14. They <u>become</u> the seven continents. (past participle)

**They have become the seven continents.**

15. Forces inside the Earth <u>make</u> the landmasses move. (past)

**Forces inside the Earth made the landmasses move.**

© Pearson Education, Inc., 5

# One Consonant or Two

| Spelling Words | | | | |
|---|---|---|---|---|
| address | collar | mirror | recess | committee |
| collect | Mississippi | immediate | command | appreciate |
| announce | possess | Tennessee | gallop | opponent |
| barricade | broccoli | accomplish | allowance | zucchini |

**Analogies** Write the word that completes each comparison.

1. Jog is to run as trot is to __gallop__.

2. Pecan is to nut as __zucchini__ is to squash.

3. Speak is to talk as own is to __possess__.

4. Friend is to enemy as teammate is to __opponent__.

5. Car is to tire as shirt is to __collar__.

6. President is to company as chairman is to __committee__.

7. Open is to close as discard is to __collect__.

8. Car is to automobile as obstacle is to __barricade__.

9. Cut is to scissors as reflect is to __mirror__.

10. Yell is to shout as proclaim is to __announce__.

**Word Clues** Write the list word that fits each clue.

11. a break in the school day — __recess__

12. the second-longest river in the United States — __Mississippi__

13. to make an effort and succeed — __accomplish__

14. your street number and name and city — __address__

15. a green vegetable with stalks and florets — __broccoli__

16. a general's job in the army — __command__

17. money received each week — __allowance__

18. a state that borders Kentucky — __Tennessee__

19. to value and treasure — __appreciate__

20. happening right now — __immediate__

 **School + Home** **Home Activity** Your child learned to spell words with double consonants. To practice at home, dictate three words with double consonants. Have your child write them.

# Troublesome Verbs

**Directions** Write the form of the underlined verb indicated in ( ).

1. Mahalia <u>leave</u> listeners dazzled by her talent. (past)

2. They <u>lay</u> down their troubles for a while. (past)

3. Her success <u>lets</u> other women dream of a career in music. (past)

4. Young Aretha Franklin <u>sit</u> with Mahalia's fans. (past participle)

5. Aretha <u>set</u> goals and achieved them. (past)

**left**

**laid**

**let**

**had sat**

**set**

**Directions** Underline the verb that correctly completes the sentence.

6. They have (<u>sat</u>, set) in this pew for years.

7. The choir (sat, <u>set</u>) their hymnals on the bench.

8. A bell (lays, <u>lies</u>) on its side.

9. Someone (lay, <u>laid</u>) it there.

10. She has (<u>left</u>, let) a cup of water on the stand.

11. (Leave, <u>Let</u>) us ask for her autograph.

12. The piano (sets, <u>sits</u>) on a platform.

**Directions** Complete each sentence with the correct form of the verb in ( ).

13. Please _____ **sit** _____ with us at the concert. (sit)

14. The singers have _____ **set** _____ their music down. (set)

15. Yesterday we _____ **left** _____ our friends at school. (leave)

16. Did you _____ **leave** _____ your guitar at home? (leave)

17. Ms. Guthrie _____ **let** _____ me pick my recital piece. (let)

18. Yesterday afternoon he _____ **laid** _____ the horn on the table. (lay)

19. The horn has _____ **lain** _____ there ever since. (lay)

20. She will _____ **lie** _____ down and rest before the performance. (lie)

© Pearson Education, Inc., 5

# Prefixes un-, de-, dis-

| Spelling Words | | | | |
|---|---|---|---|---|
| uncover | defrost | uncomfortable | discourage | disadvantage |
| unfortunate | unfamiliar | disability | discomfort | deodorant |
| unemployed | deflate | disbelief | unpredictable | disapprove |
| disappoint | unpleasant | dehydrated | disqualify | undecided |

**Synonyms** Write the list word that has the same or nearly the same meaning.

1. jobless __**unemployed**__
2. strange __**unfamiliar**__
3. handicap __**disability**__
4. reject __**disapprove**__
5. uneasiness __**discomfort**__

6. expose __**uncover**__
7. doubt __**disbelief**__
8. bar __**disqualify**__
9. dried __**dehydrated**__
10. changeable __**unpredictable**__

**Analogies** Write the word that completes each comparison.

11. Fix is to break as freeze is to __**defrost**__ .
12. Easy is to difficult as lucky is to __**unfortunate**__ .
13. Happy is to sad as relaxed is to __**uncomfortable**__ .
14. Soap is to cleanser as antiperspirant is to __**deodorant**__ .
15. Mad is to angry as uncertain is to __**undecided**__ .
16. Drain is to pool as __**deflate**__ is to balloon.
17. Freedom is to liberty as weakness is to __**disadvantage**__ .
18. Beautiful is to ugly as charming is to __**unpleasant**__ .
19. Help is to support as frustrate is to __**disappoint**__ .
20. Please is to annoy as encourage is to __**discourage**__ .

**Home Activity** Your child learned to spell words with the prefixes *un-*, *de-*, and *dis-*. Find three words with these prefixes in a newspaper. Ask your child to spell each word and name a word that means the opposite.

# Prepositions and Prepositional Phrases

**Directions** Underline the prepositional phrase in each sentence. Circle the preposition.

1. (Over) the holidays, we had a movie marathon.

2. The family watched a series (of) animated films.

3. We have quite a few (in) our film library.

4. I have watched *Dumbo* (about) 20 times.

5. Dumbo is a baby elephant (with) enormous ears.

6. Dumbo stays (near) his mother.

7. She feels protective (toward) her baby.

8. Dumbo finds a great use (for) his ears.

9. Dumbo can fly (through) the sky.

10. He is the biggest hit (at) the circus.

**Directions** Write *P* if the underlined word is a preposition. Write *O* if it is the object of the preposition.

11. Heckle and Jeckle are two crows <u>in</u> *Dumbo*.  __P__

12. They make fun <u>of</u> the baby elephant.  __P__

13. They are amazed when Dumbo soars into the <u>air</u>.  __O__

14. Some encouragement <u>from</u> a little mouse helps Dumbo.  __P__

15. I think the moral is "Believe in <u>yourself</u>."  __O__

**Directions** Underline the prepositional phrases. The number in ( ) tells how many prepositional phrases are in that sentence.

16. The theater is <u>down this street</u> and <u>around a corner</u>. (2)

17. Buy four tickets <u>at the booth</u> and two bags <u>of popcorn</u> <u>from the concession stand</u>. (3)

18. We always sit <u>toward the back</u> <u>under the balcony</u>. (2)

19. <u>At the beginning</u>, it seems very dark <u>in the theater</u>. (2)

20. The ads <u>before the show</u> make me hungry <u>for a snack</u>. (2)

Name _____

# Venn Diagram

**Directions** Fill in the Venn diagram with similarities and differences about the two things you are comparing.

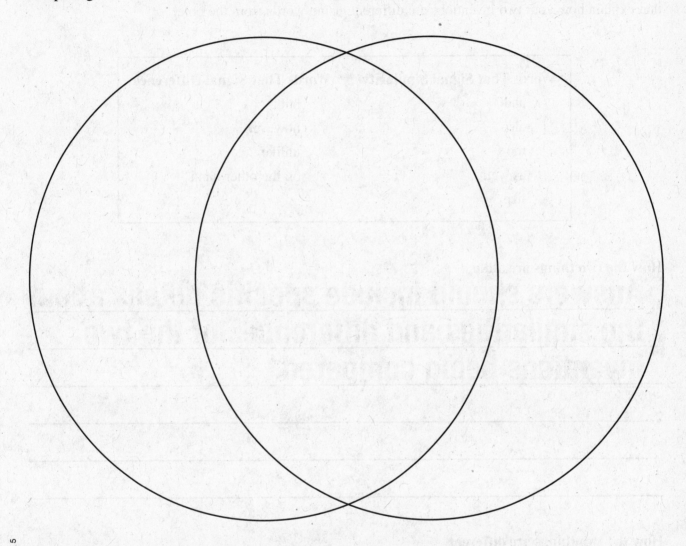

**Answers should include details to support the similarities and differences between two inventions.**

# Words That Compare and Contrast

**Directions** The words in the box signal that two things are alike or different. Write two sentences that explain how your two inventions are alike, using words from the box. Then write two sentences that explain how your two inventions are different, using words from the box.

| Words That Signal Similarity | Words That Signal Difference |
| --- | --- |
| and | but |
| also | however |
| too | unlike |
| as well | on the other hand |
| like | |

**How the two things are alike**

1. <u>Answers should include specific details about the similarities and differences of the two inventions being compared.</u>

2. _____

_____

_____

**How the two things are different**

1. _____

_____

_____

2. _____

_____

_____

# Adding and Deleting Sentences

One part of revising your writing is deciding whether you need to add or delete sentences.

**Add a sentence**    if you need another supporting detail in a paragraph or a smoother transition between paragraphs

**Delete a sentence**   if it does not support the main idea of the paragraph or the topic of the writing

**Directions**   Read the paragraphs. Answer each question by circling the letter or writing on the lines.

*The Starry Night* and *Self-Portrait 1889* are paintings by Vincent van Gogh. Both paintings feature the swirling backgrounds and heavy, visible brushstrokes Van Gogh used in many of his paintings at that time.

However, *The Starry Night* shows a night sky filled with clouds, glowing stars, and a yellow moon above houses with brightly colored windows and a church with a steeple. Viewers find many things to look at in the painting. The mood of *The Starry Night* is serene and hopeful.

*Self-Portrait 1889*, on the other hand, shows a person, the artist himself. Van Gogh painted many self-portraits during his career. The mood of *Self-Portrait 1889* is more somber because Van Gogh looks so sad and worn. His deep eyes stare directly at viewers, holding their attention in one place.

1. Which sentence should be deleted?

   **A**   Viewers find many things to look at in the painting.

   **B**   The mood of *The Starry Night* is serene and hopeful.

   **C**   Van Gogh painted many self-portraits during his career.

   **D**   His deep eyes stare directly at viewers, holding their attention in one place.

2. Why should it be deleted? **The sentence does not tell about a similarity or difference between the two paintings, which is the topic of these paragraphs.**

3. Which sentence is the best one to add?

   **A**   A dark unknown shape looms on the left in *The Starry Night*.

   **B**   Van Gogh sold only one painting while he was alive.

   **C**   *The Starry Night* is probably Van Gogh's best-known painting.

   **D**   Van Gogh painted both paintings in Saint-Rémy in 1889.

# Peer and Teacher Conferencing Compare-and-Contrast Essay

**Directions** After exchanging drafts, read your partner's essay. Refer to the Revising Checklist as you make notes about your partner's essay. Write your comments or questions on the lines. Offer compliments as well as suggestions for revisions. Take turns talking about each other's draft using your notes. Give your partner your notes.

## Revising Checklist

### Focus/Ideas
☐ Is the compare and contrast essay focused and informative?
☐ Do all sentences tell about similarities and differences? Should any sentences be deleted? Should more detail sentences be added?

### Organization
☐ Are words that compare and contrast used to signal similarities and differences?
☐ Are there smooth transitions between paragraphs?

### Voice
☐ Is the writer engaged with the topic?

### Word Choice
☐ Are specific words used to tell about similarities and differences?

### Sentences
☐ Are sentences written in a variety of types and lengths?

**Things I Thought Were Good** _____

_____

**Things I Thought Could Be Improved** _____

_____

**Teacher's Comments** _____

_____

# Draw Conclusions

- A **conclusion** is a decision you make after thinking about the details in what you read.
- Often your prior knowledge can help you draw, or make, a conclusion.
- When you draw a conclusion, be sure it makes sense and is supported by what you have read.

**Directions** Read the following passage. Then complete the diagram.

Several factors led to the formation of cities. First, small agricultural groups grew larger when farmers and hunters were able to provide a steady supply of food for more people. Also, settlers started keeping herds of animals for food and other purposes. Because of these developments there was enough food for everyone, so settlers had time to learn new skills. They started making better tools and finding new uses for them. Better tools led to improvements in living conditions. Workers built structures to protect the community and to store food. They traded with other groups for items they needed. As more people lived together, members of the community started having different responsibilities and social relationships changed. Eventually, these communities developed a system to govern themselves. They also created a written language.

## Possible answers given.

**Detail:**
1. Farmers and hunters provided food for more people.

**Detail:**
2. Settlers learned new skills.

**Detail:**
3. Settlers made better tools and found new uses for them.

**What you know:**
4. Good tools make tough jobs easier.

**Conclusion**
5. More food and better tools led to formation of cities.

**Home Activity** Your child drew a conclusion from facts or details found in a reading passage. Tell him or her a short story about an event that happened in your life. Have your child single out two or three details from the story and form a conclusion about it.

# Writing • Fictional Narrative

**Key Features of a Fictional Narrative**

- may tell a story or describe a true event
- often contains dialogue
- includes illustrations or art

## The Boy in the Mirror

The last face Jason saw at night and the first he saw in the morning was his own. He saw himself in the mirror at night when he brushed his teeth before bed. He saw himself again in the mornings as he washed his face and brushed his hair before breakfast.

Jason liked to pretend that the boy that he saw in the mirror was not a reflection of himself, but a twin who lived in a parallel universe. He didn't have a lot of friends, and this was a way he could always have someone to talk to. Jason would wish his twin good night and good morning.

One day, Jason didn't want to go to school to take his math test. "I don't feel well," he told his mother.

"Then you should stay home and rest," Jason's mother said. Later, Jason got out of bed and went to the bathroom. He splashed water on his face as usual and started to brush his hair.

That was when he saw it. Or more correctly, that was when he didn't see it. He saw no reflection of himself in the mirror. Something was terribly wrong.

Jason drew close to the glass, peering into the bottom, the sides, and even the corners. His reflection wasn't there. "Where are you?" he asked.

Jason looked at his hands and body and feet. He felt his arms, his chest, his face, and his hair. He certainly could feel himself. He stared at the mirror. But he could not see himself there. "Oh, no," he cried. "What have I done?"

He ran back to his bed and pulled the covers over his head.

Could this be his doing? Had his pretending to be sick ripped a tear in the fabric of the universe? He shivered and shook, worried and fretted until he fell into a fitful sleep.

When he awakened, the sun was setting outside. The evening air smelled sweet. Jason slipped from bed and tiptoed into the bathroom, his eyes looking away from the mirror. He forced himself to turn and look. There he was. His reflection was back. "Thank you, thank you for coming back," he said to his reflection.

"You're welcome," replied his twin.

© Pearson Education, Inc., 5

1. Name three events in this story that could be illustrated.

   **Jason sick in bed, not seeing himself, seeing himself again**

2. Circle the first key sentence that tells this narrative is fiction.

# Vocabulary

**Directions** Choose the word from the box that best matches each definition below. Write the word on the line.

**civilization**_____ 1. the ways of living of a people or nation

**strategy**_____ 2. the skillful planning and management of anything

**rustling**_____ 3. causing a light, soft sound of things gently rubbing together

**blunders**_____ 4. stupid mistakes

**Check the Words You Know**

___blunders
___civilization
___complex
___envy
___fleeing
___inspired
___rustling
___strategy

**Directions** Choose the word from the box that best fits in the sentence. Write the word on the line shown to the left.

**fleeing**_____ 5. In his dreams, dragons were after him and he was _____, or running away.

**complex**_____ 6. Cities are more _____ than tiny villages.

**inspired**_____ 7. The people who created the earliest forms of writing were motivated, or _____, by a need to communicate ideas.

**Envy**_____ 8. _____ arises when someone else gets something we wanted.

**strategy**_____ 9. To play a game or sport well, you need to form a _____.

**rustling**_____ 10. As they hiked through the woods, they could hear the fallen leaves _____.

## Write a Description

On a separate sheet of paper, describe a sport you like to play, like soccer or chess. What are the rules? What are the best strategies?

**Descriptions should include words from the vocabulary list and details such as the best strategies to use to win the game.**

**Home Activity** Your child identified and used vocabulary words from *Weslandia*. Read a short story with your child. Have him or her point out unfamiliar words. Work together to figure out the meaning of each word by using words that appear near it.

© Pearson Education, Inc., 5

# Subject and Object Pronouns

A **subject pronoun** is used in the subject of a sentence. Singular subject pronouns are *I, you, he, she,* and *it.* Plural subject pronouns are *we, you,* and *they.* When you use a person's name and a pronoun in a compound subject, be sure to use a subject pronoun.

<u>He</u> has many original ideas. <u>They</u> are exciting and unusual.
Mom and <u>I</u> made bird feeders.

An **object pronoun** is used in the predicate of a sentence after an action verb or with a preposition, such as *for, at, into, with,* or *to.* Singular object pronouns are *me, you, him, her,* and *it.* Plural object pronouns are *us, you,* and *them.* When you use a person's name and a pronoun in a compound object, be sure to use an object pronoun.

The teacher asked <u>him</u> about his project. It seemed brilliant to <u>me</u>.
This project was fun for James and <u>me</u>.

**Directions** Write *S* if the underlined word is a subject pronoun. Write *O* if the word is an object pronoun.

1. Some kids don't know what to think about <u>him</u>. **O**

2. They can't understand someone who is different from <u>them</u>. **O**

3. <u>She</u> praised his project for its originality. **S**

4. Rainelle and <u>I</u> invited him to sit with us. **S**

5. <u>We</u> were fascinated by his ideas. **S**

6. He has become a valued friend to her and <u>me</u>. **O**

**Directions** Underline the correct pronoun in ( ) to complete each sentence.

7. Most people choose friends who are like (<u>them</u>, they).

8. (Them, <u>They</u>) feel comfortable with people who agree with them.

9. You and (<u>I</u>, me) have different points of view.

10. A friend with original ideas always surprises (I, <u>me</u>).

11. (Us, <u>We</u>) need to think about what we do and say.

12. (<u>I</u>, Me) prefer independent thinkers.

13. José and (her, <u>she</u>) agree with me.

14. We have many exciting conversations with (he, <u>him</u>) and (she, <u>her</u>).

**Home Activity** Your child learned about subject and object pronouns. Read a magazine article with your child. Ask him or her to identify several subject pronouns and object pronouns in the article.

Name _____

# Words from Many Cultures

| Spelling Words | | | | |
|---|---|---|---|---|
| khaki | hula | banana | ballet | waltz |
| tomato | vanilla | canyon | yogurt | banquet |
| macaroni | polka | cobra | koala | barbecue |
| safari | buffet | stampede | karate | kiosk |

**Word Histories** Write a list word for each description.

1. This is French for a table full of different foods.
2. Many students practice this Japanese form of self-defense.
3. Native Americans introduced this fruit to the settlers.
4. This is a Turkish treat made from milk.
5. This Polynesian dance is usually performed in a grass skirt.
6. This is a Spanish word for a large group of running buffaloes or horses.
7. Although it has a French name, this dance form started in Russia.
8. This furry animal has kept its Australian name.
9. Soldiers wear this yellowish brown fabric named by the Persians and Hindus so they can't be easily seen.
10. This partner dance means "to turn" in German.
11. This is an Italian name for a well-known pasta.
12. The Spanish and Portuguese used the same name for this yellow fruit.
13. A Native American word is used to name this kind of outside cooking.
14. This Polish dance is very lively.
15. Although this word is Arabic, this type of journey is done in Africa.
16. The Spanish named this flavorful type of bean long before there was ice cream.
17. This word for a feast or a formal dinner comes from French.
18. This is a Spanish word for a very deep valley carved out by a river.
19. The name for this hooded, poisonous snake comes from the Portuguese.
20. This is a Turkish word for a newsstand.

1. **buffet**
2. **karate**
3. **tomato**
4. **yogurt**
5. **hula**
6. **stampede**
7. **ballet**
8. **koala**
9. **khaki**
10. **waltz**
11. **macaroni**
12. **banana**
13. **barbecue**
14. **polka**
15. **safari**
16. **vanilla**
17. **banquet**
18. **canyon**
19. **cobra**
20. **kiosk**

**Home Activity** Your child wrote words from other cultures. Go over the pronunciation of the French words *buffet* and *ballet*. Remind your child that in French *-et* in these words is pronounced as long *a*.

# Story Sequence C

Title _____

**Characters**

**Setting**

**Problem**

### Events

_____
_____
_____
_____
_____
_____
_____
_____
_____

**Solution**

# Vocabulary • Endings

- **Endings** are a letter or letters added to the end of a base word.
- Recognizing an ending will help you figure out the word's meaning.
- The endings *-s* and *-es* can be added to singular nouns to make them plural. The endings *-s,* *-ed,* and *-ing* can be added to verbs to change the tense. The endings *-er* and *-est* can be added to adjectives to use them to compare.
- The definition of endings can be found in dictionaries, books that list words and their meanings.

**Directions** Read the following passage. Then answer the questions below.

Lisa enjoyed camping with her brother and parents every autumn. In a way she felt they were fleeing civilization and their complex city life. She had noticed that life in the city often makes people anxious. She always felt happier while hiking through the woods and sleeping under the stars. There was no one to envy because the beauty of nature surrounded them. Even the blunders they made turned into games to play. Once they hiked down the wrong trail and got lost. Instead of worrying, they worked together to find the quickest way back. When she returned to the city, Lisa felt inspired by the beauty she had enjoyed.

**Possible answers given.**

1. In the word *fleeing,* how does the *-ing* change the meaning of the base word?

**It changes the tense of the verb.**

2. What is the difference between the *-s* in *blunders* and the *-s* in *makes*?

**The first *-s* makes a noun plural, while the second *-s* puts a verb in the present tense.**

3. How does the *-er* change the meaning of the endings in *happier*?

**It makes a comparison.**

4. What does the *-ed* in *hiked* do to the meaning of the base word?

**It puts the verb into the past tense.**

5. Change some of the endings in this sentence to put the verbs in the past tense: "Lisa calls out to her family and then walks down the trail to meet them."

**Lisa called out to her family, and then walked down the trail to meet them.**

 **Home Activity** Your child identified and used endings added to base words, such as *-s, -ed, -ing,* and *-est.* Read a newspaper or magazine article with your child. Change the endings of some of the words and discuss with him or her how the sentences' meanings change.

# Instruction Manual

- **Following directions** involves doing or making something.
- Directions are usually numbered.
- Read all the directions before starting to act on the first direction given.
- Read the first direction, do what it says to do, and then proceed to the next step.
- Try to visualize the purpose or result of the process.

**Directions** Read these directions. Then answer the questions.

---

**How to Make Crystals**

1. Gather the materials you will need. They are: a small amount of Epsom salts, water, a sponge, and a shallow dish.

2. Boil water. Remove from heat. Add about 1/4 cup of Epsom salts to about 1/2 cup of boiling water. Stir until the salts dissolve.

3. Put a sponge in a shallow dish. Pour the liquid over the sponge. (The crystals will be easier to see on a sponge.) Only pour in enough of the mixture to cover the bottom of the dish.

4. Put the glass dish in a secure spot in the sun. Soon the water will evaporate and crystals will grow.

---

1. You and a friend have decided to make crystals. What would you do first? Explain.

   **Read all the directions before starting.**

2. What would you do next?

   **Gather the needed materials.**

3. How are the directions organized to make them easier to follow?

   **The steps are numbered.**

4. Which word told you when to look for crystals?

   **soon**

5. What do you think would have happened if you hadn't heated the water before you added the Epsom salts?

   **Possible answer: The Epsom salts would not have dissolved as easily.**

Name_____

**Directions**  Read this recipe. Then answer the questions below.

---

### How to Make Pizza Dough

1. Assemble ingredients: 3 cups flour, 1 package active dry yeast, 2 tablespoons butter, 1 teaspoon salt, and water.
2. In a small mixer bowl combine 1 cup of flour and yeast.
3. In a saucepan, heat water, butter, and salt until warm, stirring constantly to melt butter. (Always work with an adult when using the stove.)
4. Add liquid ingredients to dry mixture in mixer bowl. Beat at low speed with electric mixer for 1 minute.
5. Beat 3 minutes at high speed. Then turn the dough out on a flat surface and add enough of the remaining flour to make a soft dough.
6. Cover and let rise about 45 to 60 minutes until it doubles its size.
7. Spread dough evenly on a greased pizza pan. Add toppings and cook in oven for 30 minutes to an hour.

---

**Possible answers given.**

6. How much time do you think you will need to prepare the dough? Explain.

   **About an hour or more; The dough will require 45–60 minutes to rise, plus the time spent mixing the ingredients.**

7. How much time do you think you will need from step #2 until your pizza is ready to eat? Explain.

   **About two hours; The dough will take at least an hour, and then you have to add the toppings and cook for 30–60 minutes.**

8. Describe what you will have created at the end of step #3.

   **You will have a saucepan containing warm water, melted butter, and dissolved salt.**

9. Go through the sequence of steps in making pizza. Do you think any of the steps could be rearranged? Why or why not?

   **No, because each step builds on the step before it.**

10. How can you find out what equipment you will need before you start?

    **To know what equipment you will need, read the entire recipe before starting.**

**Home Activity**  Your child learned about following directions and the concept of steps in a process. Go over an instruction manual together. Ask your child questions about the sequence of tasks and how long the project will take.

© Pearson Education, Inc., 5

# Words from Many Cultures

**Proofread a Poster** Circle the seven spelling errors in the school poster.
Write the words correctly. Write the last sentence, using correct punctuation.

**Spelling Words**

khaki
hula
banana
ballet
waltz
tomato
vanilla
canyon
yogurt
banquet

macaroni
polka
cobra
koala
barbecue
safari
buffet
stampede
karate
kiosk

---

### Our New After-School Programs

**Learn to Dance**
- (poka) and Texas two-step
- ballet (with tutus and toe shoes)
- (walts) and other ballroom dances
- hula and dances of the Pacific

**Learn Martial Arts**
- (karatie) • judo • kung fu

**Learn How to Cook**
- barbecue sauces
- (tomatoe) salads
- homemade yogurt
- (macaronie) and cheese and other pastas
- (bananana) cream pie and other desserts

Sign up at the (kyosk) outside the office.
Bring a permission form from your parents?

---

1. **polka**
2. **waltz**
3. **karate**
4. **macaroni**
5. **tomato**
6. **banana**
7. **kiosk**
8. **Bring a permission form from your parents.**

**Frequently Misspelled Words**

our
again

**Proofread Words** Circle the correct spelling of the list word.
Write the word.

9. The frightened cattle started to ____.

   stamped   (stampede)   stampeed

9. **stampede**

10. I love the assortment of foods on the restaurant ____.

   (buffet)   buffay   buffee

10. **buffet**

**Home Activity** Your child identified misspelled list words. Say a list word and spell it incorrectly. Ask your child to spell the word correctly.

© Pearson Education, Inc., 5

# Subject and Object Pronouns

**Directions** Read the passage. Then read each question. Circle the letter of the correct answer.

# Wild Foods

(1) My mother is a nature enthusiast. (2) _____ and my father know where to find foods in the wild. (3) _____ and Uncle Dick locate and use different wild plants for food. (4) <u>We</u> have made entire meals out of wild plants! (5) In the fall, my grandfather will harvest cattails. (6) Mom and <u>I</u> grind the roots to make flour for <u>him</u>. (7) She and my father hunt for mushrooms in the woods. (8) Wild foods are a lot of work, but it is fun to hunt for _____.

**1** Which pronoun best completes sentence 2?

   A   Her

   **(B)**   She

   C   Them

   D   Him

**2** Which pronoun best completes sentence 3?

   A   Him

   B   Them

   C   Her

   **(D)**   They

**3** Which best describes the underlined word in sentence 4?

   A   Object pronoun

   **(B)**   Subject pronoun

   C   Predicate

   D   None of the above

**4** Which pair describes the two underlined words in sentence 6?

   **(A)**   Subject pronoun/object pronoun

   B   Subject pronoun/subject pronoun

   C   Object pronoun/predicate

   D   Object pronoun/object pronoun

**5** Which is the correct pronoun/type of pronoun for sentence 8?

   A   they/object pronoun

   B   them/subject pronoun

   **(C)**   them/object pronoun

   D   it/object pronoun

© Pearson Education, Inc., 5

**Home Activity** Your child prepared for taking tests on subject and object pronouns. Have your child write subject pronouns and object pronouns on index cards. Then mix the cards and sort them into subject pronoun and object pronoun piles.

# Generalize

- An author may write similar details about different things or people. You can use these similar details to make a general statement that covers all the things or people. This statement is called a **generalization.**
- A **valid** generalization can be supported by facts or details. A **faulty** generalization cannot.
- Sometimes an author makes a generalization and uses a clue word such as *all, many,* or *generally* to signal it.

**Directions** Read the following passage. Then complete the diagram below.

John heard a program on the radio about diabetes. One woman described how she found out she had the disease. She always felt thirsty even though she drank a lot of water. She was also really hungry all the time, even though she ate a lot. She went to see her doctor, who said that she should be tested for diabetes because unusual thirst and hunger are generally symptoms. The test showed that she had diabetes.

A young boy spoke next. He too was always thirsty and hungry. He thought he was just growing, but one day he passed out at school. As the boy finished speaking, John realized that he was really hungry and thirsty. He was pouring some juice when he remembered he had eaten just a half-hour ago. He thought about the program, and he asked his mom to make a doctor's appointment.

## Possible answers given.

**General Statement**
1. **Unusual thirst and hunger are generally symptoms of diabetes.**          2. Clue word: **generally**

**Supporting Details**

3. **A woman with the symptoms had diabetes.**

4. **A young boy with the symptoms had diabetes.**

5. **John thought he had the symptoms of diabetes.**

**Home Activity** Your child read a short passage and recognized a generalization. Read a newspaper or magazine article together and ask your child to find a generalization along with details that support it.

© Pearson Education, Inc., 5

# Writing • Friendly Letter

**Key Features of a Friendly Letter**

- is written to a friend or someone you know well
- uses informal language to communicate ideas
- has a casual tone
- contains a date, salutation, and closing

---

May 12, 20__

Dear Jinx,

   I hope this letter finds you healthy and free from injury. I am writing to tell you that I miss you, and I have decided I want to write another story about you. If it's okay with you, I will give you a new sport to try.

   What do you think about badminton? A lot of families like to play badminton outside in their yards. All you need is a net, some rackets, and this ball-like thing called a shuttle. I imagine Mr. Deimeister has a badminton set stored somewhere at the school.

   I've tried to think of ways that you could get hurt playing badminton. It is a quick sport. I suppose you could run into another player or get hit in the head with a racket somehow. I wonder, though, would you rather turn out to be a good badminton player?

   I think I'll start writing the story. We'll just see how it turns out. After all, you are the person you are. Why mess up a good thing?

   Fondly,
   Angela Johnson

---

**1.** How does Angela Johnson's use of questions affect the tone of the letter?

**They give the letter a casual, friendly tone.**

_____

**2.** Make a list of other salutations and closings that Angela Johnson might have used.

Openings **Hello, Jinx!; Jinx,** _____

Closings **Your friend, ; Sincerely,** _____

# Vocabulary

**Directions** Choose the word from the box that best matches each definition. Write the word on the line.

**sprained**_____

1. injured tissue at a joint caused by a sudden twist or wrench

**frilly**_____

2. full of ruffles

**Dalmatian**_____

3. a large, short-haired dog, usually white with black spots

**promenading**_____

4. walking for pleasure or for show

**substitute**_____

5. something that is used instead of something else

**Directions** Choose the word from the box that best completes each sentence. Write the word on the line to the left.

**Dalmatian**_____

6. Many firehouses have a _____ as their adopted pet.

**substitute**_____

7. Mrs. Green was sick today, so we had a _____ teacher.

**sprained**_____

8. Becky _____ her ankle during basketball practice.

**frilly**_____

9. Mom had a _____ dress for parties.

**promenading**_____

10. While my sister and I played in our cabin, Mom and Dad spent time _____ around the deck.

## Write a Newspaper Article

On a separate sheet of paper, write an imaginary newspaper article about a group of local square dancers who try for First Prize at the National Square Dancing Championship. Use as many of the vocabulary words as you can.

**Articles should include words from the vocabulary list and details about a square dancing competition.**

© Pearson Education, Inc., 5

**Home Activity** Your child identified and used vocabulary words from *Tripping Over the Lunch Lady*. Together, look through newspapers or magazines for stories about people who adapt to face physical, emotional, or mental challenges. Discuss what gives people the motivation to succeed.

# Pronouns and Antecedents

A **pronoun** takes the place of a noun or nouns. An **antecedent,** or referent, is the noun or nouns to which the pronoun refers. A pronoun and its antecedent must agree in number and gender.

Before you use a pronoun, ask yourself whether the antecedent is singular or plural. If the antecedent is singular, decide whether it is masculine, feminine, or neutral. Then choose a pronoun that agrees. In the following sentences, the antecedents are underlined once and the pronouns are underlined twice.

Victoria went with Jinx to practice square dancing. She helped her practice.

**Directions** Circle the correct pronoun or pronouns in ( ) to complete each sentence. The antecedent of each pronoun is underlined to help you.

1. The girl was nicknamed Jinx because (she, her) was clumsy.

2. The square dancers were very good, and (them, they) smiled for the camera.

3. The girl talks with the gym teacher and becomes friends with (him, he).

4. Victoria helped Jinx practice, but (she, they) broke her foot.

5. People can practice sports but may never be good at (they, them).

6. The girl kept a journal, and (it, they) tells of her experiences.

**Directions** Underline the antecedent once and the pronoun twice in each sentence.

7. Nate went to tryouts with the new football he had gotten.

8. Juwon could not play because a sore knee bothered him.

9. The sky grew cloudy, and it threatened rain.

10. When Mrs. Panizzi jogged by, Nate waved to her.

11. Nate made a great catch, and it impressed the coach.

12. The coach thanked his new players, and they shook hands.

**Home Activity** Your child learned about pronouns and antecedents. Read a magazine article together and have your child find pronouns that have antecedents and identify both.

# Prefixes *over-*, *under-*, *sub-*, *super-*, *out-*

| Spelling Words | | | | |
|---|---|---|---|---|
| overlook | underline | subway | subset | supermarket |
| outlet | underground | overboard | undercurrent | superstar |
| overtime | supersonic | submarine | undercover | overcast |
| outfield | output | supernatural | subdivision | subhead |

**Classifying** Write the list word that belongs in each group.

1. city, trains, underground, ____

2. sky, clouds, gray, ____

3. diamond, mound, infield, ____

4. police officer, disguise, ____

5. grocery, bakery, butcher, ____

6. daydream, forget, omit, ____

7. highlight, line, ____

8. plane, jet engine, speed of sound, ____

9. work, extra hours, ____

10. performer, actor, singer, ____

1. **subway**

2. **overcast**

3. **outfield**

4. **undercover**

5. **supermarket**

6. **overlook**

7. **underline**

8. **supersonic**

9. **overtime**

10. **superstar**

**Definitions** Write the list word that fits each definition.

11. This is part of a community.

12. This is the result of production.

13. This means eerie and ghostly.

14. This is a small part of a larger group.

15. This means beneath the earth.

16. This is a vessel that travels underwater.

17. This comes under a heading.

18. This is a pull under the waves.

19. This means falling off a ship.

20. This can be a store that offers discounts.

11. **subdivision**

12. **output**

13. **supernatural**

14. **subset**

15. **underground**

16. **submarine**

17. **subhead**

18. **undercurrent**

19. **overboard**

20. **outlet**

**Home Activity** Your child wrote words with prefixes. Ask your child to name four words and tell you how the prefixes in each word affect its meaning.

© Pearson Education, Inc., 5

# T-Chart

# Vocabulary • Context Clues

- When you find an **unfamiliar word** in a text, look for context clues to its meaning.
- You can find context clues among the words around the unfamiliar word.

**Directions** Read the following passage about overcoming obstacles. Then use context clues to answer the questions below.

> Anita's friend Jessica asked her a hard question. "Anita, what is it like to live with your disability? Is it hard for you to be in a wheelchair?"
>
> Anita thought carefully about how she would answer. "I don't mind using a wheelchair. I get around in it very well. But because I have cerebral palsy, it's difficult for people to understand what I'm saying. Sometimes my words can sound very confusing. Sometimes my speech sounds muddled, like I have something in my mouth."
>
> Jessica said, "But I can understand you just fine."
>
> "You are used to me," said Anita. "I go to a speech therapist every week to help me learn how to speak more clearly. I want people to better understand what I'm saying."

## Possible answers given.

1. What does *wheelchair* mean? What context clues helped you to determine the meaning?

   **A wheelchair is used by people who can't walk. Because Anita can't walk, she has to use a wheelchair.**

2. What does *disability* mean? What context clues helped you to determine the meaning?

   **a handicap; Jessica asks if it's hard for Anita to be in a wheelchair.**

3. What does *muddled* mean? What context clues help you to determine the meaning?

   **unclear; Anita says it sounds like she has something in her mouth.**

4. How would using context clues help you determine the meaning of *speech therapist*?

   **A speech therapist helps people learn how to speak. Anita says the speech therapist helps her learn how to speak more clearly.**

5. What context clues helped you understand what *cerebral palsy* means?

   **disability; Anita uses a wheelchair; her speech sounds muddled.**

© Pearson Education, Inc., 5

**Home Activity** Your child identified and used context clues to understand new words of a passage. Have a discussion with your child in which you use context clues to give clues to the meanings of new words.

# Telephone Directory

A **telephone directory** is an alphabetical index of names and telephone numbers for a selected geographical area. The **white pages** list entries for individual people and businesses. The **yellow pages** list entries and ads for businesses. Entries are grouped by category or type of business, such as *restaurants*. This information is available in reference books or on the Internet. You can search online to find phone numbers for people and businesses in other cities, states, and even countries.

**Directions** The computer screen shows you how to search a directory of online white pages. Use the computer screen to answer the questions that follow.

**Enter the first and last name of the person and click *Find!***

For better results, enter the city and state also.

Last Name (required) _____

First Name _____

City _____    State _____

Country _____

( **Find!** )   If you need help, click here.

1. What entries will you get if you type "Reyes" in the field for Last Name, "Philadelphia" in the City field, and "PA" (for Pennsylvania) in the State field?

   **The results would feature telephone numbers for all the people with the last name Reyes in Philadelphia, PA.**

2. You know Sue Costello lives in Florida. Tell how to find her phone number and address.

   **Type "Costello" in the Last Name field, "Sue" in the First Name field, and "FL" in the State field.**

3. Would typing "Julia" in the First Name field and "Texas" in the State field give you good search results? Explain.

   **Possible answer: No; There are probably many people named Julia in Texas, and it would be hard to locate the person you wanted.**

4. How does using an online telephone directory rather than a telephone book increase the information you can get?

   **Possible answer: You can get information about regions for which you do not have a telephone book.**

Name_____

**Directions** The computer screen shows you how to search a directory of online yellow pages. Use the computer screen to answer the questions that follow.

## Possible answers given for 6–10.

| Enter a business category or name. Then click *Find!* |
|---|
| |
| **City** [_____]     **State** [_____] |
| **Find!**   If you need help, click here. |

5. What will you get if you enter the category "state park" and "FL" for State?

**You would be given the names and telephone numbers of state parks in Florida.**

6. If you want information on Nancy & Beth's Catering Services in St. Louis, Missouri, what should you enter?

**Enter "catering" in the Category field, "St. Louis" in the City field, and "Missouri" in the State field.**

7. If you want to find a bike rental in Phoenix, Arizona, what should you enter?

**Enter "bicycle rental" in the Category field, "Phoenix" in the City field, and "Arizona" in the State field.**

8. If you enter "toy store" in the category field, will this produce good search results? Explain.

**No; the State field has to have something in it for the search to work.**

9. Which of the three fields could you leave blank? Explain how filling in this field would narrow your search.

**the City field; Putting information in the City field would restrict your results to companies in a certain city only.**

10. Can you use an online telephone directory if you don't know how to spell the name of a business? Explain.

**Yes; If you know what kind of business it is, and the city and state it is in, you could look for it in the results of a category search.**

**Home Activity** Your child learned about using telephone directories. Look at an online telephone directory together. Ask your child to locate emergency phone numbers, maps, and phone numbers of local businesses and residences.

© Pearson Education, Inc., 5

# Prefixes *over-*, *under-*, *sub-*, *super-*, *out-*

**Proofread a Paragraph** Circle six spelling errors. Write the words correctly. Find one punctuation error and write the sentence using the correct punctuation.

© Pearson Education, Inc., 5

> If you had a choice, would you want to break the sound barrier in a (super sonic) jet? Is cruising beneath the surface of the sea in a (sub marine) more your style? What about riding underground on a large (sub way) system? Would you rather stay all night in a deserted house waiting for something (super natural) to happen? Do you like sports○ Perhaps you'd really rather be playing ball in the (out field)? Fortunately, one doesn't have to be a (super star) to do any of these things.

**Spelling Words**

overlook
underline
subway
subset
supermarket
outlet
underground
overboard
undercurrent
superstar

overtime
supersonic
submarine
undercover
overcast
outfield
output
supernatural
subdivision
subhead

1. **supersonic**
2. **submarine**
3. **subway**
4. **supernatural**
5. **outfield**
6. **superstar**
7. **Do you like sports?**

**Proofread Words** Circle the word that is spelled correctly.

8. (submarine)   submareen   submarein
9. subdivsion   subdivison   (subdivision)
10. subersonic   (supersonic)   supresonic
11. (underline)   undeline   undrline
12. outfeild   outfeeld   (outfield)
13. (overcast)   overcas   ovrcast
14. overlok   (overlook)   ovarlock
15. suparmarkit   suprmarkat   (supermarket)
16. (overboard)   overbored   ovarboard

**Frequently Misspelled Words**

outside
because

**Home Activity** Your child identified misspelled list words. Ask your child to tell you which three words are most difficult and then have your child spell them with you.

## Pronouns and Antecedents

**Directions** Read the passage. Then read each question. Circle the letter of the correct answer.

# Team Works

(1) People admired Ben and Sasha when _____ went to the gymnastics event. (2) The tournament was long, and _____ would not be easy. (3) Ben was strong, and he was a hard worker. (4) Sasha was team captain, and her was a great gymnast. (5) Sasha hurt her knee, and the team had to help her. (6) Jenny and I were there, and we cheered for the team. (7) Ben and Sasha led the way, but they got much help from the others.

1 Which pronoun best completes sentence 1?

  A  her

  B  she

  **C**  they

  D  he

2 Which pronoun best completes sentence 2?

  A  him

  **B**  it

  C  her

  D  they

3 What change, if any, should be made in sentence 4?

  A  Change *was* to **were**

  B  Remove the comma after *captain*

  **C**  Change *her* to **she**

  D  Make no change

4 In sentence 5, what is the relationship between the underlined words?

  **A**  Antecedent-pronoun

  B  Pronoun-pronoun

  C  Pronoun-antecedent

  D  Antecedent-antecedent

5 In sentence 6, which is the antecedent for the pronoun *we*?

  A  Jenny

  **B**  Jenny and I

  C  the team

  D  Jenny and I were there

© Pearson Education, Inc., 5

**School + Home**

**Home Activity** Your child prepared for taking tests on pronouns and antecedents. Have your child rewrite a paragraph from a story, replacing each pronoun with its antecedent. Ask him or her to explain why pronouns make the story sound better.

# Graphic Sources

- A **graphic source,** such as a picture, diagram, or chart, organizes information visually.
- Preview the graphic sources to help you predict what you will be reading about.

**Directions** Study the following diagram. Then answer the questions below.

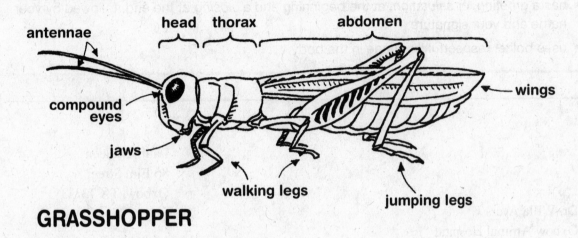

**GRASSHOPPER**

1. What is the purpose of this diagram?

   <u>Possible answer: The diagram shows the different parts of a</u>

   <u>grasshopper's body.</u>

2. What are the three main sections of the grasshopper's body?

   <u>The three parts are the abdomen, thorax, and head.</u>

3. What do grasshoppers use to hop, walk, and fly?

   <u>Grasshoppers use their jumping legs for hopping, walking legs</u>

   <u>for walking, and wings for flying.</u>

4. How many legs does the grasshopper have? How does the diagram show you this?

   <u>six; The diagram uses arrows and labels to show the legs.</u>

5. What is the location of the grasshopper's two front legs? What other job might the front legs perform in addition to walking?

   <u>close to the grasshopper's jaws; Possible answer: Grasshoppers</u>

   <u>might use the front legs to hold food while they eat.</u>

**Home Activity** Your child used a graphic source to answer questions. Together, read a newspaper or magazine article that includes a graphic source. Ask your child to answer questions about the article based on the information shown in the graphic source.

# Writing • Formal Letter

**Key Features of a Formal Letter**

- has a purpose, such as asking for information
- includes a *heading* with your address, the address of the person you are writing to, and the date you are writing the letter
- has a greeting, or *salutation*, at the beginning and a *closing* at the end, followed by your name and your signature
- uses polite, respectful language in the body

Laura Moleen
86 Elm Street
Oxbow, TX 73333

Dr. Willa Ayers
Oxbow Animal Hospital
222 State Road 202
Oxbow, TX 73330

August 11, 20__

Dear Dr. Ayers,

I asked my mother for a dog or a cat as a pet, but she has allergies to dogs and cats. She thought that I might like a Bearded Dragon and wants me to research this kind of lizard. Could you help me decide whether a Bearded Dragon would be a good pet by answering some questions or sending me information about where I can find out more about Bearded Dragons?

I would like to know whether a Bearded Dragon lizard likes to be petted. What kind of home does it need? What do I have to do to properly care for a Bearded Dragon? How big will it get? How long will it live? Is it friendly? Does it like to play? What toys should I get for it?

Thank you taking the time to answer my questions about Bearded Dragons. If you have information about Bearded Dragons, could you send it to me?

Yours sincerely,

Laura Moleen

1. What are the salutation and the closing in this letter?

   **Dear Dr. Ayers; Yours sincerely,**

2. Which sentence tells the purpose of this letter? Underline that sentence.

Name_____

# Vocabulary

**Directions** Choose the word from the box that best matches each definition. Write the word on the line.

**mucus** _____  1. a slimy substance produced in the nose and throat to moisten and protect them

**sterile** _____  2. free from germs

**enables** _____  3. gives ability, power, or means to; makes able

**specialize** _____  4. to develop in a special way

**critical** _____  5. being important to the outcome of a situation

**Directions** Circle the word or group of words that has the same or nearly the same meaning as the first word.

| *Example:* **melody** | words | (tune) | ringing |
|---|---|---|---|
| **6. scarce** | plenty | many | (rare) |
| **7. critical** | (important) | useful | relaxed |
| **8. sterile** | dirty | (germ-free) | bacteria |
| **9. enables** | teaches | makes empty | (allows) |
| **10. specialize** | stretch | (adapt) | organize |

## Write a Description

On a separate sheet of paper, write a description of a grasshopper or another insect with which you are familiar. Your description should include as many details as possible. Use as many vocabulary words as you can.

## Descriptions should include words from the vocabulary list as well as details about a grasshopper or another familiar insect.

**Home Activity** Your child identified and used vocabulary words from *Exploding Ants*. Pretend each of you is a research scientist. Use the vocabulary words to discuss a new species of insect you have discovered together.

# Possessive Pronouns

**Possessive pronouns** show who or what owns, or possesses, something. *My, mine, your, yours, her, hers, his, its, our, ours, their,* and *theirs* are possessive pronouns.

- Use *my, your, her, our,* and *their* before nouns.
  Is that your cat? It was her gerbil. They pet our dog.

- Use *mine, yours, hers, ours,* and *theirs* alone.
  The cat is yours. That gerbil is hers. The dog is ours.

- *His* and *its* can be used both before nouns and alone.
  He lost his ferret. The ferret is his.
  The dog lost its collar. The collar is its.

- Do not use an apostrophe with a possessive pronoun.

**Directions** Replace the underlined words or phrases with possessive pronouns. Rewrite the sentences.

1. An ant colony relies on the ant colony's queen.
**An ant colony relies on its queen.**

2. Both males and females have wings on the males' and females' bodies.
**Both males and females have wings on their bodies.**

3. The queen ant flies to a new location to start a colony and then sheds the queen's wings.
**The queen ant flies to a new location to start a colony and then sheds her wings.**

4. Ants are very strong for ants' size and can carry 25 times ants' weight.
**Ants are very strong for their size and can carry 25 times their weight.**

5. Most of us think that ants are pests to be swept out of most of us's way.
**Most of us think that ants are pests to be swept out of our way.**

© Pearson Education, Inc., 5

**Home Activity** Your child learned about possessive pronouns. Ask your child to make up sentences about objects at home that belong to him or her, to the family, and to others. Have your child identify the possessive pronouns he or she uses.

Name _____

# Homophones

| Spelling Words | | | | |
|---|---|---|---|---|
| cent | sent | scent | threw | through |
| weather | whether | their | there | they're |
| chili | chilly | tide | tied | pale |
| pail | aloud | allowed | course | coarse |

**Words in Context** Write homophones to complete the sentences.

On a **(1)**____ day, hot, spicy **(2)**____ with cheese really tastes good.

1. **chilly**     2. **chili**

We made sure the boats were **(3)**____ down securely against the rising **(4)**____.

3. **tied**     4. **tide**

The **(5)**____ will determine **(6)**____ or not we play the game.

5. **weather**     6. **whether**

I **(7)**____ away for that special one- **(8)**____ offer for my favorite perfume **(9)**____.

7. **sent**     8. **cent**     9. **scent**

Speaking **(10)**____ is not **(11)**____ in the library.

10. **aloud**     11. **allowed**

You **(12)**____ the ball so far that it went **(13)**____ the window!

12. **threw**     13. **through**

**(14)**____ starting **(15)**____ lemonade business over **(16)**____ near the bakery.

14. **They're**     15. **their**     16. **there**

The golf **(17)**____ is designed to be challenging. It has sand, water traps, woods, and smooth and **(18)**____ grass.

17. **course**     18. **coarse**

The **(19)**____ child carried the **(20)**____ onto the beach.

19. **pale**     20. **pail**

**Home Activity** Your child learned to use homophones in context. Ask your child to make up other sentences using list words.

**Spelling** Homophones **273**

Name _____

# Writing • Formal Letter

Sender's Name _____

Address _____

City, ST Zip _____

Date _____

Recipient's Name _____ , [Title]

Address _____

City, ST Zip _____

Salutation _____

Opening: Statement of Purpose:

_____

_____

Supporting Details:

_____

_____

_____

Desired Action:

_____

_____

_____

Thank you in advance for:

_____

Closing _____

Signature _____

# Vocabulary • Synonyms

- A **thesaurus** is a book that lists words, their **synonyms,** and their **antonyms.**
- **Synonyms** are different words that mean the same or almost the same thing, while **antonyms** are words that have the opposite meaning of each other.
- Sometimes authors write synonyms next to difficult words to help readers understand the word. To find synonyms, look for the words *or, such as,* and *like,* or a phrase set off by commas.

**Directions** Read the following passage about insects. Then answer the questions below. You may use a thesaurus.

To some people, insects such as mosquitoes are simply pests. But many insects are useful. Honeybees, for example, make honey. They also pollinate plants by carrying pollen from one plant to another. This enables, or allows, the plant to grow and develop. Pollination is essential, or critical, for many things we eat. Growers use honeybees in apple orchards, for example. Beekeepers raise colonies, or communities, of bees.

Some insects eat garbage. Others specialize in or focus on eating harmful insects. Caterpillars eat lots of plants but don't usually do permanent damage. Butterflies eat very little.

**1.** What word in the passage is a synonym for *enables*? How do you know it is a synonym?

**allows; The phrase "or allows" is set off by commas.**

**2.** What suggests that *essential* and *critical* are synonyms?

**The phrase "or critical" is set off by commas and appears near the word essential.**

**3.** The word *mosquitoes* follows the words *such as*. How do you know it is not a synonym for *insects*?

**Possible answer: *Mosquitoes* is an example of an insect, not a synonym for the word *insect*.**

**4.** What is another word for *colonies*? What context clue helps you to identify the synonym?

**communities; The phrase "or communities" is set off by commas.**

**5.** Rewrite the last sentence to provide a synonym for the word *scarce*.

**Possible answers: Many types of butterflies are abundant, though some are becoming scarce, or rare.**

**Home Activity** Your child identified and used synonyms to help him or her understand other words. Together, read an article about a scientific subject in a newspaper or magazine, noting any challenging vocabulary. Try to use synonyms and other context clues to clarify the meanings of these words.

# Magazine/Periodical

- **Magazines** and **periodicals** are excellent sources of current information. They contain news articles, opinion columns, reports, reviews, letters, cartoons, advertisements, and other features.
- A table of contents helps readers locate particular stories and other information.
- Many magazine and periodical articles follow the "5 Ws and H" format. That is, they tell you *Who? What? When? Where? Why?* and *How?* in the first few paragraphs.

**Directions** Read this table of contents for an issue of a magazine. Then answer the questions that follow.

---

**December Issue    Volume 237 Number 4**

## CONTENTS
**Year in Review**
24  Annual salute to the people who made discoveries that have changed our lives
39  Year-end updates on works-in-progress
**Features**
44  The longest-living lungfish
51  New vaccine for a dangerous disease
67  Discovery of a new species of grasshopper

**World News**
72  Monarchs winter in Mexico in record numbers
80  Alaskan dinosaurs and the Bering Strait
**Columns**
12  Letters to the editor
18  Ask the experts
93  Calendar
128 Book reviews

---

1. How would you describe the subject of this magazine?

   **Possible answer: a magazine about science and scientific discoveries**

2. On what page could you find information about lungfish?

   **page 44**

3. Where could you read what people think about a new book?

   **book reviews on page 128**

4. Do you think this is a new magazine or one that has been published for some time? How do you know?

   **It has been published for some time; The high volume number indicates the magazine's long history.**

5. If you wrote to the magazine, where might you find your comments published in the next issue?

   **They would appear under Letters to the Editor.**

**Directions** Read this passage from a magazine and answer the questions below.

**Who's Got the Longest-Living Lungfish?**

Two cities are competing for the honor of possessing the nation's longest-living lungfish. On Monday, the city of Will announced that its aquarium is celebrating the 67th birthday of its Australian lungfish on April 9. On Tuesday, one day later and fifty miles east, the city of Franklyn declared its plans to celebrate the 70th birthday of its lungfish on April 9. However, neither aquarium can prove the exact age of its lungfish.

Why the interest in elderly lungfish? Perhaps because it is a most unusual creature. It has both gills and lungs, leading scientists to believe that it is the missing link between fish and amphibians. The lungfish has the ability to be, as the saying goes, "a fish out of water." In other words, it can survive on land as well as in water. This adaptation is a big reason why the lungfish has survived for ages. Fossils show that it existed some 400 million years ago. Today the lungfish is an endangered species.

## Possible answers given for 2, 5.

**6.** What part of the passage gives you a first impression of the article's subject?

**The title gives readers the first idea of the subject.**

**7.** What would you identify as the *Who* of this article?

**The *who* is the aquarium in Will and the aquarium in Franklyn.**

**8.** What would you say is the *What* of the article?

**The *what* is the nation's longest-living lungfish.**

**9.** What is the *When* of the article?

**The *when* is April 9 (the date of the two parties) and Monday and Tuesday (when the aquariums made their announcements).**

**10.** When might you use the information in this article?

**I might use this information while writing a report about recent events in science.**

© Pearson Education, Inc., 5

**Home Activity** Your child learned about reading tables of contents and articles in magazines. Look at a current issue of a magazine together and discuss the *Who, What, When, Where, Why,* and *How* of one of the articles.

# Homophones

**Proofread an Ad** Circle six spelling errors. Write the words correctly.
Find one capitalization error. Write the sentence correctly.

> On a chilly day, shout (allowed) for our delicious (chilly!)
> It will warm you through and (threw!) Ask about our
> ninety-nine (sent) special. If the (whether) is bad, call us. We
> Deliver for free! Of course, (their) is no finer tasting treat!

1. __aloud__        2. __chili__
3. __through__      4. __cent__
5. __weather__      6. __there__
7. __We deliver for free!__

**Proofread Words** Circle the correct spelling of the list word. Write the word.

8. Burlap is a ____ fabric.

   corse        cuarse        (coarse)

9. I think ____ going on a class trip tomorrow.

   (they're)    their        they'ar

10. Sky blue is a ____ color.

    pail        (pale)        paile

11. Your perfume has a lovely ____.

    (scent)      cent          sent

12. I am not sure ____ I can go.

    wheather    (whether)      weather

13. The sailor ____ down the ship's hatch.

    tide        teid          (tied)

14. The candy cost one ____.

    scent        (cent)        sent

15. The score was even and the game was ____.

    tide        teid          (tied)

8. __coarse__

9. __they're__

10. __pale__

11. __scent__

12. __whether__

13. __tied__

14. __cent__

15. __tied__

**School + Home**

**Home Activity** Your child identified misspelled and misused homophones. Say a homophone in a sentence and have your child spell it.

Name _____

# Possessive Pronouns

**Directions** Read the passage. Then read each question. Circle the letter of the correct answer.

# Our Owls

(1) When I was young, my brother and I heard a haunting sound outside their window. (2) We ran into our yard to see what it was. (3) "It's just a screech owl," Rich said, but _____ hoot still made me nervous. (4) After that, owls became a hobby of ours. (5) Did you know that owls can turn <u>owls'</u> heads almost completely around? (6) This is an adaptation of theirs that allows them to turn their heads to follow a moving object. (7) Now biologists, my brother and I spend our time studying these birds of prey.

**1** What change, if any, should be made in sentence 1?

  **A**   Change *my brother and I* to **my brother and me**

  **B**   Change *was young* to **were young**

  **(C)**   Change *their* to **our**

  **D**   Make no change

**2** Which possessive pronoun best completes sentence 3?

  **(A)**   its

  **B**   my

  **C**   our

  **D**   their

**3** What change, if any, should be made in sentence 4?

  **A**   Change *became* to **have become**

  **B**   Change *ours* to **our**

  **C**   Change *ours* to **yours**

  **(D)**   Make no change

**4** Which possessive pronoun replaces the underlined word in sentence 5?

  **(A)**   their

  **B**   our

  **C**   theirs

  **D**   its

**5** How many possessive pronouns are in sentence 6?

  **A**   0

  **B**   1

  **(C)**   2

  **D**   3

© Pearson Education, Inc., 5

**Home Activity** Your child prepared for taking tests on possessive pronouns. Have your child choose a magazine article and find possessive pronouns in it. Ask him or her to name the person or thing each possessive pronoun stands for.

**Conventions** Possessive Pronouns   **279**

# Generalize

- To **generalize** is to make a broad statement or rule that applies to several examples.
- Active readers pay close attention to what authors tell them about story characters and make generalizations about those characters as they read.

**Directions** Read the following passage.

Matt and his family moved to a new town where he went to a new school. He disliked the school a lot. When Matt wasn't complaining, he just stayed quiet and kept to himself. He played soccer and found classmates to sit with at lunch, but longed to see his old friends. He begged to go back to his old hometown for a visit, and his parents finally agreed. As they neared his old school, Matt was excited. He raced into the school and walked around. Everything seemed strange. Even his old friends didn't seem as familiar. On the way home he found himself looking forward to soccer practice.

**Possible answers given.**

**Directions** Complete the diagram by making a generalization about Matt.

**Generalization**

1. **Students eventually adjust to a new school.**

**Support from Text**
2. **Matt's old school seems strange.**

**Support from Text**
3. **Matt's old friends seem unfamiliar.**

**Support from Text**
4. **Matt looks forward to soccer at his new school.**

5. Explain the story structure by telling the problem, rising action, climax, and outcome.

**Problem: Matt is unhappy at his new school; Rising action: Matt complains; Climax: Matt visits his old school; Outcome: Matt realizes that he likes his new school.**

© Pearson Education, Inc., 5

**Home Activity** Your child made a generalization about a character in a story. Read a short story about friendship together. Ask your child to generalize about one of the characters. Ask your child to analyze the story structure also—the problem, rising action, climax, and outcome.

# Writing • Narration Poetry

**Key Features of Narrative Poetry**

- tells a story
- uses sensory details
- may include graphic elements

## The First Day

The worst day is always the first day.
I try to stay out of everyone's way.
I talk only to myself in the noisy hall,
Maybe I could blend in to the cold wall.

Everyone stares but nobody cares.
Then I see a girl in the bathroom mirror.
WAIT—
            is that a SMILE I see?
Is she smiling at herself or at me?

I was sure this day would make me blue,
But I guess life can surprise you.
Today I made a FRIEND to stay,
So the first day isn't always the worst day!

1. Summarize the story that the poem tells.

   **The student is scared of the first day of school. She tries to**

   **avoid everyone, but then she makes a new friend.**

2. Underline two examples of sensory details in the poem.

3. Circle two examples of graphic elements, such as capital letters and varying line lengths, in the poem.

# Vocabulary

**Directions** Choose the word from the box that best matches each definition below. Write the word on the line.

cavities _____ 1. hollow places in teeth caused by decay

demonstrates _____ 2. shows how a thing is done

strict _____ 3. very careful in following a rule or making others follow it

episode _____ 4. one part of a story that is published or broadcast in several parts

profile _____ 5. attitude or position

---

**Check the Words You Know**

___cavities
___combination
___demonstrates
___episode
___profile
___strict

---

**Directions** Choose the word from the box that best matches each clue below. Write the word on the line.

episode _____ 6. This is one in a series.

combination _____ 7. This opens some locks.

strict _____ 8. Some teachers act this way.

profile _____ 9. A movie star would have a high one of these.

cavities _____ 10. If you don't brush your teeth, you might get these.

## Write a Friendly Letter

On a separate sheet of paper, write a friendly letter that you might send to a relative telling about the beginning of a new school year. Use as many vocabulary words as you can.

## Letters should include words from the vocabulary list as well as information typical to a new school year.

**Home Activity** Your child identified and used vocabulary words from *The Stormi Giovanni Club*. Read a story or nonfiction article with your child. Have him or her point out unfamiliar words. Together try to figure out the meaning of each word by using the words that appear near it.

© Pearson Education, Inc., 5

# Indefinite and Reflexive Pronouns

**Indefinite pronouns** may not refer to specific words. They do not have definite antecedents.
Someone called and left a message.

Some common indefinite pronouns are listed below.

**Singular Indefinite Pronouns**
someone, somebody, anyone,
anybody, everyone, everybody,
something, no one, either, each

**Plural Indefinite Pronouns**
few, several, both, others, many
all, some

• Use singular verb forms with singular indefinite pronouns and plural verb forms with plural indefinite pronouns: Everyone feels lonely at times. Others offer them friendship.

**Reflexive pronouns** reflect the action of the verb back on the subject. Reflexive pronouns end in -*self* or -*selves*: Vic wrote a note to himself.

**Singular Reflexive Pronouns**
himself, herself, myself,
itself, yourself

**Plural Reflexive Pronouns**
ourselves, yourselves, themselves

• There are no such words as *hisself, theirself, theirselves,* or *ourself.*

**Directions** Underline the correct pronoun in ( ) to complete each sentence.

1. (Anyone, Many) benefits by making new friends.

2. (Many, Anyone) treasure old friends too.

3. My friends and I taught (ourself, ourselves) chess.

4. We play in the cafeteria, but (few, no one) know this.

5. (Everyone, Others) is welcome to join us.

6. A new student introduced (himself, hisself).

7. (Some, Someone) calls him Dylan.

8. (Something, Many) tells me Dylan has learned chess from a master.

9. We know the moves, but he knows the game (itself, themselves).

10. (Someone, Others) tell me I'm good at chess, but Dylan beat me.

11. I hope Dylan enjoyed (herself, himself) today.

12. You should learn chess (ourself, yourself).

**Home Activity** Your child learned about indefinite and reflexive pronouns. Ask your child to make up several statements about making friends using pronouns such as *everybody, no one, many, few,* and *myself.*

# Suffixes -ible, -able

| Spelling Words | | | | |
|---|---|---|---|---|
| sensible | washable | available | agreeable | fashionable |
| valuable | flexible | reasonable | favorable | breakable |
| convertible | forgettable | laughable | sociable | allowable |
| divisible | hospitable | reversible | responsible | tolerable |

**Synonyms** Write the list word that has the same or nearly the same meaning.

1. in style                                1. __fashionable__
2. bendable                                2. __flexible__
3. welcoming                               3. __hospitable__
4. ridiculous                              4. __laughable__
5. car with top down                       5. __convertible__
6. positive                                6. __favorable__
7. permissible                             7. __allowable__
8. able to turn inside out                 8. __reversible__
9. can be cleaned                          9. __washable__
10. accountable                            10. __responsible__

**Antonyms** Write the list word that has the opposite or nearly the opposite meaning.

11. memorable                              11. __forgettable__
12. unfriendly                             12. __sociable__
13. disagreeable                           13. __agreeable__
14. unreasonable                           14. __reasonable__
15. unbreakable                            15. __breakable__
16. unavailable                            16. __available__
17. intolerable                            17. __tolerable__
18. can't be divided                       18. __divisible__
19. foolish                                19. __sensible__
20. worthless                              20. __valuable__

**Home Activity** Your child used meanings to select list words that were synonyms and antonyms. Have your child tell you the meaning of three list words and spell the words.

© Pearson Education, Inc., 5

# Story Sequence B

**Title**

**Characters**

**Setting**

**Events**

_____

_____

_____

_____

_____

_____

_____

_____

_____

# Vocabulary • Unfamiliar Words

- Sometimes when you are reading, you see an unfamiliar word. Use the **context**, or words around the unfamiliar word, to find clues to its meaning.
- Context clues include synonyms, examples, and explanations.

**Directions** Read the following passage. Then answer the questions below.

In class, Meg's teacher demonstrated, or showed, how to open the new lockers. "Dial the combination and then pull the handle," she said. Instead of paying attention, however, Meg talked to her friend about an episode of her favorite TV show, the last one of the series. "Meg, you are not supposed to talk while I am talking. I am very strict about following this rule. Please stay in class during recess," her teacher said sternly. Meg was very embarrassed, but she was glad she didn't have to stay after school. She had to go to the dentist to have her cavities filled after school.

1. What does *demonstrated* mean? What clue helps you to determine the meaning?

**_Demonstrated_ means "showed." The clue is the synonym showed.**

2. What does *combination* mean? How does the context help you to determine the meaning?

**_Combination_ means "a series of numbers used in opening a lock." The clue is the word _dial_.**

3. What is an *episode*? What clue helps you to determine this?

**_Episode_ means "a story that is one in a series." The phrase "last one in the series" helps to define _episode_.**

4. How do context clues help you determine the meaning of *strict*?

**_Strict_ means "careful in following the rules." The phrases "following this rule" and "sternly" are context clues.**

5. What does *cavities* mean? How can you use context clues to determine the meaning?

**_Cavities_ means "holes or hollow places." The word "filled" is a context clue.**

**Home Activity** Your child read a short passage and used context clues to understand new words. Work with your child to identify unfamiliar words in an article. Ask your child to find context clues to help with the understanding of the new words. Confirm the meanings with your child.

© Pearson Education, Inc., 5

# Thesaurus

A **thesaurus** is a kind of dictionary in which synonyms (words that have the same or similar meanings), antonyms (words that have the opposite meanings), and other related words are classified under headings. You can use a thesaurus to help you find new and interesting words when writing.

**Directions** Use this thesaurus entry to answer the questions that follow.

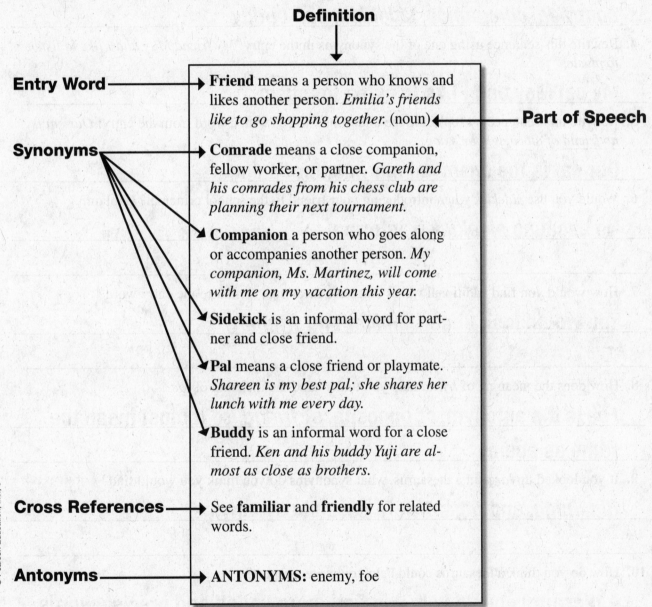

**Definition**

**Entry Word** ➔ **Friend** means a person who knows and likes another person. *Emilia's friends like to go shopping together.* (noun) ◄── **Part of Speech**

**Synonyms** ➔ **Comrade** means a close companion, fellow worker, or partner. *Gareth and his comrades from his chess club are planning their next tournament.*

**Companion** a person who goes along or accompanies another person. *My companion, Ms. Martinez, will come with me on my vacation this year.*

**Sidekick** is an informal word for partner and close friend.

**Pal** means a close friend or playmate. *Shareen is my best pal; she shares her lunch with me every day.*

**Buddy** is an informal word for a close friend. *Ken and his buddy Yuji are almost as close as brothers.*

**Cross References** ➔ See **familiar** and **friendly** for related words.

**Antonyms** ➔ **ANTONYMS:** enemy, foe

**Possible answers given for 4–6, 8–10.**

1. What entry word is shown?

___*Friend* is the entry word.___

2. Name the part of speech of the entry word.

___It is a noun.___

3. What synonyms are given for the entry word?

___*comrade, companion, sidekick, pal, buddy*___

4. Rewrite this sentence using one of the synonyms in the entry: *My friend May and I like to listen to music.*

___My pal May and I like to listen to music.___

5. Rewrite this sentence by replacing the underlined words with a word from the entry: *Our cat is no friend of our neighbor's dog.*

___Our cat is the enemy of our neighbor's dog.___

6. Would you use *sidekick* when introducing your friend to the school principal? Explain.

___No because *sidekick* is informal.___

7. How would you find additional words that have meanings similar to the entry word?

___You would look under *familiar* and *friendly*.___

8. How does the meaning of *friend* help you understand the meaning of *foe*?

___*Foe* is the antonym, or opposite, of *friend,* so it must mean the___

___same as enemy.___

9. If you looked up *large* in a thesaurus, what synonyms do you think you would find?

___*Big, huge,* and *gigantic* are possible synonyms.___

10. How do you think a thesaurus could help you write a report?

___A thesaurus could help you find more varied and precise words.___

**Home Activity** Your child answered questions about a thesaurus entry. Look at a thesaurus together. Ask your child to locate several entries using entry words you tell him or her. Discuss the synonyms for different shades of meaning.

© Pearson Education, Inc., 5

# Suffixes *-ible*, *-able*

**Proofread an Article** Find five spelling errors and one capitalization error in the article. Circle the errors and write the corrections on the lines.

**Spelling Words**

sensible
washable
available
agreeable
fashionable
valuable
flexible
reasonable
favorable
breakable

convertible
forgettable
laughable
sociable
allowable
divisible
hospitable
reversible
responsible
tolerable

---

Fashion Sense

Store buyers are responsible for ordering fashionible clothing customers will like. Last year, mrs. Clark, the store buyer, ordered dozens of reversible sweaters. The sweaters were washible, availible in a variety of colors, and sold at a reasonible price. When the sweaters sold out quickly, the buyer knew she had made a sensable choice.

---

1. **fashionable**       2. **washable**
3. **available**         4. **reasonable**
5. **sensible**          6. **Mrs.**

**Proofread Words** Circle the correct spelling of the list word.

7. The gymnast is as _____ as a rubber band.

flexable        flexibel        flexible

8. Porcelain china is delicate and _____.

breakable       brakeable       breakible

9. Be _____ to your guests when they visit.

hospital        hospitable      hospitible

10. I'd love to have a car with a _____ top.

convertible     convertable     convertibel

11. Sixty-three is _____ by seven.

dividable       divisable       divisible

12. Eat three _____ and balanced meals every day.

sensible        sensable        senseable

**Frequently Misspelled Words**

when
then
went

**School + Home**  **Home Activity** Your child identified misspelled list words. Ask your child to spell three list words that end in *-ible* and three list words that end in *-able*.

# Indefinite and Reflexive Pronouns

**Directions** Read the passage. Then read each question. Circle the letter of the correct answer.

# The New Kid

(1) "Someone new is starting today" was the buzz at school. (2) _____ likes it when a new student comes to class. (3) However, no one really likes to be the new kid. (4) Efrain, the new kid, clearly preferred to spend those first few days by himself. (5) Some tried to talk to him, but Efrain was shy. (6) Lara noticed Efrain liked to draw and told him she was an artist himself. (7) They became good friends and spent many afternoons by themselves.

**1** What is the indefinite pronoun in sentence 1?

  **A** school

  **B** buzz

  **C** new

  **(D)** Someone

**2** Which pronoun would **not** best complete sentence 2?

  **A** Everybody

  **B** Everyone

  **(C)** Either

  **D** Anyone

**3** Which describes the underlined word in sentence 4?

  **A** Singular indefinite pronoun

  **(B)** Singular reflexive pronoun

  **C** Plural indefinite pronoun

  **D** Plural reflexive pronoun

**4** Which describes the underlined word in sentence 5?

  **A** Singular indefinite pronoun

  **B** Singular reflexive pronoun

  **(C)** Plural indefinite pronoun

  **D** Plural reflexive pronoun

**5** What change, if any, should be made to sentence 6?

  **(A)** Change *himself* to **herself**

  **B** Change *him* to **her**

  **C** Change *she* to **he**

  **D** Make no change

**Home Activity** Your child prepared for taking tests on indefinite and reflexive pronouns. Have your child write each indefinite and reflexive pronoun on an index card. Mix the cards and have your child sort them by type and number.

© Pearson Education, Inc., 5

# Draw Conclusions

- A **conclusion** is a sensible decision you make after you think about facts or details that you read.
- Drawing conclusions may also be called making inferences.
- Use your prior knowledge to help you draw conclusions.

**Directions** Read the following passage. Then complete the diagram below.

Enrique is a young gymnast who is training for the Olympics. He goes to live at the Olympic Training Center in Colorado Springs. There he trains twelve hours a day with other athletes. In addition, he regularly takes part in competitions to test his skills. Enrique sets goals for himself. He wants to improve in gymnastics skills and to learn routines that are more difficult. His training schedule is so demanding, he does not have time to go to a regular school. He studies all of his school subjects with a tutor. After more years of training, Enrique hopes to make the Olympic team.

## Possible answers given.

| What does the text say? | What does the text say? | What do I already know? |
|---|---|---|
| 1. Enrique lives at a training center. | 2. He trains twelve hours a day. | 3. It is hard to make it into the Olympics. |

**What can I conclude?**

4. Enrique works hard to go to the Olympics.

5. Visualize Enrique studying with his tutor. What conclusion can you draw about the advantages or disadvantages of studying with a tutor rather than studying at a regular school?

**A disadvantage to having a tutor would be not having the time to socialize you would get at a school.**

**Home Activity** Your child read a short passage and drew a conclusion based on the details in it. Tell your child a story about an athlete you know about. Ask your child to visualize the details as you describe them. Ask your child to draw a conclusion based on the details you provide.

# Writing • Writing for Tests

## The Runner

One evening my grandfather said to me, "Come watch television with me. The show is about Jesse Owens."

"Who is he?" I asked with hesitation. My grandfather loves history, but I don't.

My grandfather turned to me with an amazed face to tell me that Jesse was the athlete whom the whole world saw as the fastest and best track star. I snuggled in next to my grandfather to watch the television show about Jesse.

After I watched the show, I wanted to be the fastest track star like Jesse. The next day, I ran to school and skidded in early! Since then, I have run home every afternoon, sometimes wincing from lack of breath. I have run fast errands for my grandfather, doing cartwheels when I arrived.

I have run so much that my brother has asked me, "Who do you think you are?" My father and teacher have asked me, "For whom do you hurry?" My grandfather has said simply, "Thank you."

I told everyone that I love running, and that I am practicing to be a track star like Jesse. However, my brother said that I have to eat more vegetables and fewer potato chips. My father said that track and field also includes long jumps and hurdles. My grandfather said, "World records come from people who are not only the fastest in short and long runs, but also the best at jumping."

My head was throbbing from all their advice. But now that I have a record of short runs to class and speedy errands, next year I will sign up for track and field!

1. What can you tell about the author's personality?

**The author is probably in elementary school because he or she will need to wait until next year to sign up for track and field. He or she is excited and enthusiastic about running, and can't wait to get started. The author is willing to work hard to become a fast runner.**

2. What details does the author give about his or her feelings? Underline sentences that tell about feelings.

Name_____

# Vocabulary

**Directions** Choose the word from the box that best matches each definition below. Write the word on the line.

<u>somersault</u>

1. to run or jump, turning the heels over the head

<u>gymnastics</u>

2. a sport in which very difficult exercises are performed

<u>hesitation</u>

3. act of failing to act promptly

<u>bluish</u>

4. somewhat blue

<u>cartwheels</u>

5. sideways handsprings with the legs and arms kept straight

### Check the Words You Know

___ bluish
___ cartwheels
___ gymnastics
___ hesitation
___ limelight
___ skidded
___ somersault
___ throbbing
___ wincing

**Directions** Choose the word from the box that matches the clues and complete the crossword puzzle.

**DOWN**

6. the pain I felt when I broke my toe
7. the color of a pale sky
8. the place the star wants to be

**ACROSS**

9. what my bicycle did when I slammed on the brakes
10. what I am doing when I eat food I don't like

|   | | | | | | | | |
|---|---|---|---|---|---|---|---|---|
| ⁶t | | | | | | | ⁸l | |
| h | | | ⁹s | k | i | d | d | e | d |
| r | | | | | m | | | |
| o | | ⁷b | | | e | | | |
| b | | l | | | l | | | |
| b | | u | | | i | | | |
| ¹⁰w | i | n | c | i | n | g | | |
| n | | s | | | h | | | |
| g | | h | | | t | | | |

## Write a News Report

Imagine you're a sports reporter covering a gymnastics meet. On a separate sheet of paper write a news report. Use as many vocabulary words as you can.

## News reports should include words from the vocabulary list and basic facts about a gymnastics meet.

**Home Activity** Your child identified and used vocabulary words from *The Gymnast*. Skim the articles about a single sport in the sports section of a newspaper. Point out and define the vocabulary word that is used to describe each type of sport.

# Using *Who* and *Whom*

People sometimes confuse the pronouns *who* and *whom* when they write. *Who* is a subject form. It is used as a subject of a sentence or a clause.

   *Who* made this mess?

   I saw a performer *who* could do four back flips. [*Who* is the subject in the dependent clause *who could do four back flips*.]

*Whom* is an object form. It is used as the object of a preposition or as a direct object.

   To *whom* did you send a letter?

   *Whom* will you ask?

In the first example, *whom* is the object of the preposition *to*. In the second example, *whom* is a direct object.

- To understand why *whom* is used in the second sentence, change the word order so that the subject comes first. (*Whom will you ask?* becomes *You will ask whom?*) This makes it easier to see that *whom* is a direct object.

**Directions**  How is the underlined word used? Write *subject*, *object of preposition*, or *direct object*.

1. Who wants to learn gymnastics? _____ **subject**

2. She is a person for whom gymnastics is hard. **object of preposition**

3. Matt is the person who did a triple somersault. **subject**

4. Whom did she help the most? _____ **direct object**

5. Who won the Olympic medal last year? _____ **subject**

**Directions**  Underline *who* or *whom* to complete each sentence correctly.

6. (Who, Whom) should we support?

7. Work with Brenda, (who, whom) has taken gymnastics for years.

8. To (who, whom) should we go for advice?

9. (Who, Whom) remembers the order of events?

10. The gymnast (who, whom) stumbled on the dismount still won a medal.

© Pearson Education, Inc., 5

**Home Activity** Your child learned about using *who* and *whom*. Ask your child to write sentences about a sport using *whom* as an object and *who* as a subject.

# Negative Prefixes

| Spelling Words | | | | |
|---|---|---|---|---|
| invisible | illiterate | irregular | irresistible | impossible |
| informal | illegal | impatient | independent | incorrect |
| inactive | imperfect | impolite | immature | illogical |
| indefinite | inappropriate | immobile | irresponsible | inexpensive |

**Missing Words** Write the missing list word.

1. If you learn to read, you are not ____.

2. If you have good manners, you'll rarely be ____.

3. If you earn a living, you can be ____.

4. If you have a "can do" attitude, little is ____.

5. If you're always trustworthy, you are never ____.

6. If you always follow the law, then you never do anything ____.

7. If you're always right, then you're never ____.

8. If you always act responsibly, then you are not ____.

9. If you set an exact time to meet, it is not ____.

10. If something always makes sense, it is not ____.

1. __illiterate__

2. __impolite__

3. __independent__

4. __impossible__

5. __irresponsible__

6. __illegal__

7. __incorrect__

8. __immature__

9. __indefinite__

10. __illogical__

**Classifying** Write the list word that completes the group.

11. cheap, reasonable, low-cost, ____

12. flawed, faulty, defective, ____

13. restless, fidgety, ____

14. unseen, faint, ____

15. casual, relaxed, ____

16. idle, quiet, immobile, ____

17. out of place, unsuitable, ____

18. stationary, motionless, ____

19. tempting, appealing, enticing, ____

20. uneven, lopsided, ____

11. __inexpensive__

12. __imperfect__

13. __impatient__

14. __invisible__

15. __informal__

16. __inactive__

17. __inappropriate__

18. __immobile__

19. __irresistible__

20. __irregular__

© Pearson Education, Inc., 5

**Home Activity** Your child wrote words with prefixes. Ask your child to spell one word for each of the four negative prefixes.

# Scoring Rubric: Writing for Tests: Autobiographical Sketch

|  | **4** | **3** | **2** | **1** |
|---|---|---|---|---|
| **Focus/Ideas** | Auto-biographical sketch clearly focused on an important event in writer's life | Auto-biographical sketch fairly clear; somewhat focused on an event in writer's life | Auto-biographical sketch with some details about an event in writer's life | Auto-biographical sketch with no focus on writer's life |
| **Organization** | Clear events in chronological order | Events largely in chronological order | Events somewhat disorganized | Little or no organization |
| **Voice** | Clearly shows writer's personality and feelings about the subject | Gives some indication of writer's personality and feelings about the subject | Gives little indication of writer's personality and feelings about the subject | No indication of writer's personality or feelings about the subject |
| **Word Choice** | First-person used appropriately throughout | First-person used correctly, but not consistently | First-person pronouns used incorrectly | First-person pronouns used incorrectly, if at all |
| **Sentences** | Sentences clear and interesting | Sentences mostly clear and interesting | Choppy sentences | Fragments or run-ons |
| **Conventions** | Excellent control and accuracy; *who* and *whom* used consistently and correctly | Good control; *who* and *whom* used correctly but not consistently | Errors may prevent understanding; *who* and *whom* used or spelled incorrectly | Frequent errors that interfere with meaning; *who* and *whom* used incorrectly, if at all |

# Vocabulary • Suffixes

- A **suffix** is a syllable added to the end of a base word to change its meaning or the way it is used in a sentence. For example, the Old English suffix *-ish* means "somewhat," as in *childish*. The Latin suffix *-ion* means "the act or state of being _____," as in *determination*. The suffix *-ics* means "study or system," as in *athletics*. The suffix *-ist* means "a member of a profession" as in *dentist*. You can use suffixes to help you figure out the meanings of words.

- In dictionaries, the definition of a base word with the suffix added is usually found near that of the base word. The base word's definition is helpful in understanding a word's meaning.

**Directions** Read the following passage. Notice the words with suffixes as you read. Then answer the questions below.

The gymnastics meet started with a spectacular balance beam routine by Amy's main competitor. Then Amy hopped onto the beam and started her routine with no hesitation. She did fine on her somersaults and cartwheels, but on one backflip she had a bad landing. Her ankle felt like a knife had ripped through it, and she saw bluish stars in front of her eyes. As she finished her routine, Amy thought, "There goes my chance to be a finalist." But when the numbers came up, she scored the highest! Although her ankle was throbbing, she stepped to the judges' table and accepted her medal.

1. What is the suffix in *gymnastics*? How does the suffix change the meaning of the base word?

   **_-ics;_ Gymnastics means "the study or system of physical exercises."**

2. What is the suffix in *hesitation*? How does the suffix change the meaning of the base word?

   **_-ion;_ The suffix _-ion_ changes _hesitate_ to a noun that means "failing to act promptly."**

3. What is the suffix in *bluish*? How does the suffix change the meaning of the base word?

   **_-ish; Bluish_ means "somewhat blue."**

4. Change the suffix of *competitor* from *-or* to *-ion*. What is the meaning of the new word?

   **competition; The meaning is "the act of being a competitor."**

5. Which word in the passage has a suffix like *dentist*? Write its definition.

   **_finalist;_ someone who finishes in the finals of a competition**

**Home Activity** Your child read a short passage and identified and used suffixes to understand new words. Work with your child to identify unfamiliar words with suffixes. Then ask your child how the suffixes help him or her to understand the meanings of the new words. Confirm the meanings by looking them up in a dictionary.

# Graphs

**Graphs** show information visually. You can use graphs to compare different pieces of information. Look at the title of a graph to see what is being compared. There are many types of graphs, but two types of graphs are bar graphs and circle graphs. A **bar graph** uses horizontal and vertical lines. Words or numbers along each line explain what is being compared. A **circle graph**, which is also called a pie chart, compares the parts of a whole.

**Directions** Use this graph to answer the questions below.

Men's Gymnastic Equipment

1. Explain what kind of graph this is and how you know.

   **This is a bar graph because it uses horizontal and vertical lines to compare things.**

2. What is the tallest piece of equipment? What is the shortest piece of equipment?

   **The tallest equipment is the rings and high bar; The shortest is the pommel horse.**

3. How many pieces of equipment are being compared?

   **Five pieces of equipment are being compared.**

4. Approximately how tall are the parallel bars? The high bar?

   **The parallel bars are 195 cm high; The high bar is 275 cm high.**

5. Would this graph be a good source for finding out information about equipment used by female gymnasts? Explain.

   **It wouldn't be a good source for information about female gymnasts because it is about men's equipment only.**

**Directions** Use this graph to answer the questions below.

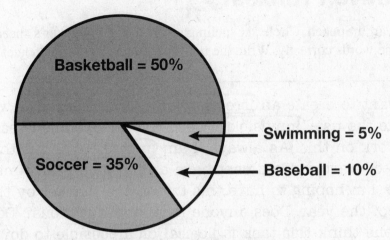

**Favorite Sports of Sawyer School Fifth Graders**

6. What kind of graph is this? How do you know?

**This is a circle graph because it is shaped like a circle and compares parts of a whole.**

7. What is the favorite sport of the fifth graders at Sawyer School? What percent of students prefer that sport?

**The favorite sport is basketball, which is preferred by 50%.**

8. What sport is second-most popular? What percent of students prefer that sport?

**The second favorite sport is soccer, which is preferred by 35%.**

9. What sport is the least popular? What percent of students prefer that sport?

**The least popular sport is swimming, which is preferred by 5%.**

10. What is being compared in this graph? Explain why you think this type of graph displays this information effectively.

**favorite sports of Sawyer School fifth graders; A circle graph shows how the parts compare to the whole.**

**Home Activity** Your child learned about using graphs as resources. With your child, look at a graph that appears in the newspaper or in a brochure. Ask your child what information is being compared. Ask your child specific questions about information the graph shows.

# Negative Prefixes

**Proofread a Speech** Circle six spelling errors in the toymaker's speech. Write the words correctly. Write the run-on sentence as two sentences.

**Spelling Words**

invisible
illiterate
irregular
irresistible
impossible
informal
illegal
impatient
independent
incorrect

inactive
imperfect
impolite
immature
illogical
indefinite
inappropriate
immobile
irresponsible
inexpensive

"I want to create an (irresistable) toy for children. It will make the user (innvisible) I need five independent teams to work on this. As always, I am (impashent) to get this project started! We do not have an (indefinute) amount of time. I'm hoping to have this toy on the market by the end of the year. Does anyone have any questions? Does anyone think this task is (ilogical) or (inpossible) to do? Do we all agree this can be done let's get to work!"

1. **irresistible**     2. **invisible**

3. **impatient**     4. **indefinite**

5. **illogical**     6. **impossible**

7. **Do we all agree this can be done? Let's get to work!**

**Proofread Words** Circle the word that is spelled correctly.

**Frequently Misspelled Words**

through
always

8. (irresistible)     unresistable     ilresistable

9. ilexpensive     imexpensive     (inexpensive)

10. inmature     (immature)     imature

11. (imperfect)     ilperfect     unperfect

12. imdependent     (independent)     ildependent

13. imactive     innactive     (inactive)

14. (impolite)     inpolite     unpolite

15. (illiterate)     iliterate     inliterate

16. imappropriate     (inappropriate)     inapropriate

© Pearson Education, Inc., 5

**Home Activity** Your child identified misspelled list words. Take turns spelling list words that begin with the four negative prefixes studied.

## Using *Who* and *Whom*

**Directions** Read the passage. Then read each question. Circle the letter of the correct answer.

# Making the Team

    (1) When Coach Reed asked, "Whom would like to try out for the basketball team?" we all raised our hands. (2) "Who will make the team?" I wondered. (3) Some of the kids were already very good at basketball. (4) It wasn't hard to see <u>who</u> had not played much. (5) I could run and shoot, but I was never sure to <u>whom</u> I should pass the ball. (6) <u>Whom</u> could I ask for help? (7) Coach Reed saw me practice and asked me to be on the team.

**1** What change, if any, should be made in sentence 1?

  **A**  Change *Coach* to **coach**

  **B**  Remove quotation marks

  **(C)**  Change *Whom* to **Who**

  **D**  Make no change

**2** What change, if any, should be made in sentence 2?

  **A**  Change *I wondered* to **I wonder**

  **B**  Remove quotation marks

  **C**  Change *Who* to **Whom**

  **(D)**  Make no change

**3** Which describes the underlined word in sentence 4?

  **(A)**  Subject

  **B**  Object of preposition

  **C**  Direct object

  **D**  None of the above

**4** Which describes the underlined word in sentence 5?

  **A**  Subject

  **(B)**  Object of preposition

  **C**  Direct object

  **D**  None of the above

**5** Which describes the underlined word in sentence 6?

  **A**  Subject

  **B**  Object of preposition

  **(C)**  Direct object

  **D**  None of the above

© Pearson Education, Inc., 5

**Home Activity** Your child prepared for taking tests on *who* and *whom*. Have your child read newspaper articles to highlight uses of *who* and *whom*. Then ask him or her to tell whether the words are used correctly, and why.

# Words from Many Cultures

| Spelling Words | | | | |
|---|---|---|---|---|
| khaki | waltz | yogurt | cobra | buffet |
| hula | tomato | banquet | koala | stampede |
| banana | vanilla | macaroni | barbecue | karate |
| ballet | canyon | polka | safari | kiosk |

**Alphabetize** Write the ten list words below in alphabetical order.

| | |
|---|---|
| kiosk | stampede |
| safari | buffet |
| koala | polka |
| banquet | karate |
| ballet | khaki |

1. **ballet**
2. **banquet**
3. **buffet**
4. **karate**
5. **khaki**

6. **kiosk**
7. **koala**
8. **polka**
9. **safari**
10. **stampede**

**Classifying** Write the list word that belongs in each group.

11. lettuce, carrots, onion, **tomato**
12. dance, ballroom, elegant, **waltz**
13. rattlesnake, boa constrictor, **cobra**
14. spaghetti, noodles, pasta, **macaroni**
15. gorge, valley, ravine, **canyon**

16. Hawaii, dance, grass skirt, **hula**
17. milk, creamy, fruit, **yogurt**
18. fruit, yellow, plant, **banana**
19. chocolate, strawberry, **vanilla**
20. food, outdoors, grill, **barbecue**

**Home Activity** Your child has learned to spell words that come from a variety of cultures. With your child, look up several of the words in a dictionary and discuss what the dictionary says about the words' origins.

© Pearson Education, Inc., 5

# Subject and Object Pronouns

**Directions** Write *S* if the underlined word is a subject pronoun. Write *O* if the word is an object pronoun.

1. In *Weslandia*, Wesley is the main character. <u>He</u> has problems.  **S**

2. Wesley doesn't act like the other kids, and they pick on <u>him</u>.  **O**

3. His parents worry that <u>they</u> have raised an odd son.  **S**

4. Wesley creates a new civilization, and <u>it</u> fascinates everyone.  **S**

5. <u>I</u> really enjoyed reading this story.  **S**

6. Wesley's ingenious uses for his crop amused <u>me</u>.  **O**

7. My friend Winnie said the suntan oil was funniest to <u>her</u>.  **O**

8. <u>You</u> should read this story too!  **S**

9. Our teacher, Mr. Su, asked <u>us</u> about civilizations.  **O**

10. Native peoples create <u>them</u> based on climate and crops in their region.  **O**

**Directions** Underline the correct pronoun in ( ) to complete each sentence.

11. Corn has many uses. Many farmers plant (<u>it</u>, they).

12. (<u>They</u>, Them) can sell the grain as a food or as a raw material for fuel.

13. The stalks can be ground up. There are several uses for (it, <u>them</u>) as well.

14. John and (<u>I</u>, me) have learned about soybeans.

15. (<u>We</u>, Us) get nutritious foods from them.

16. Do you like tofu? (<u>It</u>, Them) is a curd made from soybeans.

17. Mom served tofu to Karl and (I, <u>me</u>).

18. She didn't tell (<u>us</u>, we) what we were eating.

19. When (<u>he</u>, him) found out it was bean curd, Karl laughed.

20. Mom had disguised it in pudding. That was clever of (<u>her</u>, she)!

# Prefixes *over-*, *under-*, *sub-*, *super-*, *out-*

| Spelling Words | | | | |
|---|---|---|---|---|
| overlook | supermarket | undercurrent | submarine | output |
| underline | outlet | superstar | undercover | supernatural |
| subway | underground | overtime | overcast | subdivision |
| subset | overboard | supersonic | outfield | subhead |

**Analogies** Write the list word that completes each comparison.

1. Light is to heavy as sunny is to __overcast__.

2. Title is to subtitle as head is to __subhead__.

3. Sky is to airplane as ocean is to __submarine__.

4. Carpenter is to house as baseball player is to __outfield__.

5. Shoes are to shoe store as food is to __supermarket__.

6. Living room is to outside as cabin is to __overboard__.

7. Street is to bus as underground is to __subway__.

8. Strong is to athlete as famous is to __superstar__.

9. Comedian is to funny as ghost is to __supernatural__.

10. Store is to mall as house is to __subdivision__.

**Synonyms** Write the list word that has the same, or nearly the same, meaning.

11. underscore __underline__

12. secret __undercover__

13. category __subset__

14. extra __overtime__

15. production __output__

16. hint __undercurrent__

17. buried __underground__

18. socket __outlet__

19. fast __supersonic__

20. forget __overlook__

**Home Activity** Your child has completed analogies containing words with prefixes. Ask your child to make up two analogies containing words from the list and explain how the analogies work.

© Pearson Education, Inc., 5

# Pronouns and Antecedents

**Directions** Match the pronoun with the noun or noun phrase that could be its antecedent. Write the letter of the correct antecedent next to the pronoun.

**B** 1. her     **A** Jinx and I

**E** 2. it      **B** Victoria

**D** 3. them   **C** Uncle Jeff

**A** 4. us     **D** other students

**C** 5. he      **E** fishing rod

**Directions** Circle the antecedent of the underlined pronoun in each sentence.

6. This story reminds me of my (friend,) and <u>she</u> is named Greta.

7. (Greta and Jinx) are similar because <u>they</u> fall a lot.

8. Greta has many (casts,) and <u>they</u> prove she has had many accidents.

9. Workers poured fresh (cement,) and Greta walked into <u>it</u>.

10. (Will) nearly lost the marathon when <u>he</u> tripped over Greta's crutch.

11. (Cheerleaders) made a pyramid, and Greta toppled <u>them</u>.

12. (Greta) is nicknamed Grace because <u>she</u> is not very graceful.

**Directions** Write a pronoun to replace each underlined noun or noun phrase.

13. Jinx doesn't trip over the lunch lady, but <u>Jinx</u> has other accidents.

14. Tony choked on some gum when Jinx bounced over <u>Tony</u>.

15. Jinx crawled into boxes and boots and got stuck in <u>boxes and boots</u>.

16. Jinx looked inside her locker and got stuck inside <u>her locker</u>.

17. She saw square dancers and wanted to be like <u>the square dancers</u>.

18. Victoria and Jinx tried square dancing, but <u>Victoria and Jinx</u> hurt themselves.

<u>she</u>
<u>him</u>
<u>them</u>
<u>it</u>
<u>them</u>
<u>they</u>

# Homophones

| Spelling Words | | | | |
| --- | --- | --- | --- | --- |
| cent | through | there | tide | aloud |
| sent | weather | they're | tied | allowed |
| scent | whether | chili | pale | course |
| threw | their | chilly | pail | coarse |

**Crossword Puzzle** Use the clues to find the list words. Write each letter in a box.

**Across**
2. gave permission
6. not here
7. fastened
8. pitched
9. place to play golf

**Down**
1. said so it could be heard
3. if
4. finished
5. smell
7. belonging to them

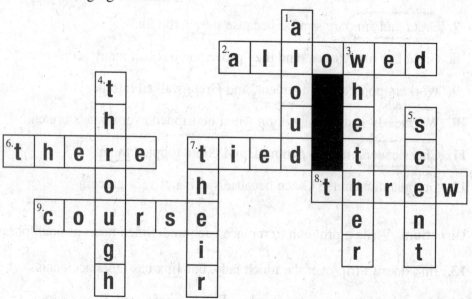

**Classifying** Write the list word that belongs in each group.

10. rain, snow, tornado, __weather__

11. cold, icy, frosty, __chilly__

12. rough, thick, __coarse__

13. taco, spaghetti, soup, __chili__

14. bucket, container, jug, __pail__

15. nickel, dime, quarter, __cent__

16. you're, we're, __they're__

17. white, colorless, sickly, __pale__

18. ocean, waves, high, low, __tide__

19. letter, mailed, transmitted, __sent__

**Home Activity** Your child has learned to spell homophones. Ask your child to find some of the list words in a newspaper or magazine. Then ask your child to spell one or more homophones for each word and use them in sentences.

© Pearson Education, Inc., 5

# Possessive Pronouns

**Directions** Write the letter of the possessive pronoun that can replace the underlined word or words in each phrase.

___A___ **1.** Lori's idea      **A** her

___E___ **2.** Nate's paper      **B** their

___B___ **3.** the twins' pet      **C** our

___D___ **4.** an owl's eyes      **D** its

___C___ **5.** Ti's and my cat      **E** his

**Directions** Underline the pronoun that correctly completes each sentence.

6. Each ant colony has (its, their) own smell.

7. The ants can recognize an intruder in (theirs, their) nest.

8. They also know which eggs are not (theirs, we).

9. A female worker will help defend (her, she) home.

10. I know some ants can sting because an ant stung (mine, my) foot!

**Directions** Write the possessive pronoun that can replace the underlined word or words.

11. Dad and I love to have honey on Dad's and my toast.     **our** _____

12. Mom likes honey on Mom's oatmeal.     **her** _____

13. Sam puts honey on Sam's peanut butter sandwiches.     **his** _____

14. Bees make honey for the bees' food.     **their** _____

15. A bee can always fly back to a bee's hive.     **its** _____

16. I washed my plate, and now you can wash the plate belonging to you.     **yours** _____

17. Paul put his glass in the dishwasher, and then I added the glass belonging to me.     **mine** _____

18. He found his fork, but she couldn't find the fork belonging to her.     **hers** _____

© Pearson Education, Inc., 5

# Suffixes *-ible*, *-able*

| Spelling Words | | | | |
|---|---|---|---|---|
| sensible | fashionable | favorable | laughable | hospitable |
| washable | valuable | breakable | sociable | reversible |
| available | flexible | convertible | allowable | responsible |
| agreeable | reasonable | forgettable | divisible | tolerable |

**Words in Context** Complete each sentence with a list word.

1. Be careful with that vase because it is __breakable__.

2. It is hot in the desert, but the dry air makes it __tolerable__.

3. Jim's mom was __hospitable__ and invited us to stay for dinner.

4. You can wear the jacket with that side in or out because it is __reversible__.

5. A(n) __convertible__ car is not practical in a cold climate.

6. Anita didn't go to the party because she was not feeling __sociable__.

7. Gold and silver are __valuable__ metals.

8. The critic liked the movie, so he gave it a(n) __favorable__ review.

9. Is that number __divisible__ by ten?

10. It's all right to get your uniform muddy because it is __washable__.

11. The magician's tricks were so obvious they were __laughable__.

12. The soccer team took care to make plays that were __allowable__.

13. Lizzy often wears new styles because she likes to be __fashionable__.

14. I can't recall the story's characters because they were __forgettable__.

15. The Henrys asked Carla to baby-sit, but she was not __available__ that day.

16. Unlike the unpleasant dog next door, our pet is always __agreeable__.

17. Who is __responsible__ for setting the table?

18. It is __sensible__ to wear sturdy shoes on a long hike.

19. If you work on the problem, you will think of a(n) __reasonable__ answer.

20. Rubber is used for many items because it is __flexible__.

© Pearson Education, Inc., 5

**Home Activity** Your child has learned to spell words with the suffixes *-ible* and *-able*. Ask your child to make up several sentences containing list words and to spell each list word used.

# Indefinite and Reflexive Pronouns

**Directions** Underline the pronoun in each sentence. Write *indefinite* or *reflexive* to identify the kind of pronoun it is. Then write *singular* or *plural* to show its number.

1. Everybody eats lunch in the cafeteria.      **indefinite**      **singular**

2. Many of the students bring a sack lunch.    **indefinite**      **plural**

3. Others eat a hot lunch.                     **indefinite**      **plural**

4. Students help themselves to milk.           **reflexive**      **plural**

5. Mom says, "Give yourself time to eat."      **reflexive**      **singular**

**Directions** Underline the correct pronoun in ( ) to complete each sentence.

6. I chose a special place for (myself, myselves).

7. (Everybody, Many) needs a place to be alone and think.

8. (Few, No one) is immune to stress.

9. The teacher said, "Do your work by (theirself, yourself)."

10. (Several, Someone) of my friends have private places.

**Directions** Choose a pronoun from the box to complete each sentence correctly. Be sure indefinite pronouns used as subjects agree in number with their verbs.

> herself    many    myself    something    everybody

11. If I see someone new, I introduce _____ **myself** _____.

12. I tell the new person _____ **something** _____ about the school.

13. The new girl said to _____ **herself** _____, "I won't make any friends."

14. _____ **Everybody** _____ appreciates a friendly welcome.

15. _____ **Many** _____ try to make newcomers feel at home.

# Negative Prefixes

| Spelling Words | | | | |
|---|---|---|---|---|
| invisible | impossible | independent | impolite | inappropriate |
| illiterate | informal | incorrect | immature | immobile |
| irregular | illegal | inactive | illogical | irresponsible |
| irresistible | impatient | imperfect | indefinite | inexpensive |

**Synonyms** Write the list word that has the same, or nearly the same, meaning.

1. restless     **impatient**
2. cheap        **inexpensive**
3. rude         **impolite**
4. motionless   **immobile**
5. casual       **informal**
6. vague        **indefinite**
7. uneven       **irregular**
8. lazy         **inactive**
9. separate     **independent**
10. fascinating **irresistible**

**Antonyms** Write the list word that has the opposite, or nearly the opposite, meaning.

11. lawful       **illegal**
12. experienced  **immature**
13. excellent    **imperfect**
14. reasonable   **illogical**
15. accurate     **incorrect**
16. educated     **illiterate**
17. suitable     **inappropriate**
18. likely       **impossible**
19. noticeable   **invisible**
20. dependable   **irresponsible**

**Home Activity** Your child has written synonyms and antonyms for words with negative prefixes. Name several list words. Ask your child to spell each word and to name a synonym and/or antonym for each.

Name _____

# Using *Who* and *Whom*

**Directions** Write *subject*, *object of preposition*, or *direct object* to identify how the underlined word is used.

1. <u>Who</u> likes cheerleading?

2. Jim is the one for <u>whom</u> the crowd is applauding.

3. Everyone <u>who</u> is watching was impressed.

4. <u>Whom</u> will the judges select?

5. To <u>whom</u> were you speaking?

**subject**
**object of preposition**
**subject**
**direct object**
**object of preposition**

**Directions** Underline *who* or *whom* to complete each sentence correctly.

6. (<u>Who</u>, Whom) would like something to drink?

7. Stu is the person to (who, <u>whom</u>) you should give your money.

8. He is the fellow with (who, <u>whom</u>) I went to the concession stand.

9. Anyone (<u>who</u>, whom) watches a gymnastics meet gets thirsty.

10. The judges, (<u>who</u>, whom) are volunteers, do a fantastic job.

11. (Who, <u>Whom</u>) shall we invite next time?

12. It should be someone with (who, <u>whom</u>) you can spend hours.

13. Spectators (<u>who</u>, whom) are veterans bring seat cushions for the bleachers.

14. Everybody (<u>who</u>, whom) sits through the entire gymnastics meet gets sore.

15. For (who, <u>whom</u>) is the meet the most fun?

**Directions** Cross out mistakes in the use of *who* and *whom* in the paragraph. Write the correct pronoun above the line. One sentence is correct.

(16) The girl watched her older brother, ~~whom~~ **who** was turning cartwheels. (17) He wondered

~~whom~~ **who** else might be looking. (18) He fell, and the dog with ~~who~~ **whom** the girl had been playing ran to

lick his face. (19) The girl shrieked with laughter, and the mother, ~~whom~~ **who** had been doing laundry,

rushed into the yard. (20) "Who is ready for a snack?" asked the mother.

# Cause-and-Effect Chart

**Directions** Most events have more than one cause and effect. Fill in the chart with each cause and effect that helps explain the change that is the main idea or thesis of your essay.

| Change (Main Idea or Thesis of My Essay) | |
|---|---|
| **Answers should include the change and details about the causes and effects behind the change for the student's cause-and-effect essay.** | |
| **Cause** | **Effect** |
| | |
| | |
| | |
| | |

# Use Cause-and-Effect Words

**Directions** Write three sentences or sets of sentences for your essay that tell about causes and/or effects. Add one of the following words or phrases to each sentence or set of sentences to make the cause and the effect clear. You may need to change some words.

| Words and Phrases for Cause-and-Effect Essays | |
| --- | --- |
| **Words and Phrases for Causes** | **Words and Phrases for Effects** |
| because | so |
| since | therefore |
| due to | for this reason |
| for the reason that | as a result |
| | as a consequence |

## Answers should include one of the words or phrases above and should accurately describe a cause-and-effect relationship.

1. _____

_____

_____

2. _____

_____

_____

3. _____

_____

_____

# Combining or Rearranging Sentences

| | |
|---|---|
| If a subject, a verb, or both are repeated in two sentences, combine the sentences to make your writing less wordy. | |
| **Wordy** | Thunderstorms often occur in hot weather. Thunderstorms occur when warm air rises. |
| **Concise** | Thunderstorms often occur in hot weather when warm air rises. |
| Rearrange your sentences to put the ideas in the most logical order. | |
| **Unclear** | Spring comes. The seed grows into a sprout. The seed gets light. |
| **Clear** | Spring comes. The seed gets light. The seed grows into a sprout. |

**Directions** Combine each pair of sentences. You may add, delete, or change words.

**Possible answers**

1. The chameleon was crawling on a brown wall. The chameleon turned from pale green to brown.

   **Crawling on a brown wall, the chameleon turned from pale green to brown.**

2. Jon began training for a marathon. He began by running one mile at a time.

   **Jon began training for a marathon by running one mile at a time.**

3. Forest fires can destroy trees in forests. Hurricanes can destroy trees in forests.

   **Forest fires and hurricanes can destroy trees in forests.**

**Directions** Rearrange each group of sentences. You may add, delete, or change words.

4. Puddles turned to ice. The temperature fell below freezing. It rained all afternoon.

   **It rained all afternoon. Then the temperature fell below freezing. Puddles turned to ice.**

5. Mr. Parker planted after the last frost. The tomato plants grew bigger. Mr. Parker put fertilizer in the soil.

   **Mr. Parker planted after the last frost. He put fertilizer in the soil. The tomato plants grew bigger.**

# Peer and Teacher Conferencing
# Compare-and-Effect Essay

**Directions** Read your partner's essay. Refer to the Revising Checklist as you write your comments or questions. Offer compliments as well as revision suggestions. Then take turns talking about each other's draft. Give your partner your notes. After you and your teacher talk about your essay, add your teacher's comments to the notes.

## Revising Checklist

**Focus/Ideas**

☐ Is the cause-and-effect essay focused on why a person, animal, or object in nature changes?

☐ Does the essay contain details about all the causes and effects?

**Organization**

☐ Does the essay have an introduction, body, and conclusion?

☐ Do any sentences need to be combined or rearranged to better connect ideas?

**Voice**

☐ Is the voice knowledgeable yet conversational?

**Word Choice**

☐ Do cause-and-effect words and phrases make the cause-and-effect relationships clear?

**Sentences**

☐ Does the essay have a variety of sentence types and lengths?

**Things I Thought Were Good** _____

_____

**Things I Thought Could Be Improved** _____

_____

**Teacher's Comments** _____

_____

# Character and Plot

- **Traits** are the qualities, such as bravery or shyness, of **characters,** or the people and animals in a story. We see characters' traits in their words and how other characters treat them.
- The **plot** is the pattern of events in a story. Usually, the events are told in sequence, from start to finish.

**Directions** Read the following passage. Then fill in the diagram.

Darcy Evans had been a rebel all her life. As a young woman, she marched for civil rights. She protested a plan to build the first mall in her small hometown. She was at the first Earth Day celebration in the 1970s, supporting efforts to protect the environment. Save the dolphins, save the whales, save the trees: Darcy could always find a good cause to support, no matter how old she was. So nobody was surprised when 83-year-old Darcy Evans was leading the fight to save the 200-year-old City Hall building in her hometown. "I'm nearly as old as City Hall," she joked. But everyone knew that if Darcy was fighting for it, the building must be worth saving.

## Possible answers given for 2–5.

**Main Character**
1. **Darcy Evans**

**Trait**
2. **rebel**

**Trait**
Concern for environment

**Trait**
3. **sense of humor**

**Trait**
4. **people respect her opinion**

5. Why does Darcy fight on behalf of various causes?

**Darcy fights on behalf of the causes she believes in.**

**Home Activity** Your child answered questions about characters and plot in a fictional passage. Have him or her describe to you a favorite character from a book.

# Writing · Rhyming Poem

**Key Features of a Rhyming Poem**

- contains rhyme and rhythm
- often uses figurative language, such as similes and metaphors, and sensory or vivid words
- often uses poetic techniques, such as alliteration and onomatopoeia
- uses graphic elements, such as capital letters

---

## Street Beat

I walk down the street.
My icy hands tapping a beat.
When suddenly before me appears
A patch of ice like a frozen tear.

My foot touches it.
I slide and slip.
Try to catch my fall,
And think *What a close call!*

WHOOSH! BANG! BAM!
I'm thinking *Oh, man.*
The fall is pretty rough,
And I thought I was tough!

---

1. Which line from the poem contains a simile?

   **A patch of ice like a frozen tear.**

2. Name one line that contains alliteration. Explain why.

   **I slide and slip. The line uses the "sl" sound twice.**

# Vocabulary

**Directions** Draw a line to connect each word on the left with its definition on the right.

1. bellow          gave up on, dismissed

2. savage          try or make an effort

3. attempt         shout or roar like a bull

4. feat            wild, ferocious, angry

5. abandoned       a difficult or skillful act

**Directions** Choose a word from the box that best matches each sentence. Write the word on the line.

**cavern**_____     6. The outlaw buried the gold in the _____ just before his arrest.

**feat**_____     7. For her latest brave accomplishment, or _____ , the escape artist freed herself from chains just in time to pull the cord on the parachute.

**attempt**_____     8. Their effort, or _____, to hike the entire Appalachian Trail in two months had little chance of success.

**immensely**_____     9. The _____ popular rock music star was greeted at the coliseum by thousands of his adoring fans.

**savage**_____     10. The _____ expression on her face would not have been out of place on a panther or some other wild animal.

## Write a News Report

On a separate sheet of paper, write an imaginary news report that describes two local youth who surprise everyone by succeeding at a difficult task. Use as many vocabulary words as you can.

**News reports should include words from the vocabulary list and a description of two imagined local youth who accomplish a difficult task.**

© Pearson Education, Inc., 5

**Home Activity** Your child identified and used vocabulary words from the story *The Skunk Ladder*. Together, come up with a list of accomplishments that you or your child performs regularly, but that might seem amazing to other people.

# Contractions and Negatives

A **contraction** is a shortened form of two words. An **apostrophe** is used to show where one or more letters have been left out. Some contractions are made by combining pronouns and verbs: *I + have = I've; you + are = you're*. Other contractions are formed by joining a verb and *not*: *should + not = shouldn't; were + not = weren't*.

- *Won't* and *can't* are formed in special ways (*can + not = can't; will + not = won't*).

**Negatives** are words that mean "no" or "not": *no, not, never, none, nothing*. Contractions with *n't* are negatives too. To make a negative statement, use only one negative word.
   **No:** Don't never ask about his leg. There won't be none left.
   **Yes:** Don't ever ask about his leg. There won't be any left.

- Use positive words instead of the negative in a sentence with *not*:

| **Negative** | **Positive** | **Negative** | **Positive** |
|---|---|---|---|
| nobody | anybody, somebody | nothing | anything, something |
| no one | anyone, someone | nowhere | anywhere, somewhere |
| none | any, all, some | never | ever, always |

**Directions** Write the letter of the two words used to form each contraction.

__F__ 1. what's      **A** has not

__B__ 2. that'll      **B** that will

__E__ 3. didn't      **C** they are

__A__ 4. hasn't      **D** could not

__C__ 5. they're      **E** did not

__D__ 6. couldn't      **F** what has

**Directions** Write the contraction for each pair of words.

7. would + have = **would've**      8. it + is = **it's**

9. she + will = **she'll**      10. will + not = **won't**

**Directions** Circle the word in ( ) that correctly completes each sentence.

11. You can't (never, (ever)) tell what those boys will do.

12. There wasn't (nobody, (anything)) in the hole.

 **Home Activity** Your child learned about contractions and negatives. With your child, scan articles in the newspaper to find contractions. Ask your child to write the words used to form each contraction.

# Multisyllabic Words

| Spelling Words | | | | |
|---|---|---|---|---|
| elementary | vehicle | miniature | probability | opportunity |
| substitute | variety | literature | elevator | Pennsylvania |
| ravioli | cafeteria | mosaic | tuxedo | meteorite |
| fascination | cylinder | intermediate | centennial | curiosity |

**Words in Context** Write the list word that best completes each sentence.

1. I'm having lunch in the ____ today.

2. Did you know that cheese ____ is on the menu?

3. Eating a ____ of foods keeps you heathy.

4. Next year our town is 100 years old, so we'll have a ____ celebration.

5. The astronauts drove a lunar ____ on the moon.

6. The colorful ____ on the table top is made of tiny tiles.

7. A shooting star is really a falling ____.

8. The capital of ____ is Harrisburg.

9. The levels of swimming at my camp are beginner, ____, and advanced.

10. Books, poetry, and short stories are types of ____.

11. Let's take the ____ to the tenth floor.

12. We had a ____ teacher for one week.

13. He had a ____ with all types of model trains.

1. **cafeteria**
2. **ravioli**
3. **variety**
4. **centennial**
5. **vehicle**
6. **mosaic**
7. **meteorite**
8. **Pennsylvania**
9. **intermediate**
10. **literature**
11. **elevator**
12. **substitute**
13. **fascination**

**Synonyms** Write the list word that has the same or almost the same meaning as the word or phrase.

14. tube

15. tiny

16. basic

17. lucky chance

18. desire to know

19. formal suit

20. likelihood

14. **cylinder**
15. **miniature**
16. **elementary**
17. **opportunity**
18. **curiosity**
19. **tuxedo**
20. **probability**

© Pearson Education, Inc., 5

**Home Activity** Your child wrote list words containing many syllables. Have your child draw a line between syllables. Use a dictionary to help you.

# Three-Column Chart

| | | |
|---|---|---|
| | | |
| | | |

# Vocabulary • Greek and Latin Roots

- Many English words are based on **Greek** and **Latin** root words. Sometimes you can use Greek and Latin roots to figure out the meaning of an unfamiliar word.
- The Latin root *spec* means "look" or "see," as in the word *inspect*. The Latin root *sect* means "to cut," as in the word *dissect*. The Latin root *pond* means "to weigh," as in the word *ponderous*.

**Directions** Read the following passage. Then answer the questions below. Look for Greek and Latin roots to help you determine the meaning of the words in italics.

The toughest section of Thursday was the morning, when I drove into town with my great-uncle Al. He couldn't see his hand in front of his face without his *spectacles*. So as we approached the stoplight with Uncle Al at the wheel, you can imagine my fright when I noticed he didn't have his glasses on. I *pondered* my options: Do I yell something? Do I scream and point? But then I saw his glasses sitting on top of his head. Not wanting to distract Uncle Al with any unnecessary *interaction*, I reached over and gently tapped his glasses. They slid right onto his nose, perfectly in place. We came to an easy stop at the red light.

## Possible answers given for 2, 3, 5.

1. What is the root of the word *section*? What does the word mean?

_*sect;* It means "a part or a piece," as in something cut from a_

_larger object._

2. How does the Latin root of the word *spectacles* help you understand the meaning of the word?

_It means "something that makes things easier to see."_

3. How does the Latin roots in the word *interaction* help you understand the meaning of the word?

_*Inter* means "between," so *interaction* must mean "activity_

_between two people or things."_

4. The Latin root word *distrahere* means "to pull away." Which word above comes from that root?

_distract_

5. How does the Latin root of the word *pondered* help you understand the meaning of the word?

_*Ponder* must mean "to weigh something in your mind," or "to_

_think about it deeply."_

**Home Activity** Your child identified and answered questions about Latin and Greek roots in words. Have your child look in the dictionary and find other words with Latin or Greek roots. Have him or her tell you the meanings of the roots he or she found. Together think of other words with the same roots.

# Print Sources

- Libraries contain many sources of information for students to use. You can use a library database or a card catalog to identify and locate these materials. In both cases, you can search for materials by author, title, or subject.
- **Print sources** include encyclopedias, newspapers, magazines, dictionaries, and other reference books.

**Directions** Read the following list of school library print sources for a report on U.S. Presidents.

**Encyclopedias**

*Encyclopedia of U.S. Presidents, Vols. I & II*

*World History Encyclopedia, Vols. I–XX*

*Encyclopedia of American History, Vols. I–XII*

*Encyclopedia of Modern Science, Vols. I–VI*

*Encyclopedia of Entertainment, Vols. I–III*

**Newspapers**

*World News Daily* (metropolitan paper)

*Weekly Wrap-Up* (community paper)

*Kingsley Chronicle* (school paper)

**Magazines**

*News Weekly*

*The Historical Reader*

*History for Children*

*Skateboard Life*

*U.S. and the World*

**Dictionaries**

*Student Dictionary of American History*

*Cultural Dictionary of the United States*

*Anders' Dictionary of Places & Events*

*Dictionary of Who's Who & What's What*

**Directions** Pretend you are writing a report on U.S. Presidents in the twentieth century. Use the list of print sources to answer the questions below.

1. Which type of print sources might be valuable to use for this report?

**Encyclopedias, magazines, and dictionaries**

2. Which would be the best source with which to start your report?

**Encyclopedia of U.S. Presidents, Vol. I and Vol. II**

3. Would all the magazines be valuable to your report? Why or why not?

**Magazines tend to be more concerned with current events, but**

**The Historical Reader or History for Children might be valuable.**

4. Suggest a topic you might research in a library's card catalog for your report.

**Possible answer: Presidents in wartime**

5. If you knew an author had written a good book about U.S. Presidents, how could you use this knowledge to get information for your report?

**Look up the author's name in the card catalog for the title.**

6. Explain how a newspaper would be helpful if you extended your report to include U.S. Presidents in the twenty-first century.

**It would have some information on the current President.**

7. How helpful would any of the newspapers be in gathering information for your report? Why?

**Not very helpful; Newspapers deal with news of the day or week**

**and not with large spans of history.**

8. If you didn't understand something that was referred to in the magazine *History for Children*, where would be a good place to find out what the reference meant?

**Student Dictionary of American History**

9. If you wanted to find out how many Presidents were from a certain state, where would you look?

**Possible answer: In the Encyclopedia of U.S. Presidents**

10. Would encyclopedias be more useful if you were writing a report on U.S. Presidents in the twentieth century or a report on children's movies currently showing in your neighborhood? Why?

**Students' answers should note that encyclopedias would have**

**a great deal more information about Presidents than current**

**children's movies.**

**Home Activity** Your child answered questions about print and media sources. Discuss where media sources are located at your local library or bookstore. How are they organized? How are they organized similarly or differently from the print sources?

# Multisyllabic Words

**Proofread an Article** Circle six spelling errors. Write the words correctly. Find one capitalization error and write the sentence correctly.

Fictional Detectives

(Literture) has its share of famous detectives. (writers) have created an enormous (variaty) of detectives. All have (curiousity) about and a (fasination) with crime. Usually, they are average people with an especially high (probility) of being right in the middle of a crime scene! As one famous detective said, "It's (elamentry,) my dear Watson!"

1. **Literature**      2. **variety**
3. **curiosity**      4. **fascination**
5. **probability**      6. **elementary**
7. **Writers have created an enormous variety of detectives.**

**Proofread Words** Circle the word that is spelled correctly.

8. A ____ looks like a rock.
   metorit          meteoright          (meteorite)

9. I made a ____ out of glass tile.
   (mosaic)          mosesic          mosiac

10. My 99-year-old grandfather will have his ____ birthday next year.
    centenial          (centennial)          cintennial

11. William Penn was the founder of ____.
    (Pennsylvania)          Pennysylvania          Pennysalvenia

12. The tour ____ can go on land and water.
    veacle          (vehicle)          vehical

13. A soup can is a ____.
    cylindar          cylander          (cylinder)

14. My dog is a ____ poodle.
    (miniature)          miniture          miniatur

## Spelling Words

elementary
vehicle
miniature
probability
opportunity
substitute
variety
literature
elevator
Pennsylvania

ravioli
cafeteria
mosaic
tuxedo
meteorite
fascination
cylinder
intermediate
centennial
curiosity

## Frequently Misspelled Words

usually
especially

**School + Home** **Home Activity** Your child identified misspelled multisyllabic words. Ask your child to select four list words and tell you how many syllables are in each word.

## Contractions and Negatives

**Directions** Read the passage. Then read each question. Circle the letter of the correct answer.

# Will Potluck's Songs

(1) My uncle, Will Potluck, lived out in the country near a small river. (2) Nobody ever saw him. (3) Uncle Will was always bothered by the badgers that dug under his house and garden. (4) When he <u>could not</u> stand it anymore, <u>he would</u> walk down to the river to escape the troublesome creatures. (5) He had _____ seen another soul there in the shade of the tall trees. (6) Dozing under the cedars, Uncle Will sang old songs, and the badgers did not never bother him. (7) With _____ around for miles, _____ ever heard Uncle Will's songs.

1  Which word from sentence 2 is a negative?

   A  didn't

   B  ever

   C  anybody

   **D  nobody**

2  Which pair of contractions could you make from the underlined words in sentence 4?

   A  couldn't/he'll

   **B  couldn't/he'd**

   C  wouldn't/he'll

   D  can't/wouldn't

3  Which word best completes sentence 5?

   **A  never**

   B  ever

   C  any

   D  no one

4  What change, if any, could be made in sentence 6?

   A  Change *cedars,* to **cedars**

   **B  Change *did not never* to didn't ever**

   C  Change *did not never* to **do not never**

   D  Make no change

5  Which pair of words best completes sentence 7?

   A  everybody/something

   B  nobody/anyone

   **C  no one/no one**

   D  nothing/something

© Pearson Education, Inc., 5

**Home Activity** Your child prepared for taking tests on contractions and negatives. Ask your child to write contractions on one side of index cards and the words used to form them on the other side. Help your child practice identifying them.

# Graphic Sources

- **Graphic sources** include charts, tables, graphs, maps, illustrations, and photographs.
- Before you read, look closely at graphic sources that accompany a selection. They will give you an idea of what you will read.

**Directions** Study the map of the *Titanic's* journey. Then answer the questions below.

1. Where did the *Titanic* begin its journey?

   **It started from Southampton, England.**

2. What other two ports in Europe did the *Titanic* visit?

   **It stopped in Cherbourg, France, and Queenstown, Ireland.**

3. In which direction was the *Titanic* sailing?

   **It was heading west.**

4. Which country was the *Titanic* closest to when it sank?

   **It was closest to Canada.**

5. The *Titanic* was headed to New York. About what portion of its journey had it completed when it sank?

   **Possible answer: The *Titanic* had completed about 3/4 of its**

   **journey.**

**Home Activity** Your child looked at a map and answered questions about it. With your child, draw a floor plan of your home. Label all the major rooms and areas.

# Writing • Notes

**Key Features of Notes**

- Includes most important dates and facts
- Restates information in one's own words; avoids plagiarism
- Cites, or names, original source or sources

## What Is Left of the Titanic

From The Unsinkable Wreck of the R.M.S. Titanic by Robert D. Ballard and Rick Archbold, pages 207–208.

Current status of ship
- First-class glass dome missing
- Titanic broken into two halves on ocean floor
- Two parts are 2,000 feet apart
- Edge of ship part is very mangled

Debris
- Very thin layer of sediment covering objects from inside the ship—Ballard thinks there should be more
- Items found include: a boiler, a tin cup, champagne bottles, the head of a porcelain doll, boots, and shoes.

1. Circle the two types of facts that appear in the notes.

2. How does the writer avoid plagiarism?

**The writer restates the facts in his/her own words.**

3. Circle where the writer cites an original source.

# Vocabulary

**Directions** Draw a line to connect each word on the left with its definition on the right.

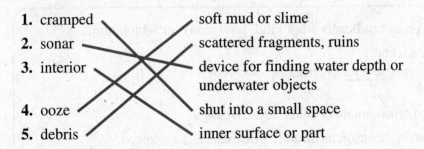

1. cramped     soft mud or slime

2. sonar     scattered fragments, ruins

3. interior     device for finding water depth or underwater objects

4. ooze     shut into a small space

5. debris     inner surface or part

**Directions** Choose words from the box to complete the crossword puzzle.

**DOWN**

6. litterbugs leave this behind

7. moving but not living

**ACROSS**

8. opposite of *exterior*

9. collected at the bottom of the ocean

10. locates objects underwater

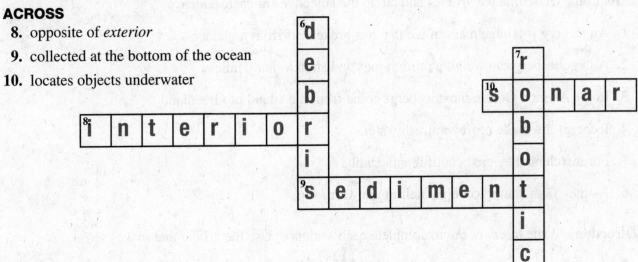

## Write a Journal Entry

Pretend you are a passenger on a huge cruise ship crossing the ocean. On a separate sheet of paper, write your first journal entry as the ship sets sail. Use as many vocabulary words as you can.

**Journal entries should be about the first day on a cruise ship and include words from the vocabulary list.**

© Pearson Education, Inc., 5

**Home Activity** Your child identified and used vocabulary words from the story *The Unsinkable Wreck of the R.M.S. Titanic.* Have your child narrate a recent adventure he or she has experienced.

**Vocabulary 329**

# Adjectives and Articles

An **adjective** describes a noun or pronoun. It tells what kind, how many, or which one.

| | |
|---|---|
| **What Kind** | a gigantic white iceberg |
| **How Many** | numerous icebergs; several chances |
| **Which One** | this lifeboat |

The **articles** *a*, *an*, and *the* appear before nouns or other adjectives.

• Use **a** before words that begin with a consonant sound: a disaster, a rapid speed.
• Use **an** before words that begin with a vowel sound or a silent *h*: an ending, an eerie noise.
• Use **the** before words beginning with any letter: the site, the passengers.

An adjective formed from a proper noun is a **proper adjective.** Proper adjectives are capitalized: American newspapers.

**Directions** Underline the articles and circle the adjectives in each sentence.

1. An iceberg is a huge mass of ice that has broken off from a glacier.

2. A large iceberg can weigh a million tons and stretch many miles.

3. In the Atlantic Ocean, most icebergs come from the island of Greenland.

4. Icebergs are made of frozen fresh water.

5. For travelers, they are beautiful and deadly.

6. As they float south, icebergs melt in the warm sun.

**Directions** Write *a, an,* or *the* to complete each sentence. Use the article that makes sense.

7. Some icebergs are carried by wind into **the** Atlantic Ocean.

8. Only **a** small part of an iceberg is visible above the water.

9. **An** iceberg is quite impressive to behold.

**Directions** Complete each sentence with an adjective or adjectives of your own.

**Possible answers:**

10. The wreck of the **British** ship lies in **two** pieces on the ocean floor.

11. A litter of belongings tells the **sad** tale of lost life.

12. The once **stately** ship is now a **rusty** heap on the ocean floor.

**Home Activity** Your child learned about adjectives and articles. Ask your child to expand sentences such as the following by adding adjectives and articles: *The ship sank. It struck an iceberg. People died. Today it's a legend.*

© Pearson Education, Inc., 5

# Spelling Words

| Spelling Words | | | | |
|---|---|---|---|---|
| music | musician | select | selection | sign |
| signal | part | partial | haste | hasten |
| protect | protection | magic | magician | resign |
| resignation | electric | electrician | condemn | condemnation |

**Words in Context** Complete each sentence with a list word.

1. John was forced to _____ as the class president.

2. The string trio was missing one _____.

3. She had a look of _____ on her face.

4. A(n) _____ works with electricity.

5. The _____ pulled a rabbit out of a hat.

6. We need a piano for _____ class.

7. The crowd's noises are a _____ of discontent.

8. She left in _____ and lost her shoe.

9. Mom said the _____ bill was due today.

10. The clown performed a few _____ tricks.

1. **resign**

2. **musician**

3. **resignation**

4. **electrician**

5. **magician**

6. **music**

7. **sign**

8. **haste**

9. **electric**

10. **magic**

**Antonyms** Write the list word that has the opposite or nearly opposite meaning.

11. whole

12. do not choose

13. harm

14. recommendation

15. delay

11. **part**

12. **select**

13. **protect**

14. **condemnation**

15. **hasten**

**Synonyms** Write the list word that has the same or nearly the same meaning.

16. incomplete

17. indicator

18. security

19. choice

20. denounce

16. **partial**

17. **sign, signal**

18. **protection**

19. **selection**

20. **condemn**

 **School + Home** **Home Activity** Your child wrote related words. Have your child tell you a synonym or an antonym for a list word.

© Pearson Education, Inc., 5

# Outline Form A

**Title** _____

**A.** _____

    1. _____

    2. _____

    3. _____

**B.** _____

    1. _____

    2. _____

    3. _____

**C.** _____

    1. _____

    2. _____

    3. _____

# Vocabulary • Unknown Words

- A dictionary lists words in alphabetical order and gives their meanings, part of speech, and pronunciations. A glossary is an alphabetical list of important words and their meanings that are used in a book. Glossaries are located at the back of a book.

- Sometimes an **unknown word** doesn't have context clues to help you find its meaning. Then you should look up the word in a dictionary or glossary.

**Directions** Read the following passage. Then use the glossary in the back of your book or a dictionary to answer the questions below.

One of the pioneers of underwater research was Jacques Cousteau. He invented the "Aqua-Lung" in 1943. The Aqua-Lung was the first compressed air diving tank that allowed divers to stay underwater for long periods of time. This tank allowed Cousteau to move freely among the fish he studied. Cousteau also helped create, or invent, a camera for filming underwater. His television series, *The Undersea World of Jacques Cousteau,* was extremely popular. People were compelled by images of the deep sea that they were able to view without leaving their homes.

## Possible answers given.

1. What is the meaning of *compressed*?

 ***Compressed* means "squeezed together."**

2. What is the meaning of *pioneer*? Is *pioneer* used as a verb or a noun in this passage?

 **A pioneer is someone who does something first; It is used as a noun.**

3. What is the meaning of *invent*?

 ***Invent* means "to make something up for the first time."**

4. Look up *Jacques Cousteau* in your dictionary. Did you find him listed under *C* or *J*? When was he born?

 **Jacques Cousteau is listed under *C*. He was born in 1910.**

5. Find an unfamiliar word in the passage. Write a sentence using this word.

 ***compelled;* The apple was so tasty, I was compelled to eat another one.**

**Home Activity** Your child read a short passage and used a dictionary and glossary to find the meanings of unknown words. Read an article together and pick a few unknown words. If your child cannot find context clues to help with the meanings, ask him or her to find the meanings in a dictionary.

© Pearson Education, Inc., 5

# Note Taking

**Taking notes** about what you read can help you understand and remember the text better. It can also help you organize information to study for a test or to include in a research report. There is no one right way to take notes. You might make a list, an outline, or a story map or paraphrase what you've read. When you **paraphrase,** you rewrite what you've read using your own words. Avoid plagiarism, or copying another person's words. When you record findings, you synthesize, or combine information. Use key words, phrases, or short sentences when taking notes.

**Directions** Read the following article. On a separate sheet of paper, take notes properly as you read.

Remotely-operated vehicles, or ROVs, are the primary means for underwater exploration to take place in deep waters. The first ROV was created by a Russian photographer, Demitri Rebikoff, in 1953. Since the first ROV, which was connected by rope or cable above water, many improvements have been made to the technology. The earliest innovations in ROV technology were made by the U.S. Navy in the 1960s. The Navy used CURV, Cable-Controlled Underwater Recovery Vehicle, to recover a hydrogen bomb lost off the coast of Spain. CURV was also used to save the lives of the pilots of a submersible that sunk off the coast of Cork, Ireland, in 1973. In the past two decades, private oil companies have searched ever deeper for new oil resources. As a result, they are responsible for the greatest developments in ROV technology.

The most famous development in ROV technology, however, came in 1986 when *Alvin* was "flown" down to the wreck of the *Titanic* in the Atlantic Ocean. Created by the scientists at Woods Hole Oceanographic Institution, *Alvin* was a human-driven submersible tethered by a line that reached the water's surface. A person was able to steer it and operate the camera equipment attached to the exterior. Scientist Martin Bowen was the first person to take *Alvin* to the wreck of the *Titanic,* some 13,000 feet below sea level. Because the pressure at such a depth is far too great for the human body to withstand, only a protective submersible like *Alvin* could provide the necessary protection for such a journey.

Currently, more advanced ROVs, like Triton XL (which is about the size of a small car), can perform a variety of tasks deep underwater. Construction, underwater surveying, and pipeline maintenance are a few of the things these advanced ROVs can accomplish.

**Directions** Answer the questions below based on the article you read and the notes you took.
## Possible answers given for 6–10.

**1.** When was the first ROV developed?

**The first ROV was designed by a Russian photographer in 1953.**

**2.** Why did the U.S. Navy develop ROV technology?

**They developed it to recover a lost atomic bomb.**

**3.** Why was *Alvin* developed?

***Alvin* was developed to better explore the wreck of the *Titanic*.**

**4.** How far below sea level is the wreck of the *Titanic* located?

**It is located 13,000 feet below sea level.**

**5.** Paraphrase the last two sentences of the first paragraph.

**Private oil companies are responsible for recent developments in ROVs because they are always searching for oil.**

**6.** Synthesize the information in the second paragraph.

***Alvin*, a human-driven ROV, was created by Woods Hole Oceanographic Institution to explore the *Titanic*. The driver controlled the steering and a camera.**

**7.** How would you organize your notes about this article? Why?

**I would organize my notes in three parts because there are three paragraphs.**

**8.** Why is it important for you to take notes about what you read?

**Taking notes can help you understand and remember the text better when you are studying.**

**9.** How does paraphrasing help you to understand and recall material that you read?

**Putting ideas into your own words can help you understand and remember information that you read.**

**10.** On a separate piece of paper, make a simple time line of the major developments in ROV technology.

**Check students' time line for accuracy.**

**Home Activity** Your child read a short article, took notes, and recorded findings from it. With your child, read an article from a newspaper or magazine and practice taking notes and recording findings from the article.

# Related Words

**Proofread an E-Mail** Shawnelle wrote an e-mail to her friend. Circle six spelling errors and one capitalization error. Write the corrections on the lines.

Dear (nancy,)

I had a great time at the outdoor (musick) festival. The (hole) group played so well. I especially liked the (selecshun) played by the (alectric) guitars. Playing without a conductor must be hard. It was difficult to see who gave the (signle) to start. When it began raining I wondered what they would do to (protek) the instruments. Luckily I had a raincoat which kept me dry! Thanks again for giving me your extra ticket.

Your friend,

Kim

**Spelling Words**

music
musician
select
selection
sign
signal
part
partial
haste
hasten

protect
protection
magic
magician
resign
resignation
electric
electrician
condemn
condemnation

1. **music**   2. **whole**
3. **selection**   4. **electric**
5. **signal**   6. **protect**
7. **Nancy**

**Proofread Words** Circle the correct spelling of the word.

8. musishun — (musician) — musicshun

9. magisshun — magicshun — (magician)

10. (partial) — partshel — parshel

11. (select) — selekt — selek

12. haston — hastin — (hasten)

13. resignashun — resinashun — (resignation)

14. finaly — (finally) — finely

15. (electrician) — electreshun — aletrician

16. (condemnation) — condemmation — condennation

**Frequently Misspelled Words**

finally
whole
want

**Home Activity** Your child identified misspelled words in a paragraph. Ask your child to name a pair of list words and describe how one of the consonants is pronounced differently in each.

## Adjectives and Articles

**Directions** Read the passage. Then read each question. Circle the letter of the correct answer.

# Trouble at Sea

(1) From the deck of the <u>small</u> boat, the waves were giant mountains crashing down on us every few seconds. (2) It was a great feat to catch our breath. (3) There was nothing we could do to keep out of the way of the _____ waves. (4) We could only hope that our tiny boat was strong enough to hold up against _____ force of _____ storm and _____ battering of _____ huge waves. (5) The storm seemed endless, and all hope appeared lost. (6) Suddenly, _____ small flash of sunlight streaked across the _____ deck. (7) The waves began to recede, and we looked at each other with joy.

**1** In sentence 1, the underlined word answers which question about the boat?
  **(A)** What kind?
  **B** How many?
  **C** Which one?
  **D** How much?

**2** What is the article in sentence 2?
  **A** It
  **B** was
  **(C)** a
  **D** to

**3** Which adjective best completes sentence 3?
  **A** wonderful
  **(B)** colossal
  **C** soft
  **D** boring

**4** Which article could be used in all four places in sentence 4?
  **A** a
  **B** an
  **(C)** the
  **D** None of the above

**5** Which pair of words best completes sentence 6?
  **A** an/distraught
  **B** the/relieved
  **C** a/happy
  **(D)** a/battered

© Pearson Education, Inc., 5

**School + Home** **Home Activity** Your child prepared for taking tests on adjectives and articles. Copy a page from a storybook. Have your child highlight the adjectives in red and the articles in blue.

**Conventions** Adjectives and Articles **337**

# Author's Purpose

- The **author's purpose** is the main reason an author writes a selection. An author may write to persuade, to inform, to entertain, or to express ideas or feelings.
- Sometimes an author may write with more than one purpose in mind.
- What the author says and the details given help you figure out the author's purpose.

**Directions** Read the following passage and fill in the diagram below.

Jenna dreamed of being an astronaut. She read books about astronauts, she watched documentaries on TV about space exploration, and she even insisted her parents take her on vacation to the NASA launch site in Florida. At school, Jenna's science projects always had something to do with the planets or space or famous astronauts. It seemed she knew more about the space shuttle than some of her teachers did. Although she had only been in an airplane once, she spent the whole three-hour flight staring out the window at the clouds and the vast sky. Jenna wasn't sure how long it would take, but she knew one day she would see the Earth from as far away as the moon.

## Possible answers given.

| AUTHOR'S PURPOSE | 1. **The author is writing to inform about Jenna's dream to be an astronaut.** |
|---|---|
| **DETAIL** What is one example of Jenna's interest in astronauts? | 2. **She made her parents take her to a launch site for vacation.** |
| **DETAIL** What is another example of Jenna's interest in astronauts? | 3. **She watches documentaries about space exploration.** |

4. Does the author meet his or her purpose successfully? Why do you feel this way?

   **yes; The author describes a variety of activities that reflect Jenna's dream of becoming an astronaut.**

5. If you did not understand the passage, what could you do to help yourself understand?

   **You could go back and re-read the passage at a much slower rate.**

**Home Activity** Your child answered questions about an author's purpose in a fictional passage. Read a favorite book and have your child describe the author's purpose for writing.

© Pearson Education, Inc., 5

# Writing • Biographical Sketch

**Key Features of a Biographical Sketch**

- tells about a real person's life
- uses precise language and sensory details
- can show the subject's personality
- may use quotations to reveal the subject's personality

## Tonya's Sweet Tea Stand

My friend Tonya is a natural business person. She can sell anything to anyone, from cookies to T-shirts with a special pattern that she has made. Last summer, Tonya decided to try a new kind of business: selling sweet tea from a stand in front of her house.

I helped Tonya prepare a tall pitcher of tea on the first day of her new enterprise. As we worked in her mother's kitchen, she told me, "This'll be a great idea. The key to any good business is giving people what they want. It's so hot in the summertime that everyone will want a cool, refreshing drink."

But that first day didn't go quite as well as she had hoped. She sat in front of her house next to a big, bright sign advertising "Tea 25 cents." The afternoon was dry and hot. It was the perfect weather for a cool drink. But only a few cars passed by her narrow yard, and only one car stopped.

That night, Tonya asked her mother for advice. Tonya gets a lot of her business knowledge from her mother, who's a buyer for the department store downtown. Her mother told her, "Tonya, you can't wait for your customers to come to you. You have to go where your customers are."

Early the next morning, I helped Tonya set up her stand in a different spot. We went to the park by the train station, where crowds of people were on their way to work. The morning was hot, the people were thirsty, and by ten-thirty we'd sold out of all the tea we'd brought. Tonya was right: her tea stand was a great idea!

1. What sensory details does the author use to describe the weather?

   **The weather is dry and hot.**

2. Underline the quotation from Tonya. What does this quotation show about her?

   **It shows that she has put thought into her business idea and that she is enthusiastic about it.**

# Vocabulary

**Directions** Draw a line to connect each word on the left with its definition on the right.

1. monitors — part played in real life

2. role — the force that causes objects to move or tend to move toward the center of the Earth

3. gravity — computer screens

4. accomplishments — definite

5. specific — achievements

**Check the Words You Know**

___ accomplishments
___ focus
___ gravity
___ monitors
___ role
___ specific

**Directions** Choose a word from the box that best matches each clue. Write the word on the line.

**focus** _____ 6. what gets the most attention

**gravity** _____ 7. this keeps our feet on the ground

**monitors** _____ 8. they show information

**accomplishments** _____ 9. things you can successfully complete

**specific** _____ 10. not just anything

## Write a Scene from a Play

On a separate sheet of paper, write a short scene from a play about an astronaut telling his granddaughter what it was like to fly to the moon. Use as many vocabulary words as you can.

**Scenes should include words from the vocabulary list and reflect dialogue between the astronaut and his granddaughter describing a flight to the moon.**

© Pearson Education, Inc., 5

**School + Home** **Home Activity** Your child identified and used vocabulary words from the interview *Talk with an Astronaut*. Have your child interview you about the work you do.

Name _____

# This, That, These, and Those

> The adjectives *this, that, these,* and *those* tell which one or which ones. *This* and *that* modify singular nouns. *These* and *those* modify plural nouns. *This* and *these* refer to objects that are close by. *That* and *those* refer to objects farther away.
>
> This shirt I have on is like that one in the store window.
>
> These pencils just fit in the pocket, but those pens on the desk did not fit.
>
> • Do not use *here* or *there* after *this, that, these,* or *those.*
>
> **No:** This here article is about NASA. That there one is about new computers.
>
> **Yes:** This article is about NASA. That one is about new computers.
>
> • Do not use *them* in place of *these* or *those.*
>
> **No:** She wrote them articles for *Newsweek.*
>
> **Yes:** She wrote those articles for *Newsweek.*

**Directions** Write the letter of the sentence in which the underlined part is correct.

**B** 1. **A** That there space capsule is smaller than I realized.
   **B** That space capsule is smaller than I realized.

**B** 2. **A** I think them astronauts were brave to travel in it.
   **B** I think those astronauts were brave to travel in it.

**A** 3. **A** Is that spacesuit the one worn by John Glenn?
   **B** Is those spacesuit the one worn by John Glenn?

**B** 4. **A** This here time line shows the history of space flight.
   **B** This time line shows the history of space flight.

**A** 5. **A** Robert Goddard helped design these early rockets.
   **B** Robert Goddard helped design them early rockets.

**Directions** Write each sentence. Use the correct adjective in ( ).

6. Will (that, those) storm reach Florida today?

## Will that storm reach Florida today?

7. If it does, NASA will postpone (this, these) shuttle launch.

## If it does, NASA will postpone this shuttle launch.

8. Use (them, those) binoculars to view the launch.

## Use those binoculars to view the launch.

 **Home Activity** Your child learned about *this, that, these,* and *those.* Write the words on four index cards. Ask your child to match each word with the appropriate category: singular near, singular far, plural near, plural far.

# Greek Word Parts

| Spelling Words | | | | |
|---|---|---|---|---|
| artist | tourism | biology | phobia | heroism |
| geology | cartoonist | technology | journalism | hydrophobia |
| violinist | ecology | patriotism | vocalist | meteorology |
| zoology | claustrophobia | capitalism | novelist | technophobia |

**Classifying** Write the list word that best fits each group.

1. animal, study, science, ____
2. travel, pleasure, recreation, ____
3. soprano, bass, tenor, ____
4. paint, canvas, sculpture, ____
5. rocks, minerals, earth, ____
6. plants, animals, study, ____
7. courage, bravery, fortitude, ____
8. weather, forecast, barometer, ____
9. writing, reporting, news, ____
10. fear, water, abnormal, ____

1. __zoology__
2. __tourism__
3. __vocalist__
4. __artist__
5. __geology__
6. __biology__
7. __heroism__
8. __meteorology__
9. __journalism__
10. __hydrophobia__

**Definitions**

11. a persistent, abnormal fear or dislike
12. one who draws a comic strip
13. a person who writes novels
14. the development of new ways to solve problems
15. an abnormal fear of technology
16. a person who plays the violin
17. love and devotion to one's country
18. economic system based on the private ownership of industry
19. fear of being in small or enclosed spaces
20. study of the relation of living things to their environment and one another

11. __phobia__
12. __cartoonist__
13. __novelist__
14. __technology__
15. __technophobia__
16. __violinist__
17. __patriotism__
18. __capitalism__
19. __claustrophobia__
20. __ecology__

© Pearson Education, Inc., 5

**Home Activity** Your child wrote words that have Greek word parts. Have your child underline the Greek word part in each word.

# Story Sequence B

**Title**

**Characters**

**Setting**

**Events**

_____

_____

_____

_____

_____

_____

_____

_____

_____

# Vocabulary · Multiple-Meaning Words

- Some words have more than one meaning. They are called **multiple-meaning words.**
- If you read a word that you recognize, but it is used in an unfamiliar way, look for clues about its meaning in the words nearby. Then use a dictionary to help you understand its meaning.

**Directions** Read the following passage. Then answer the questions below. Look for context clues to help you understand words with multiple meanings.

> You could say astronomers are monitors of the skies. They focus in on the details of our vast universe so we can understand the bigger picture. Even though the serious work astronomers do has a lot of gravity, or seriousness, most of them will admit they feel as excited as kids when a major discovery is made.
>
> To become an astronomer, you have to study many elements of science, such as gravity, with a dedication and focus most people find hard to have. But once you complete your education and are a working astronomer studying space, the sky truly is the limit.

1. How would you define the word *monitors* as it is used in the passage?

   **Monitors are people who focus on details and observe them.**

2. What is another definition for the word *monitors*?

   **Monitors can also be TV or computer screens.**

3. What context clues helped you understand the way the word *gravity* was used in the passage the first time?

   **"seriousness"**

4. What does *focus* mean the first time it is used in the passage?

   **It means "to concentrate on."**

5. What does *focus* mean the second time it is used in the passage?

   **It means "a central point of attention."**

**Home Activity** Your child used context clues to help define words with multiple meanings. Work together to try to use other words with multiple meanings to make up a silly poem.

# Readers' Guide to Periodical Literature

- The **Readers' Guide to Periodical Literature** is a set of books that lists, alphabetically by author and subject, the articles that are published in more than 200 periodicals. Each entry provides an article's title, author, volume, pages, and date.
- You can find a *Readers' Guide* in most libraries.

**Directions** Read the following page, which is similar to one you would find in the *Readers' Guide to Periodical Literature*. Then answer the questions below.

---

**ASTRONAUTS—**
> See also
> Moonwalk
> NASA
> Shuttle

Astronaut interviews. *School Zone* v496 p18 Ja '02
Astrophysics. L. Jones. *Science Explorers* v117 p87 My '02
Calling Earth [astronaut talks about mission] G. Calwell. *The Northwest Herald*  Sec D p1
   Au 17 '02
Miraculous Adventure [astronaut orbits Earth] R. Gold. *Discover the World* v198 p29 Jy '03
Where is NASA's Latest Mission? S. Bobrick. *Mysteries of Space* v48 p31 Mr '03
The Years Before Space Exploration [training astronauts in 1950s] A. Hether. *Our Times* p44
   F '03

---

1. Which article would probably be the best to read if you were writing a research paper on the training of the first astronauts?

   **"The Years Before Space Exploration" in *Our Times***

2. In each listing, where does the title of the article appear?

   **The article's title appears first in each listing.**

3. What do the words in brackets tell you?

   **They provide additional information about the article and its title.**

4. Are there any books listed in this section? How do you know?

   **no; The *Readers' Guide* lists only periodicals, not books.**

5. Why is the *Readers' Guide to Periodical Literature* a valuable tool?

   **Possible answer: It provides a listing of hundreds of periodicals and magazines, making it easy to find these resources.**

**Directions**  Read the following page. Then answer the questions below.

---

**MARS**

  *See also*
  Martians
  Red Planet
  Solar System–Planets
  Space Exploration

Are the Martians Coming? A. Wilson. *Mysteries of Space* v22 p24 D '03

Astral Recordings. *Science Sounds* v6 p33 F '04

Earth's Neighbors [Venus and Mars] T. Charleston. *The Jersey Times* Sec 1 p3 O 7 '03

Ice on Mars [NASA's report on ice deposits] W. M. Walters. *This Great Planet* v8 p29 Ja '04

Life on Mars? [research by University of Minnesota] L. Fulkner. *Science Research Weekly* p8
 S 18 '03

The Trouble with Hubble [information on Hubble] J. Randolph. *Astrophysical Magazine* v68
 p356 Mr '04

---

## Possible answers given for 6, 9, 10.

**6.** Why do you think the *"See also"* references are placed at the top of the listing?

## These refer to related topics that may contain useful information.

**7.** According to the listing above, what is the focus of the article in *The Jersey Times*?

## The focus of the article is the planets Venus and Mars.

**8.** If you were writing a report on the possibility of water existing on Mars, which article or articles would be most helpful?

## "Life on Mars?" in *Science Research Weekly* and "Ice on Mars" in *This Great Planet*

**9.** How would you describe one of the major differences between a library card catalog and the *Readers' Guide*?

## The card catalog lists all of the books found in the library. The *Readers' Guide* is an index of periodical articles.

**10.** If you were writing a research paper, why might you use the *Readers' Guide?*

## I could use it to find up-to-date magazine and journal articles about my subject.

**Home Activity**  Your child answered questions about the *Readers' Guide to Periodical Literature*. Together, gather several magazines and create your own *Readers' Guide* listings for them. Encourage your child to catalog as many articles from the magazines as possible.

© Pearson Education, Inc., 5

# Greek Word Parts

**Proofread an Article** Circle six spelling errors in the article. Write the corrections on the lines. Find the sentence with two punctuation errors and write the sentence correctly.

**Spelling Words**

artist
tourism
biology
phobia
heroism
geology
cartoonist
technology
journalism
hydrophobia

violinist
ecology
patriotism
vocalist
meteorology
zoology
claustrophobia
capitalism
novelist
technophobia

Vacation in Millville

This year many of Millville's families will spend their summer vacations at home. The city's bureau of tourism has great ideas on where to go and what to see. The Museum of Natural History has exhibits on geology and metorology Meanwhile Millville's war memorial holds stories of local herosm and patritism Kids of all ages are invited to the park's month-long festival of ecology and zology. With all that Millville has to offer, its bound to be a fun summer!

1. **tourism**          2. **meteorology**

3. **heroism**          4. **patriotism**

5. **zoology**          6. **it's**

7. **Meanwhile, Millville's war memorial holds stories of local heroism and patriotism.**

**Proofread Words** Circle the correct spelling of the word.

8. journlism        (journalism)       jurnalism

9. (violinist)       vilinist           vylinist

10. captalism        (capitalism)       capetlism

11. tecknology       teknology          (technology)

12. (cartoonist)     cartunist          cartoonis

13. eclogy           ekology            (ecology)

14. (biology)        bilogy             biologie

15. clastrofobia     claustraphobia     (claustrophobia)

16. hidrofobia       (hydrophobia)      hydrofobia

**Frequently Misspelled Words**

I'm
it's
let's

**Home Activity** Your child identified misspelled list words. Ask your child to spell four words, each with a different Greek word part, and tell you what the words mean.

## This, That, These, and *Those*

**Directions** Read the passage. Then read each question. Circle the letter of the correct answer.

# Man on the Moon

(1) Today, we continued to analyze the surface of <u>this</u> dark moon.
(2) Temperatures here are very low, and we would freeze without these here suits.
(3) Them early astronauts were extremely brave to come here. (4) Regarding those
rumors of life on this moon, we believe they are false. (5) _____ old report
submitted by Colonel Brown appears to be correct. (6) We have collected rocks
and soil samples. (7) We have found no evidence in those there rocks that water
ever ran here.

**1** In sentence 1, the underlined word suggests what?

  **A**  The author is cold.
  **(B)**  The author is on the moon.
  **C**  The author is lonely.
  **D**  The author had once gone to the moon.

**2** What change, if any, should be made in sentence 2?

  **A**  Change *here* to **there**
  **B**  Change *we would* to **we did**
  **(C)**  Change *these here suits* to **these suits**
  **D**  Make no change

**3** What change, if any, should be made in sentence 3?

  **(A)**  Change *Them* to **Those**
  **B**  Change *Them* to **This**
  **C**  Change *were* to **was**
  **D**  Make no change

**4** Which article could be used to complete sentence 5?

  **A**  These
  **(B)**  That
  **C**  Those
  **D**  All could be used

**5** What change, if any, should be made in sentence 7?

  **A**  Change *those* to **this**
  **B**  Change *those* to **these**
  **(C)**  Change *those there* to **those**
  **D**  Make no change

© Pearson Education, Inc., 5

**School + Home**  **Home Activity** Your child prepared for taking tests on *this, that, these,* and *those*. Ask your child to use these adjectives with the names of objects you point out in a room to describe their number and location.

# Cause and Effect

- A **cause** (what makes something happen) may have several effects. An **effect** (what happens as a result of a cause) may have several causes.

- Sometimes clue words such as *since, as a result, caused, thus, therefore,* and *consequently* are used to show cause-and-effect relationships.

**Directions** Read the following passage. Then complete the diagram below.

Kai was determined to dig straight through to the other side of the Earth. He had the tools: his mom's garden shovel and his dad's metal rake. When he started digging, things went smoothly. As he dug deeper, the digging got harder. As Kai pounded away at the clay below the topsoil, the tip of his shovel began to flatten. He knew he'd need a sharp tip on his shovel to dig deep into the mantle of the Earth, so he went back to the garage and got another shovel. The harder he dug, the sweatier he became. Pretty soon, Kai was exhausted. He sat down in the shade of a nearby tree and quickly fell asleep.

He dreamed he had dug through Earth's mantle, through the boiling hot core, and was making his way out on the other side of the globe. Dream-digging was so much easier.

**Cause**

1. **The clay was hard.**

**Effect**

2. **Pounding at the clay, Kai flattened the tip of his mom's shovel**

**Effect**

Kai had to get another shovel to keep digging.

**Effect**

Kai dreamed he was on the other side of the globe.

**Cause**

3. **Kai was tired and he fell asleep.**

**Cause**

4. **He dreamed he dug through the Earth.**

5. Summarize the passage in one or two sentences.

**Possible answer: Kai tried to dig to the other side of the planet, but found it was easier to dream about digging.**

**School + Home** **Home Activity** Your child read a short passage and identified causes and effects. Read a favorite story together and discuss the causes and effects you find.

© Pearson Education 5

# Writing · Writing for Tests

To the Editor:

The Oregon Street Park is in desperate need of repair and renovation. Between the crumbling pavement on the basketball and tennis courts and the rusty, broken slides and swing sets, the park is unsafe for the many children who visit it daily. The park must be fixed before someone gets hurt.

First, the park must be cleaned up. Broken bottles and pieces of litter are scattered all over the ground. My fifth-grade class at Windber Elementary has arranged a field trip to clean up the park. We will gather at Oregon Park at 9 AM on October 11th. We ask our neighbors in the community to join us and help clean up our park.

Next, we ask the members of the city government to visit the park and see the problems for themselves. It is up to the city government to remove the old, broken parts of the park and replace them with safe, new materials. Specifically, we believe that the basketball and tennis courts, along with the slides and swing sets, should be replaced.

If we work together as a community, we could have the safest, cleanest, and most enjoyable park around. A new park will provide the community with a place to meet, to exercise, and to play. We students are ready to help make this change. We hope we can count on the support of the adults in our community.

Thank you,
Cooper Jackson
Windber Elementary School

1. Reread the letter. What purpose does the writer state in paragraph one?

   **Oregon Street Park must be cleaned up and repaired. Unsafe**

   **equipment must be replaced.**

2. What are two facts the writer includes to support the purpose for writing?

   **Broken bottles and rusty slides show that the park is unsafe.**

   **Crumbling pavement on the basketball and tennis courts**

   **shows that the park needs repairs.**

3. From whom does the writer ask support for this purpose?

   **members of the city government and neighbors in the**

   **community**

© Pearson Education, Inc., 5

# Vocabulary

**Directions** Choose the word from the box that best completes each sentence. Write the word on the line shown to the left.

**extinct**_____

1. No one is really sure how the dinosaurs vanished, or became _____.

**plunged**_____

2. Some think a giant asteroid collided with the Earth and _____ it into darkness.

**armor**_____

3. Some dinosaurs looked as though they were covered in heavy, protective _____.

**hideous**_____

4. Although they looked strong, they were not protected from starvation, a painful and _____ way to die.

**encases**_____

5. Today, a scientist who finds any remains from the age of the dinosaurs covers, or _____, them in special boxes that will preserve them into the future.

> ### Check the Words You Know
> ___armor
> ___encases
> ___extinct
> ___hideous
> ___plunged
> ___serpent

**Directions** Fill in the crossword puzzle using the clues below.

**DOWN**

6. very ugly, horrible

7. protective covering

8. covers completely

**ACROSS**

9. snake

10. no longer existing

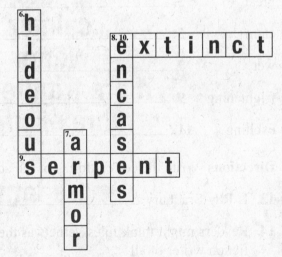

## Write a Newspaper Article

On a separate sheet of paper, pretend you are a news reporter and dinosaur fossils have been discovered somewhere in your town. Use as many vocabulary words as you can to write an article about the fossils.

**Newspaper articles should include words from the vocabulary list and be about fossils found in the student's town.**

**Home Activity** Your child identified and used vocabulary words from the story *Journey to the Center of the Earth*. With your child, make up a story about what is at the center of the Earth using the vocabulary words.

# Comparative and Superlative Adjectives

**Comparative adjectives** are used to compare two people, places, things, or groups. Add *-er* to most short adjectives to make their comparative forms. Use *more* with longer adjectives.
**Superlative adjectives** are used to compare three or more people, places, things, or groups. Add *-est* to most short adjectives to make their superlative forms. Use *most* with longer adjectives.

| Adjective | Comparative | Superlative |
|---|---|---|
| great | great<u>er</u> | great<u>est</u> |
| enormous | <u>more</u> enormous | <u>most</u> enormous |

• Adjectives such as *good* and *bad* have irregular comparative and superlative forms: *good, better, best; bad, worse, worst.*

• Never use *more* or *most* with *-er* and *-est.*
 **No:** more sillier, most ancientest
 **Yes:** sillier, most ancient

**Directions** Complete the table. Add *-er*, *-est*, *more*, or *most* as needed.

| Adjective | Comparative | | Superlative | |
|---|---|---|---|---|
| primitive | 1. | **more primitive** | 2. | **most primitive** |
| great | 3. | **greater** | 4. | **greatest** |
| calm | 5. | **calmer** | 6. | **calmest** |
| wet | 7. | **wetter** | 8. | **wettest** |
| frightening | 9. | **more frightening** | 10. | **most frightening** |
| exciting | 11. | **more exciting** | 12. | **most exciting** |

**Directions** Write the correct forms of the adjectives in ( ) to complete the sentences.

13. Is Ray Bradbury ____**more famous**____ (famous) than Jules Verne was?

14. Readers might think Jules Verne was the ____**luckiest**____ (lucky) science fiction writer of all.

15. Did Verne write ____**better**____ (good) fiction than Lewis Carroll?

16. His **most important** ____ (important) legacy of all was his influence on twentieth-century scientists, inventors, and explorers.

© Pearson Education, Inc., 5

**Home Activity** Your child learned about comparative and superlative adjectives. Ask your child to use these forms to expand these sentences: *Science fiction is fascinating. Reading is fun.* ____ *is a good book.*

# Latin Roots

| Spelling Words | | | | |
|---|---|---|---|---|
| describe | interruption | inspection | scribble | respectful |
| bankrupt | project | injection | manuscript | suspect |
| subscription | spectacular | eruption | eject | abruptly |
| prescribe | reject | aspect | rupture | inscribe |

**Words in Context** Write the list words that complete each sentence.

She paged through the mystery **(1)**____ and became convinced that the **(2)**____ was guilty.

1. <u>**manuscript**</u>     2. <u>**suspect**</u>

She needed to give it a close **(3)**____ before she announced that she would **(4)**____ it.

3. <u>**inspection**</u>     4. <u>**reject**</u>

It was a long-term **(5)**____ and would look bad if it ended **(6)**____.

5. <u>**project**</u>     6. <u>**abruptly**</u>

She had to **(7)**____ in detail any pause or **(8)**____ that occurred.

7. <u>**describe**</u>     8. <u>**interruption**</u>

Even when the company lost money and went **(9)**____, she remained **(10)**____.

9. <u>**bankrupt**</u>     10. <u>**respectful**</u>

**Word Definitions** Write the list word that has the same meaning.

11. purchase of a series of things
12. a burst, split, or break
13. write carelessly
14. an element to be considered
15. a way of administering a substance, such as a drug
16. an order, set down as a rule or guide
17. carve into a material
18. put out from a place

11. <u>**subscription**</u>
12. <u>**rupture**</u>
13. <u>**scribble**</u>
14. <u>**aspect**</u>
15. <u>**injection**</u>
16. <u>**prescribe**</u>
17. <u>**inscribe**</u>
18. <u>**eject**</u>

© Pearson Education, Inc., 5

**Home Activity** Your child wrote words that have Latin roots. Have your child tell you five list words and identify the Latin root in each word. Have your child spell each word.

# Scoring Rubric: Letter to the Editor

| | 4 | 3 | 2 | 1 |
|---|---|---|---|---|
| **Focus/Ideas** | Focused letter with clearly stated purpose; inclusion of supporting arguments or reasoning | Somewhat focused letter with clearly stated purpose; some supporting arguments included | Unfocused letter; purpose apparent but not stated; few supporting arguments included | Letter with no clear purpose; no supporting arguments included |
| **Organization** | Logical organization; properly uses letter conventions | Mostly logical organization; some letter conventions missing or incorrect | Weak organization; letter conventions missing or incorrect | No identifiable organizational scheme; letter conventions missing or incorrect |
| **Voice** | Engaging, effective, and confident; shows writer's feelings about stated purpose | Fairly engaging voice; shows writer's feelings about stated purpose | Weak voice showing few feelings about stated purpose | Flat writing with no identifiable voice |
| **Word Choice** | Vivid, precise word choice including words that appeal to the reader's thoughts and emotions | Accurate word choice including some words that appeal to the reader's thoughts and emotions | Limited or repetitive word choice with few or no words that appeal to the reader's thoughts and emotions | Incorrect or very limited word choice with no words that appeal to the reader's thoughts and emotions |
| **Sentences** | Varied sentences in logical progression | Not as much variety; order mostly logical | Too many similar sentences; order lacking | Many fragments and run-ons |
| **Conventions** | Excellent control and accuracy; comparative and superlative adjectives used correctly | Good control, few errors; comparative and superlative adjectives generally used correctly | Weak control, many errors; comparative and superlative adjectives used incorrectly | Serious errors that obscure meaning |

# Vocabulary · Unfamiliar Words

- As you read, you may come to a word you do not know. Look for **context clues,** or words and sentences around the words, to help you figure out the meaning of the unknown word.

**Directions** Read the following passage. Then answer the questions below.

The *ichthyosaurus* isn't one specific dinosaur; it refers to a category of dinosaurs. Throughout history, *Ichthyosaurs* have been described as hideous, or disgusting to look at, creatures. That description has more to do with the imagination of artists than with actual fact.

*Icthyosaurs* were the ancestors that came before modern dolphins and serpents (or snakes). Though extinct for millions of years, we can see similarities between *ichthyosaurs* and snakes and dolphins today: they can live in water, they can be up to 10 feet long, and they have flexible spines. They all have sharp teeth.

1. What do you think *hideous* means?

   **Possible answer:** *Hideous* **means "very ugly."**

2. What context clue helped you understand its meaning?

   **The passage says "or disgusting to look at" separated by commas.**

3. How do context clues help you understand the meaning of *serpent*?

   **The passage says "or snakes" in parentheses.**

4. How do context clues help you understand the meaning *ancestor*?

   **The passage says "came before" later in the sentence.**

5. What context clues help you to figure out what *extinct* means?

   **The sentence contrasts animals living today with** *ichthyosaurs,* **which suggests that dinosaurs no longer exist.**

**Home Activity** Your child read a short passage and used context clues to understand unfamiliar words. With your child, read a piece of mail you received and help him or her use context clues to understand unfamiliar words.

© Pearson Education, Inc., 5

# Diagram/Scale Drawing

- A **diagram** is a drawing that shows how something is put together, how its parts relate to one another, or how it works. The parts are usually labeled in a diagram, and they often have text that explains how the different parts work.

- A **scale drawing** is a diagram that uses a mathematical scale, such as 1 inch on the drawing equals 1 foot in "real life."

**Directions** Use this Web page to answer the questions below.

## GEOLOGY SITE

[                                        ] **Search**

Note: The more specific your search terms, the more successful your search will be.

**Student Question of the Day**

How hot is magma?
Click here to find out.

**Today in History**

1891: British spelunker Ed Jensen discovers new mineral in Southeast Asia.

## Possible answers given for 2–5.

1. Where would you begin your search on this site for a diagram of the Earth's layers?

**You would begin in the Search bar in the upper right corner.**

2. What keywords would you use to search for a diagram of the Earth's layers?

**Earth, layers, and diagram**

3. If you want to get an idea of the size of the diagram area, what specific keyword would you need to use?

**scale**

4. If you wanted help understanding the diagram, what might be a helpful keyword to include in a search?

**help**

5. Why would a geology site be a good place to start looking for your diagram?

**This is a site about geology and the natural sciences, and studying the layers of the Earth is a part of geology.**

© Pearson Education, Inc., 5

Name_____

**Directions** Use the diagram below to answer the questions.

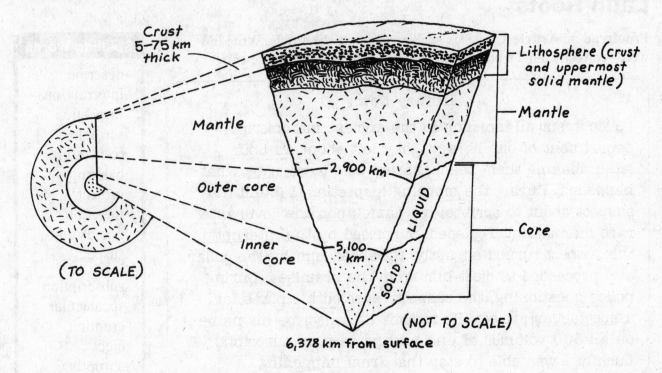

Crust 5–75 km thick

Mantle

Outer core

Inner core

2,900 km

5,100 km

(TO SCALE)

(NOT TO SCALE)

6,378 km from surface

Lithosphere (crust and uppermost solid mantle)

Mantle

Core

LIQUID

SOLID

6. Which of the two images of the Earth's layers is to scale?

**The smaller image to the left is to scale.**

7. What is the Earth's core made of?

**It is made of solid and liquid materials.**

8. Looking at the "To Scale" image, what makes up the largest part of the Earth: the core, the mantle, or the crust?

**The mantle makes up the largest part.**

9. The Earth is 8,000 miles in diameter. If you made a scale drawing with a scale of 1 inch to 2,000 miles, how big would the drawing be?

**4 inches in diameter**

10. How might you interpret what the drawing shows about the Earth's core?

**Possible answer: The core is the innermost part of the Earth, and it's made of solid and liquid matter.**

© Pearson Education, Inc., 5

**School + Home**

**Home Activity** Your child learned how to locate and interpret a scale drawing. With your child, create a scale drawing of your home using a size ratio of 1 inch equaling 2 feet (this should fit on a standard piece of paper).

# Latin Roots

**Proofread an Article** Circle six spelling errors in the article. Write the words correctly. Find a punctuation error and write the sentence correctly.

## Library News

Police spent all morning in the ancient manuscript department of our library. They left about an hour later, shaking their heads, barely able to (discribe) what happened. During the morning inspection, I found the suspect about to (scribbel) his name (apon) the cover of a rare manuscript. I gasped. Surprised by the (interuption) the suspect turned abruptly. I grabbed him by the collar and proceeded to eject him from the premises. During police questioning, the suspect revealed his plans for a (spectacilar) project. He intended to (enscribe) his name on all 600 volumes of ancient and rare manuscripts. Luckily, I was able to stop that from happening.

1. **describe**
2. **scribble**
3. **upon**
4. **interruption**
5. **spectacular**
6. **inscribe**
7. **Surprised by the interruption, the suspect turned abruptly.**

**Proofread Words** Circle the correct spelling of each word.

8. bankupt    (bankrupt)    bankrup
9. (injection)    enjection    injekshun
10. aruption    erubtion    (eruption)
11. respectfull    (respectful)    rispectful
12. (preescribe)    preescribe    preskribe
13. subsription    (subscription)    subscreption
14. rejekt    rejict    (reject)
15. rupshure    repture    (rupture)
16. (aspect)    espekt    aspict

### Spelling Words

describe
interruption
inspection
scribble
respectful
bankrupt
project
injection
manuscript
suspect

subscription
spectacular
eruption
eject
abruptly
prescribe
reject
aspect
rupture
inscribe

### Frequently Misspelled Words

into
upon

**School + Home**    **Home Activity** Your child identified misspelled list words. Ask your child to say five list words, tell the Latin root for each, and then spell and define each word.

© Pearson Education, Inc., 5

## Comparative and Superlative Adjectives

**Directions** Read the passage. Then read each question. Circle the letter of the correct answer.

# Uncovering Dinosaurs

(1) Most dinosaurs were (big) than today's reptiles. (2) Although he was not the (large), the *Tyrannosaurus rex* was the (scary) dinosaur of them all. (3) Scientists today have a _____ idea of what dinosaurs looked like than they used to. (4) Sue is the largest *T. rex* ever found. (5) She stands in the Field Museum, one of the country's _____ museums. (6) Their collection of dinosaurs is exquisite. (7) Most dinosaurs at the Field Museum are much (small) than *T. rex* and much (frightening)!

**1** Which form of the word in parentheses best completes sentence 1?

  **A** big

  **B** bigger

  **C** biggest

  **D** more big

**2** Which forms of the words in parentheses best completes sentence 2?

  **A** larger/scarier

  **B** larger/scariest

  **C** largest/scary

  **D** largest/scariest

**3** Which word best completes sentence 3?

  **A** good

  **B** better

  **C** best

  **D** great

**4** Which superlative adjective would not be used to complete sentence 5?

  **A** finest

  **B** dirtiest

  **C** best known

  **D** most respected

**5** Sentence 7 could best be replaced with which sentence?

  **A** Most dinosaurs at the Field Museum are much smaller than *T. rex* and much less frightening!

  **B** Most dinosaurs at the Field Museum are much more smaller than *T. rex* and much less frightening!

  **C** Most dinosaurs at the Field Museum are much small than *T. rex* and much less frightening!

  **D** Most dinosaurs at the Field Museum are much more small than *T. rex* and much less frightening!

© Pearson Education, Inc., 5

**Home Activity** Your child prepared for taking tests on comparative and superlative adjectives. Ask your child to use the correct adjective forms on this page in sentences to compare sets of two objects, then sets of three objects.

# Generalize

- To **generalize** means to make a broad statement or rule that applies to several examples. Clue words such as *all, many,* and *most* can signal generalizations.

- If generalizations are supported by the text, they are *valid generalizations.* If they are not supported by the text or by logic, they are *faulty generalizations.*

**Directions** Read the following passage. Then complete the diagram below by writing a valid generalization and two ideas that support your generalization.

President Thomas Jefferson led an effort to make the Louisiana Purchase in 1803. The United States bought an 828,000-square-mile stretch of land west of the Mississippi River from France for a mere three cents per acre. The Louisiana Purchase is widely considered to be the greatest land bargain in American history.

Jefferson asked Lewis and Clark to explore the territory. For more than two years they investigated the land along the Missouri River seeking a route to the Pacific Ocean. They were greeted as heroes when they returned to St. Louis in 1806. President Jefferson was pleased, as he had doubled the size of the United States. You might say that he got the deal of the century!

**Possible answers given.**

**Generalization**

1. **The Louisiana Purchase was the greatest land bargain in American history.**

**Support from Text**

2. **Land only cost three cents per acre.**

**Support from Text**

3. **The U.S. bought 828,000 square miles of land.**

**Support from Text**

The Louisiana Purchase doubled the size of the United States.

4. In box #1, what word suggests the statement is a generalization?

**The word *greatest* suggests that it is a generalization.**

5. Would you say this generalization is valid or faulty? Why?

**valid; The statistics and facts support the generalization.**

**Home Activity** Your child made and supported a generalization about a nonfiction text. Choose a familiar generalization from everyday life, and discuss with your child whether or not it is valid.

# Writing · Summary

### Key Features of a Summary

- uses the writer's own words
- restates the most important facts and details
- leaves out unimportant details

## Summary of "Going West"

During the 1800s, the Homestead Act caused many people to pack up their belongings and move to a place they had never seen before. Under the Homestead Act, the government freely gave away 160 acres of land to anyone who would build a house on it, dig a well, farm it, and live on it for five years.

The journey west could be extremely difficult for these pioneers. Their lives were certainly not easy. But if they made it through all the hardships, they had something to show for it in the end—the American Dream!

**1.** Which sentence expresses the main idea?

**During the 1800s, the Homestead Act caused many people to pack up their belongings and move to a place they had never seen before.**

**2.** Circle an important detail the writer included in the summary.

# Vocabulary

**Directions** Draw a line to connect each word on the left with its definition on the right.

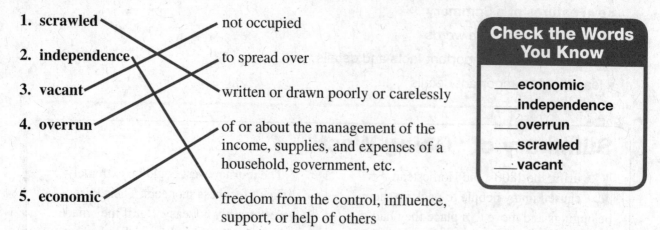

1. scrawled

2. independence

3. vacant

4. overrun

5. economic

not occupied

to spread over

written or drawn poorly or carelessly

of or about the management of the income, supplies, and expenses of a household, government, etc.

freedom from the control, influence, support, or help of others

**Directions** Choose the word from the box that best completes the sentences below. Write the word on the line.

6. You can find evidence of the Old West in the run-down, **vacant**_____

old buildings that stand like ghosts in Colorado. **7.** At one time these booming towns were

**overrun**_____ with prospectors. **8.** The prospectors had come in search of gold

and **economic**_____ freedom. **9.** **Scrawled**_____ on old walls and

doors are the names and dates of particularly wealthy gold rushers. **10.** Unfortunately, their

financial success and **independence**_____, or freedom, was short-lived, as the gold

boom busted within a few years.

## Write an Advertisement

On a separate sheet of paper, write an advertisement for a new theme park celebrating the Old West. Your advertisement should describe some appealing exhibits and activities, as well as noting details that reflect ways of life in the Old West. Try to use as many vocabulary words as possible.

**Advertisements should include words from the vocabulary list, as well as describe the park's features and note details that show elements of life in the Old West.**

© Pearson Education, Inc., 5

**Home Activity** Your child identified and used vocabulary words from the story *Ghost Towns of the American West*. Together, make up a story about a relative who lived in the Old West.

# Adverbs

**Adverbs** tell more about verbs. They explain *how, when,* or *where* actions happen. Many adverbs that tell *how* end in *-ly*. Adverbs can appear before or after the verbs they describe.

**How**     Cowboys rode expertly. They worked hard.
**When**    They seldom slept past daybreak. They always took care of their horses.
**Where**   A cowtown existed here. Cowboys visited there for entertainment.

Some adverbs tell more about an adjective or another adverb:

A ghost town seems rather spooky to me. I very rarely go to such places.

**Comparative adverbs** compare two actions. Add *-er* to form a comparative adverb. **Superlative adverbs** compare three or more actions. Add *-est* to form a superlative adverb. If an adverb ends in *-ly*, use *more* or *most* instead of *-er* or *-est*.

**Comparative Adverb**    The stagecoach rolled more slowly going up the mountain than going down.
**Superlative Adverb**    When they were fresh, the horses pulled most quickly of all.

• The adverbs *well* and *badly* use special forms to show comparison.

| Adverb | Comparative | Superlative |
|--------|-------------|-------------|
| well   | better      | best        |
| badly  | worse       | worst       |

**Directions** Underline the adverb or adverbs in each sentence. Circle the word that each adverb tells more about.

1. Pioneer women bravely (risked) their lives.

2. They (worked) tirelessly to feed and clothe their families.

3. They seldom (shopped) at a store.

4. They were often (lonely) in their isolated homes.

5. They (toiled) outdoors in gardens and indoors at wood stoves.

**Directions** Underline the correct adverb in ( ) to complete each sentence.

6. We can point (proudly, more proudly) at the staying power of pioneers.

7. They lived with hardship (better, more better) than I would have.

8. If crops failed, they faced a (terrible, terribly) hard winter.

9. Towns needed railroads (more desperately, most desperately) than they needed settlers.

10. Railroads connected settlers (direct, directly) to supplies and goods.

**Home Activity** Your child learned about adverbs. Ask your child to expand these sentences using adverbs to tell how, when, and where: *Settlers traveled. They built homes and towns. They raised food.*

© Pearson Education, Inc., 5

# Greek Word Parts

| Spelling Words | | | | |
|---|---|---|---|---|
| telephone | graphic | thermometer | photographer | centimeter |
| paragraph | telescope | diameter | photocopy | speedometer |
| telegraph | millimeter | autograph | television | barometer |
| telecommute | pedometer | phonograph | kilometer | telephoto |

**Classifying** Write the list word that best fits each group.

1. circle, radius, circumference, **diameter**

2. microscope, binoculars, **telescope**

3. letters, words, sentences, **paragraph**

4. tape cassette, compact disc, mp3 player, **phonograph**

5. air pressure, weather, instrument, **barometer**

6. instrument, measure, speed, **speedometer**

7. communicate, wire, electric, **telegraph**

8. call, dial, talk, **telephone**

9. camera, pictures, person, **photographer**

10. mile, furlong, fathom, **kilometer**

**Definitions** Write the list word that has the same meaning.

11. one hundredth of a meter

12. a person's own signature

13. a photographic copy of written or printed work

14. instrument for measuring temperature

15. electronic device that shows images on a screen

16. instrument for measuring distance walked

17. one thousandth of a meter

18. to work at a location remote from one's place of employment, making use of a computer

19. a lens that makes distant objects appear magnified

20. a picture, design, or visual display

11. **centimeter**

12. **autograph**

13. **photocopy**

14. **thermometer**

15. **television**

16. **pedometer**

17. **millimeter**

18. **telecommute**

19. **telephoto**

20. **graphic**

© Pearson Education, Inc., 5

**Home Activity** Your child wrote related words that are spelled similarly but pronounced differently. Say list words and have your child say and spell the list word that is related.

# Outline Form A

**Title** _____

**A.** _____

    1. _____

    2. _____

    3. _____

**B.** _____

    1. _____

    2. _____

    3. _____

**C.** _____

    1. _____

    2. _____

    3. _____

# Vocabulary • Prefixes

- A **prefix** is a word part added at the beginning of a base word that has a meaning of its own.
- Prefixes do not stand alone in sentences. They usually have their own definitions listed in dictionaries, as well as their own origins, such as the Greek or Latin languages.
- Sometimes you can use prefixes to figure out the meaning of an unfamiliar word. For example, one meaning of the prefix *over-* is "too much." An *overheated* engine is too hot. The prefix *in-* can mean "not." An *informal* party is not formal.

**Directions** Read the following passage. Then answer the questions below. Look for prefixes in words to help determine their meanings.

Independence is something that many people strive to attain. In fact, the United States of America was established in response to such an idea. You might say the founders of our nation were overrun with ideas of freedom and independence.

They believed that any form of government that limited freedom was invalid. The patriots' ability to overpower the stronger and more experienced British army illustrates how strong this urge to be free really was.

1. If *independence* means "freedom from the control, influence, support, or help of others," what does its base word mean and why? Use a dictionary to help you.

**"needing the support of others"; The prefix means "not."**

2. What word uses the prefix *over-*? How does this prefix change the meaning of its base word?

**_overrun;_ The prefix changes "run" to "running too much."**

3. If *invalid* means "not acceptable under the law," what does its base word mean and why?

**"acceptable under the law"; Since the prefix means "not,"**

**without the prefix you have only the meaning of the base word.**

4. What do you think might be the definition of *overpower*? Why? Use a dictionary to help you.

**"to conquer by greater strength"; The base word _power_ means**

**"strength," and the prefix _over-_ means "too much."**

5. What prefix could you add to the word *experienced* to describe the colonial army? How would the prefix change the meaning of the base word?

**Adding the prefix _in-_ would make the word _inexperienced;_ The**

**prefix reverses the meaning of the base word.**

**Home Activity** Your child identified prefixes as a way of understanding the meanings of words. Together, try to make a rhyming song featuring base words with different prefixes. For example, the base word *view* could be used to make the rhyming words *review* and *preview*, and the base word *done* could be used to create the rhyming pair *overdone* and *underdone*.

© Pearson Education, Inc., 5

Name_____

# Outline

- An **outline** is a good way to organize information that you find in an article, report, or other nonfiction text. Creating an outline can help you better understand a text. It can also help you focus your own thoughts before you write something of your own.
- An outline includes a title, main topics, subtopics, and details.

**Directions** Read the following outline. Then answer the questions below.

### The Gold Rush

I.  Traveling West
    A. Searching for new lands
    B. Meeting the natives
        1. Establishing friendships
        2. Conflicts arise
    C. The California coast
        1. New settlements
        2. Towns are established

II.  The Rush for Gold
    A. They came in droves
        1. Prospectors
        2. Easterners flock to new towns
    B. The newly rich
    C. An overnight economy
        1. Merchants and merrymakers
        2. Banking and loan sharks
        3. Golden staircases

**1.** What are the two main topics of this outline?

**"Traveling West," "The Rush for Gold"**

**2.** Under the first subtopic of "The Rush for Gold," what details are listed?

**"Prospectors," "Easterners flock to new towns"**

**3.** Which subtopic describes dealings with Native Americans?

**"I.B., Meeting the natives"**

**4.** Which is the first subtopic to contain information about people striking it rich during the Gold Rush?

**"II.B., The newly rich"**

**5.** How can an outline help you plan a report?

**Possible answer: An outline can help you organize information so that you can present it in a clear, reasonable way.**

# Research and Study Skills

**Directions** Read the following passage. Then complete the outline below.

### Purchase of the Louisiana Territory

The Louisiana Territory covered 828,000 square miles of North America west of the Mississippi River.

**A Spanish Territory** With Spain's permission, Americans used the Mississippi and Missouri Rivers, and the port of New Orleans for trade. However, President Jefferson believed that the United States should control both waterways.

**French Acquisition** France's leader, Napoleon, also wanted more control in North America. In April 1802, Jefferson wrote a letter to the U.S. Minister to France. He discussed his interest in obtaining the territory around New Orleans. In October 1802, France acquired the territory from Spain. Americans were angered, and a conflict between the U.S. and France seemed unavoidable.

**The U.S. Purchase** In spring 1803, President Jefferson sent James Monroe to France to purchase the area around the mouth of the Mississippi, including New Orleans. When Monroe arrived, he found France in an uneasy position. Disease had weakened the French army. Moreover, French officials were worried that Britain would soon declare war on them. Napoleon was convinced that he should forget about establishing French power in North America. For these reasons, James Monroe made a deal with Napoleon to purchase the Louisiana Territory by the end of 1803. The size of the United States was doubled in a day.

## Possible answers given.
Purchase of the Louisiana Territory

I. **Spain Controls Louisiana Territory**

  A. Spain allows U.S. to use Mississippi River, port of New Orleans for trade

  B. President Jefferson wants control of Mississippi and New Orleans

  C. **Napoleon wants control of Louisiana Territory**

II. France Acquires Louisiana Territory from Spain

III. United States and France at Bargaining Table

  A. **U.S. wishes to buy New Orleans and mouth of Mississippi**

  B. **France lets go of plan to control mid-North America**

    1. French army weakened by disease

    2. Napoleon fearing war with Britain

  C. **U.S. purchases Louisiana Territory from France**

**Home Activity** Your child answered questions about outlines and completed an outline, using information from a nonfiction article. Together, make an outline that organizes your family's daily activities. Try to break down the day into main sections, subtopics, and important details.

Name _____

# Greek Word Parts

**Proofread an Article** Circle six spelling errors in the article. Write the words correctly. Find a punctuation error and write the sentence correctly.

### From Feet to Kilometers

Each time your feet hit the pavement, your body vibrates. A (pedimeter) senses these vibrations and moves a counter forward, counting the total number of steps. Then (it's) computer changes the number of steps into miles or meters. A bicycle odometer does something similar. It counts the number of times a wheel goes around. A computer uses the (dimeter) of the wheel to compute the distance traveled, changing (centameters) to meters. Rather than counting wheel revolutions, automobile odometers count the number of turns made by the car's transmission gears. A computer changes the (milimeters) the gears move to the kilometers the automobile moves. Can you guess how a (speedameter) works.

**Spelling Words**

telephone
graphic
thermometer
photographer
centimeter
paragraph
telescope
diameter
photocopy
speedometer

telegraph
millimeter
autograph
television
barometer
telecommute
pedometer
phonograph
kilometer
telephoto

1. **pedometer**
2. **its**
3. **diameter**
4. **centimeters**
5. **millimeters**
6. **speedometer**
7. **Can you guess how a speedometer works?**

**Proofread Words** Circle the correct spelling of each word.

8. telecomute    telacommute    (telecommute)
9. photacopy    (photocopy)    photocoppy
10. (telescope)    telascope    teliscope
11. grafic    graphik    (graphic)
12. thermameter    (thermometer)    thermemeter
13. (photographer)    photagrapher    photographor
14. baramater    barimeter    (barometer)

**Frequently Misspelled Words**

I'm
it's
let's

 **School + Home** **Home Activity** Your child identified misspelled words. Ask your child to spell four words, each with a different Greek word part, and tell you what the words mean.

## Adverbs

**Directions** Read the passage. Then read each question. Circle the letter of the correct answer.

# Gold Rush

(1) In 1848, James Marshall discovered gold in northern California. (2) Although Marshall quietly tried to keep his discovery secret, word <u>eventually</u> spread to San Francisco and other western towns. (3) Gold was free to anyone who could find it, so people went <u>hurriedly</u> to California seeking riches. (4) Mining towns were hastily built to house the miners and families who emigrated west. (5) While some miners found wealth, others fought _____ over the gold. (6) Some mining towns died <u>more suddenly</u> than others as the mines were gradually spent. (7) San Francisco watched its population grow rapidly, and it became the <u>most important</u> city in the west.

**1** Which question is answered by the underlined adverb in sentence 2?

   (**A**)  How?

   **B**  When?

   **C**  Where?

   **D**  None of the above

**2** The underlined word in sentence 3 tells about which word?

   **A**  Gold

   **B**  free

   **C**  people

   (**D**)  went

**3** Which adverb best completes sentence 5?

   **A**  most greedy

   **B**  more greedy

   (**C**)  greedily

   **D**  greediest

**4** Which best describes the underlined adverb in sentence 6?

   (**A**)  Comparative adverb

   **B**  Superlative adverb

   **C**  Incorrect adverb

   **D**  Not an adverb

**5** Which best describes the underlined adverb in sentence 7?

   **A**  Comparative adverb

   **B**  Superlative adverb

   **C**  Incorrect adverb

   (**D**)  Not an adverb

**Home Activity** Your child prepared for taking tests on adverbs. Have your child read a favorite story aloud, point out the adverbs, and tell what words they describe. Encourage your child to add adverbs to the story.

# Multisyllabic Words

| Spelling Words | | | | |
| --- | --- | --- | --- | --- |
| elementary | opportunity | elevator | mosaic | cylinder |
| vehicle | substitute | Pennsylvania | tuxedo | intermediate |
| miniature | variety | ravioli | meteorite | centennial |
| probability | literature | cafeteria | fascination | curiosity |

**Analogies** Write the list word that completes each comparison.

1. Store is to shop as lunchroom is to **cafeteria**_____.

2. Poodle is to dog as poem is to **literature**_____.

3. Building block is to cube as tin can is to **cylinder**_____.

4. Huge is to giant as tiny is to **miniature**_____.

5. Chicago is to Illinois as Philadelphia is to **Pennsylvania**.

6. Silk is to fabric as car is to **vehicle**_____.

7. Apple is to fruit as **ravioli**_____ is to pasta.

8. Pleasant is to nice as basic is to **elementary**_____.

9. Casual is to jeans as formal is to **tuxedo**_____.

10. Beginning is to elementary as middle is to **intermediate**_____.

**Alphabetize** Write the ten list words below in alphabetical order.

| | |
| --- | --- |
| meteorite | elevator |
| curiosity | opportunity |
| probability | substitute |
| fascination | centennial |
| mosaic | variety |

11. **centennial**_____

12. **curiosity**_____

13. **elevator**_____

14. **fascination**_____

15. **meteorite**_____

16. **mosaic**_____

17. **opportunity**_____

18. **probability**_____

19. **substitute**_____

20. **variety**_____

**Home Activity** Your child has completed analogies for multisyllabic words. Take turns making up analogies for list words and completing them.

# Contractions and Negatives

**Directions** Write the words used to form the contractions.

1. wouldn't <u>**would not**</u>

2. she'll <u>**she will**</u>

3. he's <u>**he is** *or* **he has**</u>

4. we're <u>**we are**</u>

5. isn't <u>**is not**</u>

6. can't <u>**cannot**</u>

**Directions** Write the contraction for each pair of words.

7. will + not <u>**won't**</u>

8. I + am <u>**I'm**</u>

9. he + had <u>**he'd**</u>

10. you + are <u>**you're**</u>

**Directions** Write the contraction for the underlined words.

11. What is the craziest project <u>you have</u> ever done?    <u>**you've**</u>

12. Ashley says <u>she has</u> started a zoo.    <u>**she's**</u>

13. <u>She had</u> collected a turtle, a mouse, and a snake.    <u>**She'd**</u>

14. Ashley says <u>she will</u> make another zoo in the future.    <u>**she'll**</u>

**Directions** Circle the word in ( ) that correctly completes each sentence.

15. My friend and I aren't (ever, never) without a new plan.

16. We don't ever do (anything, nothing) without our parents' permission.

17. They wouldn't (ever, never) let us do anything dangerous.

18. We don't want (anybody, nobody) to get hurt.

# Related Words

| Spelling Words | | | | |
|---|---|---|---|---|
| music | musician | select | selection | sign |
| signal | part | partial | haste | hasten |
| protect | protection | magic | magician | resign |
| resignation | electric | electrician | condemn | condemnation |

**Analogies** Write the word that completes each sentence.

1. Pieces are to puzzle as notes are to **music**.
2. Postpone is to delay as speed up is to **hasten**.
3. Pipes are to plumber as lights are to **electrician**.
4. Complete is to undone as whole is to **partial**.
5. Food is to nourishment as defense is to **protection**.
6. Sign up is to enroll as drop out is to **resign**.
7. Approve is to disapprove as praise is to **condemn**.
8. Route is to path as choice is to **selection**.
9. Smart is to intelligent as symbol is to **sign**.
10. Drill is to carpenter as wand is to **magician**.

**Word Clues** Write the list word that fits each clue.

11. a strong statement of disapproval    **condemnation**
12. a person who plays music    **musician**
13. to choose    **select**
14. a portion    **part**
15. tricks and illusions    **magic**
16. an action or gesture to communicate    **signal**
17. great speed    **haste**
18. watch over    **protect**
19. full of electricity    **electric**
20. a formal letter that you're leaving    **resignation**

**School + Home** **Home Activity** Your child has learned to spell related words. To practice at home, make up clues about related words and ask your child to spell the words.

Name _____

# Adjectives and Articles

**Directions** Underline the articles and circle the adjectives in each sentence.

1. A few brave adventurers are searching for shipwrecks.

2. They dive deep beneath the surface in search of an exciting find.

3. One group of divers found the treasure of a Spanish galleon.

4. The jewels, coins, and other artifacts are priceless.

5. Five hundred years ago, these ships sailed from Mexico loaded with silver and gold.

**Directions** Write *what kind, how many,* or *which one* to tell what question each underlined adjective answers about a noun.

6. That sunken ship is scary.  **which one**

7. All tour boats pass by it.  **how many**

8. The captain explains its tragic wreck.  **what kind**

9. A million tourists have seen it.  **how many**

10. Some sad songs have been written about it.  **what kind**

11. This song tells about a sailor's wife.  **which one**

12. She looked for her husband for ten years.  **how many**

**Directions** Write *a, an,* or *the* to complete each sentence. Choose the article that makes sense and follows the rules for articles.

13. Have you ever found _____ **a** _____ real treasure?

14. Once I found _____ **an** _____ old box.

15. It was buried in _____ **the** _____ bushes behind my house.

16. Inside _____ **the** _____ box were some rocks.

17. It was _____ **a** _____ disappointing moment.

18. Later, I found out _____ **the** _____ rocks were valuable.

19. One rock was _____ **a** _____ rare geode.

20. It was _____ **an** _____ amazing experience.

**374** Conventions

# Greek Word Parts

| **Spelling Words** | | | | |
|---|---|---|---|---|
| artist | tourism | biology | phobia | heroism |
| geology | cartoonist | technology | journalism | hydrophobia |
| violinist | ecology | patriotism | vocalist | meteorology |
| zoology | claustrophobia | capitalism | novelist | technophobia |

**Words in Context** Write the list words that complete each sentence.

The School of the Arts is the best if you want to be an **(1)** _____ and paint or a
**(2)** _____ and write.

1. __artist__                    2. __novelist__

The soldiers in the platoon showed great courage, **(3)** _____, and **(4)** _____.

3. __patriotism__              4. __heroism__

Rafael studies environmental science, or **(5)** _____; he wants to use engineering science, or
**(6)** _____, to improve the environment.

5. __ecology__                 6. __technology__

The **(7)** _____ titled his humorous drawing about the market economy, "**(8)** _____ at Work."

7. __cartoonist__              8. __Capitalist__

The **(9)** _____ students presented a news program about **(10)** _____, the fear of small,
enclosed spaces.

9. __journalism__             10. __claustrophobia__

Azir studied all living things, or **(11)** _____, before he decided to major in **(12)** _____, the
study of animals.

11. __biology__               12. __zoology__

Earth science courses include **(13)** _____, the study of rocks, and **(14)** _____ the study of
weather and climate.

13. __geology__               14. __meteorology__

**Synonyms** Write the list word that has the same, or nearly the same, meaning.

15. violin player __violinist__          16. recreational travel __tourism__

17. singer __vocalist__                  18. fear of technology __technophobia__

19. strong fear __phobia__               20. fear of water __hydrophobia__

**Home Activity** Your child has learned to spell words with Greek word parts. Ask your child to organize
the list words into groups according to word parts and tell what each word part means.

Name _____

# This, That, These, and Those

**Directions** Write *this*, *that*, *these*, or *those* to describe each object.

1. a book in your hands    **this** _____ book

2. a store a mile away    **that** _____ store

3. dogs in a neighbor's yard    **those** _____ dogs

4. shoes on your feet    **these** _____ shoes

**Directions** Underline the word in ( ) that completes each sentence correctly.

5. (That there, <u>That</u>) constellation is called Orion.

6. (<u>This</u>, This here) observatory will give us a good view.

7. (Them, <u>Those</u>) astronauts who have gone into space have not reached the stars.

8. (<u>These</u>, Them) articles tell about their trips to the moon.

9. I have reached (<u>this</u>, those) conclusion: Astronauts must be brave.

10. Can someone tell me if (this, <u>these</u>) facts are accurate?

**Directions** Write each sentence correctly.

11. That there telescope is called the Hubble Telescope.

**That telescope is called the Hubble Telescope.**
_____

12. These here photographs I'm showing you were made by that telescope.

**These photographs I'm showing you were made by that telescope.**

13. Can you believe that this here photograph shows the birth of a galaxy?

**Can you believe that this photograph shows the birth of a galaxy?**

14. A telescope on Earth could not take them photographs.

**A telescope on Earth could not take these photographs.**

# Latin Roots

| Spelling Words | | | | |
| --- | --- | --- | --- | --- |
| describe | interruption | inspection | scribble | respectful |
| bankrupt | project | injection | manuscript | suspect |
| subscription | spectacular | eruption | eject | abruptly |
| prescribe | reject | aspect | rupture | inscribe |

**Classifying** Write the list word that belongs in each group.

1. book, pamphlet, brochure, **manuscript**
2. shot, vaccine, inoculation, **injection**
3. draw, write, doodle, **scribble**
4. write, etch, chisel, **inscribe**
5. tear, void, break, **rupture**
6. break, gap, discontinuity, **interruption**
7. ejection, geyser, outburst, **eruption**
8. appearance, part, perspective, **aspect**
9. review, survey, examination, **inspection**
10. magazines, monthly, newspapers, **subscription**

**Synonyms** Write the list word that has the same, or nearly the same, meaning.

11. turn down **reject**
12. distrust **suspect**
13. suddenly **abruptly**
14. broke **bankrupt**
15. dictate **prescribe**
16. task **project**
17. throw out **eject**
18. tell details **describe**
19. courteous **respectful**
20. wonderful **spectacular**

**Home Activity** Your child has learned to spell words with Latin roots. Take turns brainstorming a word that has one of the list word roots. Look up each word in the dictionary to confirm it comes from a Latin word.

# Comparative and Superlative Adjectives

**Directions** Complete the table. Add *-er, -est, more,* or *most* as needed.

| Adjective | Comparative | Superlative |
|---|---|---|
| fierce | 1. **fiercer** | 2. **fiercest** |
| small | 3. **smaller** | 4. **smallest** |
| ridiculous | 5. **more ridiculous** | 6. **most ridiculous** |
| icy | 7. **icier** | 8. **iciest** |
| hot | 9. **hotter** | 10. **hottest** |

**Directions** Underline the adjective form in ( ) to complete each sentence correctly.

**11.** Which dinosaur was the (stronger, strongest) of all?

**12.** *Triceratops* had a (more dangerous, most dangerous) horn and tail than *Tyrannosaurus.*

**13.** However, *Tyrannosaurus* probably had the (greater, greatest) speed and strength of all the dinosaurs.

**14.** Bill has a (larger, largest) collection of dinosaur figures than I do.

**15.** He has the (more complete, most complete) collection of anyone I know.

**Directions** Write the correct forms of the adjectives in ( ) to complete the sentences.

**16.** Do you think description is ___**more important**___ than plot in a story? (important)

**17.** I think stories with good characters are ___**more memorable**___ than stories with good plots. (memorable)

**18.** The ___**most interesting**___ characters of all are the villains. (interesting)

**19.** A ___**longer**___ book may not be better than a shorter one. (long)

**20.** The ___**best**___ books of all are the ones that make you think. (good)

# Greek Word Parts

| Spelling Words | | | | |
|---|---|---|---|---|
| telephone | graphic | thermometer | photographer | centimeter |
| paragraph | telescope | diameter | photocopy | speedometer |
| telegraph | millimeter | autograph | television | barometer |
| telecommute | pedometer | phonograph | kilometer | telephoto |

**Words in Context** Write the list words that complete each sentence.

A (1) _____ lens magnifies distant objects; a (2) _____ also magnifies distant objects.

1. **telephoto**

2. **telescope**

A (3) _____ keeps track of the distance walked; a (4) _____ keeps track of a vehicle's speed.

3. **pedometer**

4. **speedometer**

A (5) _____ and a land line (6) _____ both carry communication over wires.

5. **telegraph**

6. **telephone**

A (7) _____ and a (8) _____ are each smaller than an inch.

7. **millimeter**

8. **centimeter**

You can use a (9) _____ and a (10) _____ to learn about the weather.

9. **thermometer**

10. **barometer**

**Word Definitions** Write the list word that matches the definition.

11. a group of sentences developing a single idea

12. record player

13. picture or other visual representation

14. a copy made with a photocopier

15. twice the length of a circle's radius

16. a person's own signature

17. one thousand meters

18. person who takes photographs

19. work from home using computers, and other electronic devices

20. a device that shows images on a screen

11. **paragraph**

12. **phonograph**

13. **graphic**

14. **photocopy**

15. **diameter**

16. **autograph**

17. **kilometer**

18. **photographer**

19. **telecommute**

20. **television**

**Home Activity** Your child has learned to spell words with Greek word parts. Ask your child to organize the list words into groups according to word parts and tell what each word part means.

# Adverbs

**Directions** Write the comparative and superlative forms of each adverb.

| Adverb | Comparative | Superlative |
|--------|-------------|-------------|
| sadly | 1. __more sadly__ | 2. __most sadly__ |
| wildly | 3. __more wildly__ | 4. __most wildly__ |
| late | 5. __later__ | 6. __latest__ |
| well | 7. __better__ | 8. __best__ |

**Directions** Underline the adverb in each sentence. Circle the word or words that each adverb tells more about.

9. Settlers (waited) impatiently for the mail.

10. Mail (traveled) slowly by stagecoach.

11. The Pony Express was a very (welcome) change.

12. Riders on horseback (raced) westward day and night.

13. The mail (had) never (moved) faster.

14. Soon railroads (replaced) the Pony Express.

**Directions** Underline the correct word in ( ) to complete each sentence.

15. The Pony Express moved the mail (most quickly, more quickly) than stagecoaches did.

16. The daring riders (certain, certainly) appealed to the public.

17. Of all western heroes, these young men lived (more dangerously, most dangerously).

18. The Pony Express worked (better, best) for some than for others.

19. It cost more to send a letter than most people could (possible, possibly) afford.

20. Today, airplanes serve the public (better, best) of all.

# Persuasive Essay Chart

**Directions** Fill in the graphic organizer with ideas for the introduction, supporting reasons, and conclusion in your persuasive essay. **Answers will vary.**

**Introduction: State your position or thesis**

↓

**First reason**

↓

**Second reason**

↓

**Third reason (most important)**

↓

**Conclusion**

# Persuasive Words

**Directions** Add a persuasive word from the box or a word of your own to each sentence. Rewrite the sentence. **Possible answers:**

| Persuasive Words | | | | |
|---|---|---|---|---|
| better | worse | should | never | most important |
| best | worst | must | necessary | effective |

1. A camping trip in the Alaskan wilderness is the _____ excursion for our class.

**A survival trip to the Alaskan wilderness is the best excursion for our class.**

2. It is _____ to set up camp away from any bear habitats.

**It is most important to set up camp away from any bear habitats.**

3. Plenty of protective gear is _____ for survival.

**Plenty of protective gear is necessary for survival.**

4. While camping in Alaska, we'll learn that teamwork is _____ than working alone.

**While camping in Alaska, we'll learn that teamwork is better than working alone.**

5. You _____ experience the wide-open spaces on our adventure in Alaska.

**You must experience the wide-open spaces on our adventure in Alaska.**

© Pearson Education, Inc., 5

# Adding, Deleting, or Rearranging Sentences

**Directions** Revise this paragraph by adding, deleting, or rearranging sentences as instructed below.

---

(1) Scores of people attempt to climb Mount Everest each year. (2) Many dangers are involved in climbing this mountain. (3) The air is very thin above 26,000 feet. (4) <u>The weather is extremely harsh on the top of the mountain. (5) Many climbers take bottled oxygen because of the thin air.</u> (6) The weather can also be unpredictable. (7) A huge blizzard can occur in a matter of minutes. (8) Finally, the mountain itself presents many dangers. (9) There are wide crevasses, or canyons, as well as moving ice blocks. (10) Many climbers have died on the mountain. (11) Another dangerous mountain is Mount Rainier in Washington. (12) Despite the dangers, Mount Everest is a popular destination for both professional and amateur climbers.

---

**1.** Write the number of the sentence that should be deleted. Tell why you think it should be deleted.

**11; The sentence does not stick to the main topic.**

**2.** Underline the two sentences that need to be rearranged. Write the sentences in the correct order.

**Many climbers take bottled oxygen because of the thin air. The weather is extremely harsh on the top of the mountain.**

**3.** Tell where you would add each fact below to the paragraph.

A. Some professional mountain climbers object to the use of oxygen, though.

**after sentence 5**

B. In 1996 alone, fifteen people died while climbing Mount Everest.

**after sentence 10**

C. At 29,029 feet, Everest is the highest mountain in the world.

**after sentence 1**

# Editing 3

**Directions** This is part of a persuasive essay. Edit the paragraph. Look for errors in spelling, grammar, and mechanics. Use proofreading marks to show the corrections.

| Proofreading Marks | |
|---|---|
| Delete (Take out) | ⌿ |
| Add | ∧ |
| Spelling | ⬭ |
| Uppercase letter | ≡ |
| Lowercase letter | / |

**performed**

Astronauts have (preformed) many exciting feats. Some astronauts have walked

on the moon. Others have lived in a space station for more than a year. These

**amazing**

(amazeing) adventures began in 1962 with a trip that seems simple today. In that

year an astronaut named John Glenn became the first american to orbit Earth. He
≡

was launched into space by a rocket and was soon orbiting Earth in his spacecraft,

**He was o**

*Friendship 7.* One of the first people in the world to see Earth from space. He
∧

**flew**

said, "It's a beautiful sight, looking eastward across the Atlantic." Soon he ~~flown~~
∧

**already**

over Perth Australia, where it was (allready) night. People in Perth had turned on
∧

their lights so Glenn could spot them from space. Glenn's spacecraft orbited Earth

three times the flight took about five hours. Then the spacecraft splashed down in
∧≡
⊙

**smoothly**

the Atlantic ocean. The first orbit of Earth went ~~smooth~~, paving the way for many
≡                                                    ∧

**journeys**

future space (journies)

Name_____

# Draw Conclusions

- Active readers **draw conclusions,** or make decisions, based on information in the text and their own knowledge.

- Examine your own conclusions as you read. Ask yourself, "Can I support them with information from the text or with facts I already know?"

**Directions** Read the following story. Then complete the diagram by writing a conclusion and listing details from the story that support your conclusion.

> On most summer weekends, Tina went to the beach with her aunt and younger cousins. She built sand castles with her cousins and watched the kids carefully as they toddled near the shore. If they waded into the water, Tina held their hands. She taught them to watch out for big waves, and she showed the older cousins how to swim. She also brought snacks for all the children to share. When it was time to go home, Tina carried the youngest cousins to keep their feet from burning on the sand. On the way home, she was already looking forward to the next day at the beach.

## Possible answers given.

**What Can I Conclude?**

1. Tina is a very caring and responsible cousin.

**What Does the Text Say?**

2. She watches the younger children carefully.

3. She plays with and teaches the children.

4. She brings the children snacks.

**What Do I Already Know?**

5. I already know that toddlers need to be watched carefully. I know also that beaches can be dangerous for young children.

**School + Home**

**Home Activity** Your child drew a conclusion based on the details of a passage. Together, read a story about children. Work with your child to draw one or more conclusions about a character or event, using the text and prior knowledge.

# Writing · Journal

(Sunday, June 5)

Dear Journal,

What a crazy week it has been! It all started last Saturday. You see, Dad has been planning a surprise party for Mom's birthday this year. Each member of the family had a task to do to help make the party happen. It was my job to ride my bike around the neighborhood and drop off the party invitations to people.

So last Saturday, I told Mom I was going to ride my bike to my friend Derek's house. I put all of the invitations in my backpack, so Mom had no clue what I was doing. Well, while I was out delivering invitations, Derek called my house and asked for me! I can't believe I forgot to let him in on the secret! Needless to say, Mom was furious at me when I got home. She wanted to know where I was and why I lied to her. Well, I couldn't tell her! I'd ruin the whole surprise party just to save myself from trouble. Mom grounded me for a week because I refused to answer her.

Her party was the next Saturday, and the surprise went off just perfectly. She cried when she saw everyone. When I walked up to her to say happy birthday, she hugged me and asked, "Did your lie last Saturday have to do with this party?" I told her I was out delivering invitations, but I couldn't tell her because I would have ruined everything. She felt so bad that I had been grounded the whole week over the misunderstanding. In fact, she said that I had earned a get-out-of-trouble-free card. She said the next time I get grounded, and there's something I really want to do, I can give her the card and not be grounded for the night. Even though I had to be grounded this past week, it was soooo worth it!

1. Circle the date written for this journal entry.

2. Summarize the main events and ideas told in this journal entry.

   **The writer got into trouble because he lied to his mom. The writer had to lie because he was planning a surprise party for his mom. In the end, the party went well and the writer's mom gave the writer a free pass for the next time he gets into trouble.**

3. Underline several words and phrases that show how journal entries are informal and personal.

Name_____

# Vocabulary

**Directions** Choose the word from the box that best matches each definition. Write the word on the line.

bizarre_____ **1.** strikingly odd in appearance or style

headline_____ **2.** the words printed in heavy type at the top of a newspaper article telling what it is about

vital_____ **3.** very important

breathtaking_____ **4.** thrilling; exciting

roost_____ **5.** to sit as birds do on a support; settle for the night

high-pitched_____ **6.** a high tone or sound

> **Check the Words You Know**
>
> ___ bizarre
> ___ breathtaking
> ___ headline
> ___ high-pitched
> ___ roost
> ___ vital

**Directions** Choose the word from the box that best completes each sentence. Write the word on the line to the left.

high-pitched_____ **7.** The baby's _____ squeal could be heard three rooms away.

vital_____ **8.** It is _____ that you get plenty of rest when you are sick.

headline_____ **9.** The morning's newspaper _____ was about the fire at McGill's Warehouse.

bizarre_____ **10.** Andre's costume was so _____ that no one knew exactly what it was supposed to be.

## Write a Journal Entry

On a separate sheet of paper, write about a bat or bird you have seen outdoors or in a book. Use as many vocabulary words as you can.

**Journal entries should use vocabulary words to describe bats or birds.**

**Home Activity** Your child identified and used vocabulary words from *The Truth About Austin's Amazing Bats*. With your child, write a story about an interesting animal native to your area. Use as many vocabulary words as you can.

# Modifiers

Adjectives, adverbs, and prepositional phrases are **modifiers**, words or groups of words that tell more about, or modify, other words in a sentence. Adjectives modify nouns and pronouns. Adverbs modify verbs, adjectives, or other adverbs. Prepositional phrases can act as adjectives or adverbs.

**As Adjective** The bats <u>over the river</u> are amazing.
**As Adverb** They swirl <u>above the bridge</u>.

To avoid confusion, place modifiers close to the words they modify. Adjective phrases usually come right after the word they modify. Adverb phrases may appear right after a verb or at the beginning of a sentence.

The meaning of a sentence can be unclear if the modifier is misplaced.

*No:* The bats flew by the girls <u>with sharply curved wings</u>.
*Yes:* The bats <u>with sharply curved wings</u> flew by the girls.

The position of *only* in a sentence can affect the sentence's entire meaning. Place *only* directly before the word or words it modifies.

*Example:* <u>Only</u> he watches the bats. (Nobody else watches them.)
He <u>only</u> watches the bats. (He doesn't do anything except watch.)
He watches <u>only</u> the bats. (He doesn't watch anything else.)

**Directions** Write *adverb, adjective,* or *prepositional phrase* to identify each underlined modifier. Write *adjective* or *adverb* to identify how a prepositional phrase is used.

1. Austin's bats roost <u>under a bridge</u>. **prepositional phrase—adverb**

2. The bats are attracted to <u>dark</u> crevices. **adjective**

3. At sunset, the bats appear <u>gradually</u> in the sky. **adverb**

**Directions** Each sentence has a misplaced modifier. Rewrite the sentence and put the phrase where it belongs.

4. A bat caught the boy's eye with fluttering wings.

**A bat with fluttering wings caught the boy's eye.**

5. He watched the bats as they multiplied with a smile. **Possible answers: He watched with a smile as the bats multiplied. With a smile, he watched the bats as they multiplied.**

**Home Activity** Your child learned about modifiers. With your child, read a newspaper article. Ask your child to identify several modifiers, including adjectives, adverbs, and prepositional phrases.

# Suffixes -ous, -sion, -ion, -ation

| Spelling Words | | | | |
|---|---|---|---|---|
| famous | invention | election | furious | imagination |
| education | nervous | explanation | various | decision |
| relaxation | conversation | tension | humorous | exhibition |
| attraction | invasion | creation | occupation | destination |

**Synonyms** Write the list word that has the same or almost the same meaning as the underlined word or phrase.

1. We will reach our <u>journey's end</u> after four days of traveling.

2. People who are <u>well known</u> are often stopped by fans on the street.

3. Sometimes it's very hard to make a <u>choice</u>.

4. I had a very long <u>talk</u> on the phone with my cousin.

5. The 5th graders had a special <u>art show</u> in the auditorium.

6. I felt <u>worried</u> and had butterflies in my stomach.

7. The army ants launched an <u>attack</u> at our picnic.

8. It takes a lot of <u>creative thoughts</u> to write a story.

9. What was your <u>excuse</u> for being late?

10. Who won that close <u>vote</u> last month?

1. **destination**
2. **famous**
3. **decision**
4. **conversation**
5. **exhibition**
6. **nervous**
7. **invasion**
8. **imagination**
9. **explanation**
10. **election**

**Definitions** Write the list word that fits each definition.

11. stretching or a strain

12. a thing that delights

13. something that is created

14. funny and amusing

15. knowledge and skills learned

16. differing from one another

17. condition of being relaxed

18. something made for the first time

19. what someone does to earn a living

20. full of wild, fierce anger

11. **tension**
12. **attraction**
13. **creation**
14. **humorous**
15. **education**
16. **various**
17. **relaxation**
18. **invention**
19. **occupation**
20. **furious**

 **School + Home** **Home Activity** Your child wrote words that have suffixes. Have your child underline the suffix in each word.

# Story Sequence C

Title_____

| Characters |
|---|
|  |

| Setting |
|---|
|  |

| Problem |
|---|
|  |

## Events

_____

_____

_____

_____

_____

_____

_____

_____

| Solution |
|---|
|  |

Name_____

# Vocabulary • Unknown Words

- If you cannot figure out the meaning of an unknown word through context clues or word structure, look up the word in a **dictionary** or **glossary.**

- Glossaries and dictionaries contain definitions of entry words. The entry words are arranged alphabetically. Use guide words at the top of each page to locate the word quickly.

**Directions** Read the following passage about a day at the beach. Then use your glossary or a dictionary to answer the questions below.

> Keiko lamented that she had never been to the beach. Deciding to give her a treat, her parents drove several hours with her to the shore. For the first time, she played in huge waves. She saw creatures of the sea, including jellyfish and sea urchins. She marveled at the green algae coating the rocks and the smooth driftwood at the shoreline. Her best surprise, though, was a tiny crab she found concealed under a shell. Keiko didn't want her day at the beach to end.

## Possible answers given for 1, 3, 5.

1. What is the definition of *lamented*? Use it in a sentence of your own.

   **_Lamented_ means "showed grief for someone or something." Todd lamented that he had hurt his mother's feelings.**

2. What kind of creature is a sea urchin? Which of these pairs of guide words—*scuttle* and *seal,* or *season* and *second*—is a likely place to find the entry word *sea urchin*?

   **Sea urchins are small sea animals with spiny shells. The entry word would be found with the guide words _season_ and _second_.**

3. What is the definition of *marveled*?

   **_Marveled_ means "felt wonder and astonishment."**

4. What is the definition and part of speech of the word *driftwood*?

   **_Driftwood_ is a noun meaning "wood carried along by water or washed ashore from the water."**

5. What does *concealed* mean in the passage? Put the definition in your own words.

   **_Concealed_ means "hidden."**

**Home Activity** Your child used a dictionary or glossary to find the meanings of unfamiliar words. Work with him or her to identify unfamiliar words in an article. Then ask your child to look up each new word in a dictionary or glossary. Confirm the meaning in the sentence together.

© Pearson Education, Inc., 5

# Follow and Clarify Directions

- Directions are instructions that are given in order, usually in numbered steps.
- Read through all the directions before you begin. Then **follow directions** by doing what is instructed, one step at a time.
- Try to visualize the end result of the directions. If you need to **clarify directions,** reread them, review them, or ask questions.

**Directions**  Use the following directions to answer the questions below.

**Rhythmic Breathing**

The following directions will help you learn rhythmic breathing for swimming.

1. Stand in water that is about chest deep.

2. Lean forward, and turn your face to one side so that your ear is underwater but your face is just above the water line.

3. Breathe in and hold your breath.

4. Turn your head so your face is down, and exhale slowly through your mouth.

5. Rotate your head back to the start position and inhale again.

6. Try performing this action to the right and to the left to see which is more comfortable.

7. Then repeat steps 3 through 5 over and over in a regular rhythm.

8. Practice until you can do steps 3 through 5 smoothly.

## Possible answers given for 4, 5.

**1.** What is the purpose of these directions?

**The purpose is to learn how to do rhythmic breathing.**

**2.** What is the first step in the directions? What is the last step?

**The first step is to stand in chest-deep water. The last step is to practice rhythmic breathing.**

**3.** To do rhythmic breathing, which steps must be repeated? Why?

**Steps 3 through 5 must be repeated to do the rhythmic breathing. The repetition allows for continuous breathing.**

**4.** Why must these steps be done in order?

**The steps must be done in order to inhale and exhale at the right times.**

**5.** Explain how you were able to visualize the directions. How were you able to clarify directions you didn't understand?

**I imagined each body motion as it was described. Rereading and reviewing also helped me understand the directions.**

© Pearson Education, Inc., 5

**Directions** Use the following directions to answer the questions below.

---

**Coral Reef Word Puzzle**

Follow these directions to complete the coral reef word puzzle.

1. Write down the letters of the word *seal,* the sea mammal that has four flippers, lives in cold water, and eats fish.

2. Next to these four letters, write down the first letter of a word that means the opposite of *push.*

3. Now add the four letters of a word that rhymes with *wrong* and means "the opposite of *short.*"

4. Cross out the letters *a, l,* and *l.*

5. Finally, unscramble the remaining six letters to find the name of something you might find at a coral reef.

---

6. What is the purpose of these directions? What did you do to follow step 1?

**The purpose of the directions is to help me solve a word puzzle.**

**To complete step 1, I wrote down the letters of the word *seal.***

7. What is the word you wrote down to complete step 2? What letters do you have after completing step 2?

**Step 2 refers to the word *pull.* After step 2, I have the letters *s, e,* *a, l,* and *p.***

8. What is the word you wrote down to complete step 3? What letters do you have after completing step 3?

**Step 3 refers to the word *long.* After step 3, I have the letters *s, e,* *a, l, p, l, o, n,* and *g.***

9. What answer do you find for the puzzle after completing steps 4 and 5?

**After completing steps 4 and 5, I have the answer *sponge.***

10. Why would it be impossible to solve this word puzzle without following the directions in order?

**I can only complete step 4 if I have already completed steps 1,** **2, and 3. I wouldn't be able to unscramble the word correctly** **without completing the previous four steps.**

© Pearson Education, Inc., 5

**Home Activity** Your child learned about following directions step by step. Talk about a simple recipe for one of your child's favorite foods. Work together to follow the directions for making the recipe step by step.

# Suffixes -ous, -sion, -ion, -ation

**Proofread an Essay** Circle five spelling errors in the essay. Write the words correctly. Find a sentence with a capitalization error and write the sentence correctly.

Laughing Helps

When I feel (nervos) or edgy, I call my friend. Having a friendly (conversasion) really helps. My friend is truly funny and tells (humorus) stories. I told my friend that she would be (famus) one day. She laughed and said, "well, I don't want to be a performer. I have to finish my (educasion) first." Still, I think being a comedian seems like a great occupation for her.

1. __nervous__          2. __conversation__

3. __humorous__          4. __famous__

5. __education__

6. __Well, I don't want to be a performer.__

**Proofread Words** Circle the word that is spelled correctly. Write the word.

7. varius        varous        (various)         7. __various__

8. invension     (invention)   invensiun         8. __invention__

9. tention       tensiun       (tension)         9. __tension__

10. (furious)    furyous       furius           10. __furious__

11. attration    (attraction)  attracshun       11. __attraction__

12. destinashun  destinasion   (destination)    12. __destination__

13. relacsation  (relaxation)  relaxasion       13. __relaxation__

14. exsibition   exabition     (exhibition)     14. __exhibition__

15. (election)   elektion      elecsion         15. __election__

16. invation     (invasion)    invashion        16. __invasion__

© Pearson Education, Inc., 5

**Home Activity** Your child identified misspelled list words. Say a suffix and have your child tell you a list word ending in that suffix. Then have your child spell the word.

Name _____

# Modifiers

**Directions** Read the passage. Then read each question. Circle the letter of the correct answer.

# Creatures of the Night

(1) The night is dark and quiet, and most animals lie down to sleep. (2) Still, many animals are busy after dark. (3) These nocturnal animals include some venomous snakes, agile monkeys, and tiny bats. (4) The kinkajou is a yellowish-brown animal that hops freely <u>along the treetops</u> at night. (5) Great horned owls are fearsome nighttime hunters, soaring <u>from the trees</u> to snatch its prey. (6) A bat uses high-pitched sounds to help tell what lies in its path. (7) The jaguar, <u>with its eight-foot body</u>, is a huge and ferocious predator.

**1** What two adjectives are found in sentence 1?

   **A** dark/most

   **B** night/dark

   **(C)** dark/quiet

   **D** most/down

**2** How many adjectives are found in sentence 3?

   **(A)** 4

   **B** 3

   **C** 2

   **D** 1

**3** Which best describes the underlined phrase in sentence 4?

   **A** Adjective phrase

   **B** Adverb phrase

   **(C)** Prepositional phrase

   **D** None of the above

**4** The underlined phrase in sentence 5 describes which word?

   **A** hunters

   **(B)** soaring

   **C** snatch

   **D** fearsome

**5** Which best describes the underlined modifier in sentence 7?

   **(A)** Adjective phrase

   **B** Adverb phrase

   **C** Prepositional phrase

   **D** None of the above

**Home Activity** Your child practiced for taking tests on modifiers. Copy a paragraph from one of your child's favorite stories, leaving blanks where modifiers go. Ask your child to suggest possible modifiers for the blanks. Compare with the original.

# Main Idea and Details

- The **topic** is the overall subject of a piece of writing. The **main idea** of a selection is the most important idea about the topic of that selection. **Details** are small pieces of information that tell more about the main idea.

- Sometimes the author states the main idea in a single sentence. When the author does not state the main idea, the reader must figure it out.

**Directions** Read the following passage. Then complete the diagram below.

Plants, just like animals, can become endangered as a result of the actions of human beings. Some plants are threatened after the insects that pollinate the plant die off. For example, one type of milkweed has nearly disappeared because chemicals killed off the butterfly that pollinates the milkweed. In addition, a plant can become endangered when buildings and roads take over the open lands where it grows. Other human activities such as farming and logging can threaten plants too. Finally, human pollution of land and water threatens many types of natural life, including plants. People are often unaware of it, but human activities can have harmful effects on plants and other parts of the natural world.

## Possible answers given for 2–5.

**Main Idea**

1. **Plants can be endangered by human actions.**

**Details**

2. **Plants are threatened if the insects that pollinate them are killed by human chemicals.**

3. **Plants are threatened when land is taken over for buildings and roads.**

4. **Farming and logging can endanger plants.**

5. **Pollution of land and water can endanger plants.**

**Home Activity** Your child identified the main idea and details of a nonfiction passage. Together, work to identify the main idea and details of individual paragraphs in a magazine article about animals.

© Pearson Education, Inc., 5

# Writing • Mystery

**Key Features of a Mystery**

- presents a problem or mystery early in the story with a clearly defined focus
- has a specific, believable setting described with sensory detail
- has a clearly defined plot with facts, details, and examples to help solve the mystery
- explains or resolves the mystery by the end of the story

## It's in the Cards

I was asleep when the telephone jangled me awake. It was my grandma. She was frantic. "You must come over right away," she pleaded. "It's my secret fudge recipe. I was going to make a batch for your birthday, but the recipe has vanished!"

I was at her house in five minutes. "Where did you keep the recipe?" I asked.

"With my other recipe cards," she answered, pulling a shoebox from her pantry. It was full of index cards, all with recipes written on them. "See," she said, pointing to a table of contents, "here it is, Number 112. Fudge. I had the card two weeks ago. But when I looked for it tonight, it was gone."

"Who has been here in the last two weeks who might have had access to your cards?" I asked. Grandma said she had three visitors recently: a plumber, a visiting nurse, and a lady from the senior citizen center.

I found the plumber fixing a water fountain at the Boy's Club. "I need to ask you about a missing card that belongs to my grandma," I said. "Have you seen a missing card?"

"Card, you say," the plumber said calmly. "What kind of cards does she play?"

I asked the nurse the same question I had asked the plumber. <u>Taking a deep breath, she said, "Why would your grandma keep her recipes on cards?</u> Just about everybody uses a computer these days," she said, looking away quickly.

I repeated the same question to the lady at the senior citizen center. "No, I don't think so," she said thoughtfully, "and I think I would have noticed. I always send out greeting cards for every holiday."

"I know who took your fudge recipe card," I told my grandma.

"You solved the case already? Who was it?" she asked in a puzzled tone.

"It was the nurse. I asked all three suspects the same question. I never mentioned what kind of a card I was talking about. The nurse is the only one who knew I was talking about a recipe card, and the only way she would know it was missing is if she took it."

Grandma sighed. "Although she shouldn't have taken the card without asking, I'll tell her that I would be happy to let her make a copy of the recipe if she brings back my original card."

"Sounds like a sweet ending to me," I said.

**1.** Paraphrase the problem or mystery in the story.

   <u>**Grandma's recipe card is missing.**</u>

**2.** What clue tells us who took the recipe card? Underline the clue.

# Vocabulary

**Directions** Choose the word from the box that best matches each definition. Write the word on the line.

tundra_____ 1. a vast, treeless plain in arctic regions

parasites_____ 2. living things that live on or in others, from which they get food

scrawny_____ 3. having little flesh; lean; thin

bleached_____ 4. whitened by exposure to sunlight or the use of chemicals

suspicions_____ 5. beliefs; feelings; thoughts

**Directions** Choose the word from the box that best matches each clue. Write the word on the line.

tundra_____ 6. This ground is frozen even in summer.

parasites_____ 7. Lice and tapeworms are examples of these.

starvation_____ 8. This is an extreme form of hunger.

carcasses_____ 9. These are dead bodies of animals.

decay_____ 10. This is the process of rotting.

## Write a Memo

Imagine that you are a zookeeper reporting on illnesses among animals at a zoo. On a separate sheet of paper, write a memo to the zoo's director about what you have observed. Use as many vocabulary words as you can.

## Memos should include words from the vocabulary list and details about ailing animals.

**Home Activity** Your child identified and used vocabulary words from *The Mystery of Saint Matthew Island*. Together, read a story or nonfiction article. Have him or her point out unfamiliar words. Work together to figure out the meaning of each word by using other words that appear near it.

© Pearson Education, Inc., 5

# Conjunctions

> A conjunction is a word such as *and, but,* or *or* that joins words, phrases, and sentences.
>
> - Use *and* to join related ideas: The snowy owl <u>and</u> snow bunting are arctic birds.
> - Use *but* to join contrasting ideas: I like the snow <u>but</u> not the cold.
> - Use *or* to suggest a choice: Is that a ringed seal <u>or</u> a hooded seal?
>
> You can use conjunctions to make compound subjects, compound predicates, and compound sentences. Place a comma before the conjunction in a compound sentence.
>
> **Compound Subject**    Frigid cold <u>and</u> deep snow make arctic life difficult.
> **Compound Predicate**  Arctic foxes do not hibernate <u>but</u> withstand the cold.
> **Compound Sentence**  They feed on live prey, <u>or</u> they can eat remains of a polar bear's meal.

**Directions** Underline the conjunction(s) in each sentence.

1. The arctic fox makes a burrow in a hill <u>or</u> cliff, <u>but</u> it does not hibernate.

2. It is well adapted for the cold with its furry feet <u>and</u> small, rounded ears.

3. A polar bear is huge <u>but</u> surprisingly fast <u>and</u> can outrun a caribou.

**Directions** Underline the conjunction in ( ) that completes each sentence.

4. The tundra has very little moisture (or, <u>and</u>) a short growing season.

5. The climate is harsh, (or, <u>but</u>) more than 1,700 kinds of plants live in the Arctic.

**Directions** Use the conjunction *and, but,* or *or* to join each pair of sentences. Write the new sentences. Remember to add a comma.

6. The Arctic is frigid in winter. It is much warmer in summer.

## The Arctic is frigid in winter, but it is much warmer in summer.

7. Arctic plants must grow quickly. They won't have time to reproduce.

## Arctic plants must grow quickly, or they won't have time to reproduce.

**Home Activity** Your child learned about conjunctions. Have your child write *and, but,* and *or* on index cards and then read a short article, making a tally mark on the appropriate card each time he or she sees that conjunction.

© Pearson Education, Inc., 5

# Final Syllable -*ant*, -*ent*, -*ance*, -*ence*

| Spelling Words | | | | |
|---|---|---|---|---|
| important | experience | ignorant | entrance | difference |
| instance | absence | appearance | intelligent | evidence |
| pollutant | clearance | confidence | conference | insurance |
| ambulance | hesitant | consistent | excellence | persistent |

**Antonyms** Write the list word that has the opposite or almost the opposite meaning of the underlined word or phrase.

1. I was <u>certain</u> to ask for help on my assignment.

2. We thought his <u>presence</u> was the cause of the loss.

3. We had trouble finding the <u>exit</u> to the building.

4. The facts in the case are <u>unimportant</u>.

5. Our students strive for <u>poor quality</u> in all they do.

6. That constant buzzing in the television is a(n) <u>occasional</u> annoyance.

7. A good employee is hard working and <u>inconsistent</u>.

8. It takes a while to develop self-assurance and <u>shyness</u>.

9. Car exhaust is an air <u>cleaner</u>.

10. By human standards, slugs and snails are not <u>stupid</u>.

1. __hesitant__
2. __absence__
3. __entrance__
4. __important__
5. __excellence__
6. __persistent__
7. __consistent__
8. __confidence__
9. __pollutant__
10. __intelligent__

**Definitions** Write the list word on the line that has the same meaning.

11. anything that shows what is true and what is not

12. a kind of sale

13. financial protection against harm, illness, or loss

14. vehicle that provides transportation to the hospital

15. a change

16. a person or thing serving as an example

17. knowing little or nothing

18. what is seen, done, or lived through

19. a meeting of interested persons to discuss a particular subject

20. the act of coming into sight

11. __evidence__
12. __clearance__
13. __insurance__
14. __ambulance__
15. __difference__
16. __instance__
17. __ignorant__
18. __experience__
19. __conference__
20. __appearance__

© Pearson Education, Inc., 5

**Home Activity** Your child wrote words that have syllables ending in -*ant*, -*ent*, -*ance*, -*ence*. Have your child underline the final syllable in each word.

# T-Chart

# Vocabulary · Endings

- An **ending** is a letter or letters added to the end of a base word. Recognizing an ending will help you figure out the word's meaning.
- In a dictionary, listings for words with endings are found near their base words.
- The ending *-ed* is added to a verb to make it past tense. The ending *-ing* is added to a verb to make it tell about present or ongoing actions. The endings *-s* and *-es* are added to a singular noun to make it refer to more than one person, place, or thing.

**Directions** Read the following passage. Then answer the questions below. Use a dictionary to help you.

The pilot flew above the arctic tundra, looking for baby seals. He was checking on the population of seals for a conservation organization. Although hunters were not allowed to kill the seals, some people had suspicions that seals were disappearing. The pilot was strongly hoping he wouldn't find any seal carcasses bleached, or made white, by the sun. As he steered the airplane closer to the frozen ground, he glimpsed a few seals. They did look scrawny, probably because of minor illnesses, but they were alive. Then he saw more and more seals coming into view. The pilot was very pleased.

1. What part of speech is *suspicions*? What meaning does the ending give the word?

   ___*Suspicions* is a noun; the *-s* creates more than one suspicion.___

2. How does the ending in *checking* affect the word's meaning?

   ___The *-ing* shows that the action "to check" is ongoing.___

3. What is the meaning of *bleached* in the passage? What effect does the ending have on the word's meaning?

   ___*Bleached* means "made white by exposing to the sun." The *-ed* ending means that the effect of the sun happened in the past.___

4. How would removing the *-es* ending in *illnesses* change the meaning of the word?

   ___The word would become singular instead of plural.___

5. Rewrite the second sentence of the passage to make the action occur in the past.

   ___He checked on the population of seals for a conservation organization.___

**Home Activity** Your child identified and used word endings to help determine the meanings of new words in a passage. Work with your child to identify unfamiliar words in another article. Together, identify word endings that help you understand the words.

# Time Line

- A **time line** is a chart that shows a sequence of events. Usually a time line uses a bar divided into periods of time to show the order of events. Some time lines are read left to right, and others are read top to bottom.
- You can use a time line to show the time order of events in a nonfiction text. A time line can also show the order of events in a work of fiction.
- A time line may cover any length of time, such as a day or thousands of years. Pay attention to the title and labels on a time line.

**Directions** Read the following time line. Then answer the questions below.

**The Life of a Reindeer**

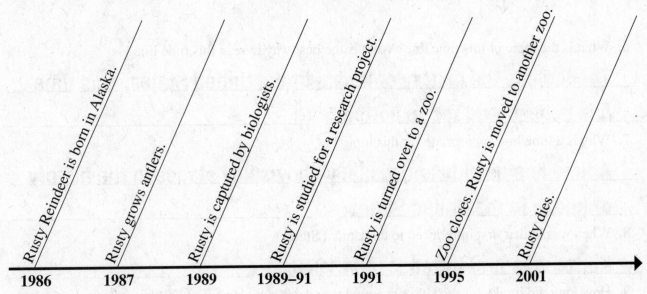

1986   1987   1989   1989–91   1991   1995   2001

1. How is this time line organized? What is the topic of this time line?

**It is organized in time order from earliest to latest. The topic is the life of a reindeer named Rusty.**

2. How many years passed between Rusty's birth and his capture?

**Three years passed.**

3. How long was Rusty in zoos?

**Rusty was in zoos for ten years.**

4. How old was Rusty when he died?

**Rusty was fifteen years old when he died.**

5. The average age of a reindeer in the wild is ten to twelve years. How does the time line help you draw a conclusion about Rusty's life span? Explain.

**The time line shows Rusty had an above average life span.**

**Directions** Read the following time line. Then answer the questions.

| | **History of the Plant That Grew Too Well** |
|---|---|
| 1876 | Kudzu, a vine from Japan, arrives in U.S. |
| 1900s | Florida farmers begin to feed kudzu to animals. |
| 1930s | U.S. Soil Conservation Service urges use of kudzu to prevent erosion. |
| 1930s | U.S. Civilian Conservation Corps plants kudzu. |
| 1940s | Government pays farmers to plant kudzu. |
| 1940s | Georgia radio personality starts Kudzu Clubs. |
| 1953 | Government discourages use of kudzu. |
| 1972 | Government declares kudzu a weed. |
| 2004 | Kudzu covers 6 million acres in South; people work to eliminate it. |

**6.** What is the topic of this time line? What is the best way to read this time line?

**The topic is the history of kudzu in the United States. This time line is best read top to bottom.**

**7.** Why is a time line appropriate for this topic?

**A time line quickly and visually shows key stages in the history of kudzu in the United States.**

**8.** When was kudzu first introduced to the United States?

**Kudzu was first introduced in 1876.**

**9.** How long did it take for the U.S. government to declare kudzu a weed? When was kudzu planted most heavily?

**It took 96 years for the United States government to declare kudzu a weed; Kudzu was planted most heavily in the 1920s, 1930s, and 1940s.**

**10.** What happened with kudzu most recently, according to the time line?

**Kudzu now covers six million acres, and people are trying to eliminate it.**

© Pearson Education, Inc., 5

**Home Activity** Your child learned about using time lines as resources. Together, look at a time line in a history book. Ask your child to explain entries and to answer your questions about time order.

# Final Syllable *-ant*, *-ent*, *-ance*, *-ence*

**Proofread an Article** Circle and write six spelling errors. Circle one capitalization error and write the sentence correctly.

**Spelling Words**

Help Is on the Way

With sirens wailing, the (ambulence) driver carefully winds through traffic. It takes a lot of (confidents) to do this (importent) job. In large cities, with (persistant) traffic, a driver must be extra careful. Still, the (D)river must take the fastest route to the emergency room. Time makes all the (differants) when people need emergency care. All drivers try to get each (won) of their patients to the emergency room entrance as quickly as possible.

1. **ambulance**
2. **confidence**
3. **important**
4. **persistent**
5. **difference**
6. **one**
7. **Still, the driver must take the fastest route to the emergency room.**

**Spelling Words**

important
experience
ignorant
entrance
difference
instance
absence
appearance
intelligent
evidence

pollutant
clearance
confidence
conference
insurance
ambulance
hesitant
consistent
excellence
persistent

**Proofread Words** Circle the correct spelling of the list word. Write the word.

| | | | | |
|---|---|---|---|---|
| 8. absense | abcense | (absence) | 8. **absence** |
| 9. intelligant | (intelligent) | intellagent | 9. **intelligent** |
| 10. (insurance) | insurants | insurence | 10. **insurance** |
| 11. pollutent | (pollutant) | pollutint | 11. **pollutant** |
| 12. ignorent | ignorint | (ignorant) | 12. **ignorant** |
| 13. apperence | (appearance) | appearants | 13. **appearance** |
| 14. (important) | importent | inportant | 14. **important** |
| 15. hezitent | hesitent | (hesitant) | 15. **hesitant** |

**Frequently Misspelled Words**

off
one
tired

**Home Activity** Your child identified misspelled list words. Ask your child to name the four words he or she has the most difficulty spelling and spell them for you.

## Conjunctions

**Directions** Read the passage. Then read each question. Circle the letter of the correct answer.

# The Living Arctic

(1) Although <u>you and I</u> might not like to live in the Arctic, many animals make their home in this cold _____ hostile land. (2) Reindeer are found across the northernmost parts of Canada and Asia. (3) Bitter cold but deep snow do not bother the Arctic Fox. (4) A year-round hunter, this fox can be snowy white or brown, depending on the season. (5) The climate here is harsh, _____ some plants do grow and provide food for the Arctic herbivores. (6) The muskox and Arctic hare are two animals that rely on plants and grasses for food. (7) Polar bears pose no threat to the hare, and wolves do prey the small Arctic animals.

1 Which best describes the underlined phrase in sentence 1?

   **A** Compound sentence

   **B** Compound predicate

   **(C)** Compound subject

   **D** None of the above

2 Which conjunction best completes sentence 1?

   **A** however

   **B** but

   **C** or

   **(D)** and

3 What change, if any, should be made in sentence 3?

   **A** Change *do not bother* to **does not bother**

   **(B)** Change *Bitter cold but deep snow* to **Bitter cold and deep snow**

   **C** Change *Bitter cold but deep snow* to **Bitter cold, but deep snow**

   **D** Make no change

4 Which conjunction best completes sentence 5?

   **A** however

   **(B)** but

   **C** or

   **D** and

5 What change, if any, should be made in sentence 7?

   **(A)** Change *and wolves* to **but wolves**

   **B** Change *and wolves* to **or wolves**

   **C** Change *and wolves* to **because wolves**

   **D** Make no change

© Pearson Education, Inc., 5

**Home Activity** Your child prepared for taking tests on conjunctions. Have your child find and circle *and, but,* and *or* in ads. Ask your child to explain why each word is used.

# Compare and Contrast

- Writers sometimes use **comparison** and **contrast** to organize their writing. Clue words such as *same, also, before, although,* and *however* signal comparisons and contrasts.
- Good readers notice the author's comparisons and contrasts and make their own as they read.

**Directions** Read the following passage. Then complete the diagram below.

Hillary and her family wanted to move to New York City because it seemed exciting compared to their quiet hometown. They saved money for a year to afford the move. When it was time to move, their friends gave them a big send-off party.

After they moved to New York, they enjoyed the energy of the crowds as they bustled down the streets. They visited museums with amazing collections of art and artifacts. They experimented with new foods from all over the world.

They were unprepared, however, for how expensive everything was. And even though they were surrounded by people, they found it hard to make friends. They were surprised, but sometimes they longed for the peace and quiet of their home town. Over time, they understood that their new home was a mixture of advantages and disadvantages.

## Possible answers given.

| Advantages and Disadvantages of Moving to New York City | |
|---|---|
| Advantages | Disadvantages |
| 1. **the energy of the crowds** | 3. **expensive** |
| 2. **new foods from all over the world** | 4. **difficult to make friends** |

5. What prior knowledge do you have about the advantages and disadvantages of living in a big city helps you makes comparisons and contrasts?

**When my sister moved to Chicago, she called home every day because she was homesick.**

**Home Activity** Your child read a short passage and made comparisons and contrasts. After reading a historical article, work with your child to compare and contrast something at two different points in time.

© Pearson Education, Inc., 5

# Writing • Parody

## Key Features of Parody

- imitates a familiar story's plot, style, and language
- changes details of the original story for comic effect
- may include action that rises to a climax

## The Three Pigs

Frank was the oldest of the three pigs. He always had his own way of doing things. He thought he was smarter than everyone else, including his two little brothers. He also thought that you should work as little as possible.

The three pigs lived in a small brick house with their mother. Four pigs in one tiny house was too many! The pigs' mom decided it was time for the boys to move out.

"Build your own homes," she said. "Make them just right for you."

Frank decided he would think before working on his house. He would watch his brothers. He thought he would learn from their mistakes.

Frank's youngest brother built a house from straw. A wolf blew it down and ate Frank's brother. Frank's mom cried and cried. "You have to make your houses safe," she warned.

Frank's middle brother built a house from sticks. He tied them together tightly with rope.

Frank watched and waited. A week after his brother moved in, the wolf blew the sticks apart and ate Frank's middle brother. Frank's mom cried and cried. "Don't move out!" she said to Frank. "This brick house is safe. Stay here with me. You're all I have now."

Frank wiped his own eyes. He did miss his little brothers.

Soon, though, Frank smiled. Watching and waiting was so much better than working. He had decided he should build his own house from bricks. But bricks were heavy. Building with them was hard work. Yes, Frank decided, he was the smartest pig around.

As for the wolf, who also liked to watch and wait, he was sad.

1. Which character from the original "Three Little Pigs" story is most different in this parody? How is this character different?

   **The oldest pig. In the original story the pigs are all alike, with no personality. In this story, this pig is selfish and lazy.**

2. What is the turning point? Circle the sentence that proves the tension is broken.

# Vocabulary

**Directions** Choose the word from the box that best matches each definition below. Write the word on the line.

**adorn**_____

1. to add beauty to; put ornaments on

**lifeless**_____

2. without life

**spoonful**_____

3. as much as a spoon can hold

**realm**_____

4. kingdom

**cleanse**_____

5. to make clean

---

**Check the Words You Know**

___adorn
___cleanse
___lifeless
___precious
___realm
___spoonful

---

**Directions** Fill in the crossword puzzle using the clues below.

**DOWN**

6. to make pure
7. a king's empire
8. valuable

**ACROSS**

9. to decorate
10. without life

[Crossword grid:]

9. a d o r n (with 8. p r e c i o u s down through the r)

10. l i f e l e s s (with 6. c l e a n s e down through the l, and 7. r e a l m down through the r)

# Write a Description

On a separate sheet of paper, write a short description of a king's castle. Use as many vocabulary words as you can.

**Descriptions should include words from the vocabulary list and specific details about a king's castle.**

**School + Home**

**Home Activity** Your child identified and used vocabulary words from *King Midas and the Golden Touch.* Read a myth or fairy tale with your child. Ask your child to point out any of the vocabulary words he or she sees.

## Commas

Commas can clarify meaning and tell readers when to pause.

- Put a comma after every item in a *series* but the last.
  Poets pay attention to the sounds, meanings, and emotions of words.
  The audience applauded, cheered, and stood up.

- When you speak or write to someone, you may use the person's name or title. This noun of *direct address* is set off with a comma, or two commas if it is in the middle of a sentence.
  Will you read some more, Mr. Berry?
  I'd love to, children, if you aren't tired of sitting.

- *Appositives* are noun phrases that describe another noun. They are set off by commas.
  Ted Kooser, a wonderful poet, lives in Nebraska.

- Put a comma after an *introductory word or phrase*, such as *yes, no, well, of course*, or *in fact*.
  No, I haven't read the new book. As usual, I'm too busy.

**Directions** Add commas to each sentence where they are needed.

1. Harry enjoys writing stories, poems, and articles.

2. Voni, do you prefer reading fairy tales, tall tales, or myths?

3. *King Midas*, a myth about values, features a greedy king.

4. Were you surprised, Kaela, when the glowing young man appeared?

5. No, I expect magical things to happen in tales.

6. King Midas's gift is deadly because he cannot eat, drink, or touch people.

**Directions** Rewrite each sentence. Add commas where they are needed.

7. By the way King Midas what did you learn about gold?

## By the way, King Midas, what did you learn about gold?

8. I learned that gold is cold hard and meaningless by itself.

## I learned that gold is cold, hard, and meaningless by itself.

**Home Activity** Your child learned about commas. Record a short conversation with your child about his or her favorite foods or activities. Ask your child to write the conversation adding commas where they are needed.

Name _____

# Latin Roots

| Spelling Words | | | | |
|---|---|---|---|---|
| portable | audience | decade | territory | auditorium |
| dictionary | terrace | reporter | December | contradict |
| export | decimal | audit | transport | audition |
| prediction | import | jurisdiction | decathlon | terrain |

**Words in Context** Write the list words that complete each sentence.

She sang for her **(1)** _____ in the large **(2)** _____.

1. __audition__

2. __auditorium__

Most of the **(3)** _____ was hilly but we found a nice flat **(4)** _____ for a short rest.

3. __terrain__

4. __terrace__

We **(5)** _____ grain to China and **(6)** _____ Chinese toys and clothes.

5. __export__

6. __import__

The **(7)** _____ took her notes using a **(8)** _____ recorder.

7. __reporter__

8. __portable__

He was bold enough to insist his definition was right and **(9)** _____ the **(10)** _____.

9. __contradict__

10. __dictionary__

**Word Definitions** Write the list word that has the same meaning.

11. move something

12. a statement made about the future

13. a number written using base ten

14. those who view or listen to a performance

15. land or region

16. a ten-year period

17. examine carefully for accuracy

18. legal power

19. a competition having ten events

20. twelfth month of the year

11. __transport__

12. __prediction__

13. __decimal__

14. __audience__

15. __territory__

16. __decade__

17. __audit__

18. __jurisdiction__

19. __decathlon__

20. __December__

© Pearson Education, Inc., 5

**Home Activity** Your child wrote words that have Latin roots. Have your child tell you five list words and identify the Latin root in each word. Have your child spell each word.

# Story Sequence A

**Title** _____

```
┌─────────────────────────────────────────┐
│  Beginning                               │
│                                          │
│                                          │
│                                          │
│                                          │
│                                          │
└─────────────────────────────────────────┘
                    │
                    ▼
┌─────────────────────────────────────────┐
│  Middle                                  │
│                                          │
│                                          │
│                                          │
│                                          │
│                                          │
│                                          │
└─────────────────────────────────────────┘
                    │
                    ▼
┌─────────────────────────────────────────┐
│  End                                     │
│                                          │
│                                          │
│                                          │
│                                          │
│                                          │
└─────────────────────────────────────────┘
```

Name_____

# Vocabulary • Suffixes

- A **suffix** is added to the end of a base word to change its meaning or the way it is used in a sentence.
- The Old English suffix *-ful* can mean "full of _____," as in *careful,* or "an amount that fills something," as in *spoonful.* The suffix *-less* means "without," as in *harmless.*
- A dictionary is a book that helps us find the meanings of words we do not know.

**Directions** Read the following passage. Then answer the questions below. Use a dictionary to help you.

> A wealthy king had all he could ask for except the one thing he needed most. His precious daughter was sick and lifeless. He sent out a message to all in his realm that he would give his fortune to anyone who could cure his daughter. In response, a penniless beggar came to the king's castle with a special potion. "If she takes a spoonful, she will improve," he said. Sure enough, with a spoonful she woke up, and with a cupful she was dancing around. As you might guess, the homeless beggar was well rewarded by the joyful king.

1. What is the base word in *lifeless*? How does the suffix help you understand its meaning?

   **_Life_ is the base word; _-less_ means "without," so _lifeless_ means "without life."**

2. What is the base word in *penniless*? How does the suffix help you understand its meaning?

   **_Penny_ is the base word; _Penniless_ means "without a penny."**

3. What is the base word in *homeless*? How does the suffix help you understand its meaning?

   **_Home_ is the base word; _-less_ means "without," so _homeless_ means "without a home."**

4. Change the word *powerful* so that it has the opposite meaning. Find the meanings of both words in a dictionary.

   **By adding _-less_ to _power_ instead of _-ful,_ the meaning is changed from "full of power" to "without power."**

5. How does the suffix in the word *joyful* help you understand its meaning?

   **_-ful_ means "full of"; so _joyful_ means "full of joy."**

**Home Activity** Your child identified and used suffixes to understand new words of a passage. Work with your child to identify unfamiliar words in an article. Ask your child if any suffixes can help him or her understand the new words. Confirm the meanings using a dictionary.

© Pearson Education, Inc., 5

# Order Form/Application

**Order forms** and **applications** are charts with columns and spaces in which you can write or type. An order form is the means by which a person can purchase merchandise. An application is a form by which a person can apply for a job.

**Directions** Use this order form from an online catalog to answer the questions below.

---

### *GLITTER GOLD* ORDER FORM
Click *SUBMIT* when you have completed this form.

| Item Number | Item | Quantity | Price |
|---|---|---|---|
| 13715 | Big Bracelet | | $ |
| 20166 | Big Ring | | $ |
| | | | + $5 shipping and handling |
| | | TOTAL PRICE | $ |

**Billing Address**

* Name
* Street Address
* City
* State _____ * ZIP
* Country
  Phone
* E-mail address

**Shipping Address**
☐ Check this box if same as billing address

* Name
* Street Address
* City
* State _____ * ZIP
* Country
  Phone

**PAYMENT METHOD**
* Type of Credit Card
* Account Number
* Expiration Date

Your comments and messages here.

* REQUIRED FIELD

**Submit**

---

1. When would you fill out only one of the two address fields shown?

   **If the addresses are identical, fill out only the billing address.**

2. If you are buying an item, what information do you need to specify on the order form?

   **You need to specify the quantity of each item you order.**

3. If you wish to submit an online order at Glitter Gold, what payment options do you have?

   **You must pay using a credit card.**

4. How could you send comments to Glitter Gold?

   **Use the "comments and messages" field on the order form.**

5. If you are ordering from this Web page, what information is optional?

   **The only information that is not required is the phone numbers.**

**Directions** Use this online job application form to answer the questions below.

<table>
<tr><td colspan="3" align="center">**MIDAS MINING CO. EMPLOYMENT APPLICATION**<br>Click *SUBMIT* when you have completed this form.</td></tr>
<tr><td colspan="3">**PERSONAL INFORMATION**</td></tr>
<tr><td>Last Name</td><td>First Name</td><td>Middle Initial</td></tr>
<tr><td>Address</td><td>City</td><td>State/ZIP</td></tr>
<tr><td>Phone Number</td><td>E-mail Address</td><td>Social Security No.</td></tr>
<tr><td>Position Applied For</td><td>Full-Time/Part-Time</td><td>Date Available to Start</td></tr>
</table>

| **EDUCATION** | | | |
| --- | --- | --- | --- |
| High School | | Address | Graduated |
| College | | Address | Graduated |

| **WORK EXPERIENCE** | | | | |
| --- | --- | --- | --- | --- |
| Current Employer | Address | Duties | | Start/End Dates |
| Employer Name | Address | Duties | | Start/End Dates |

**OTHER SKILLS**

| **REFERENCES** | | | |
| --- | --- | --- | --- |
| Name | Address | Phone | Relationship |

SUBMIT

6. What is the purpose of this form?

## The purpose of the form is to apply for a job at Midas Mining Co.

7. What is the first piece of information you need to provide on this form?

## the applicant's last name

8. In what section would you say when you could start working?

## in the Personal Information section

9. What are three of the five main sections of the application?

## Possible answer: Education, Work Experience, and Other Skills

10. What directions are given on this form?

## "Click *SUBMIT* when you have completed this form."

**Home Activity** Your child learned about filling out order forms and applications. Look at an order form or application together. Discuss how to fill it out.

# Latin Roots

**Proofread an Article** Circle six spelling errors in the article. Write the words correctly. Find a punctuation error and write the sentence correctly.

Hard Work

Only a superb athlete can prevail in a (decathalon) The competition includes five events on each of two days. There is an enthusiastic audience for most events, especially those held in an (auditorum) Races may be won by less than a thousandth of a second. However, the jumps, shot put, and javelin events may be won by as much as a decimeter. (Reportors) find it difficult to make a (predikshion) regarding a winner because winners are determined by a system which awards (decemal) values based on performance. Today, only male athletes may enter (in too) a decathlon. Women athletes compete in a heptathlon, a competition with seven events.

portable
audience
decade
territory
auditorium
dictionary
terrace
reporter
December
contradict

export
decimal
audit
transport
audition
prediction
import
jurisdiction
decathlon
terrain

1. **decathlon**
2. **auditorium**
3. **Reporters**
4. **prediction**
5. **decimal**
6. **into**
7. **Only a superb athlete can prevail in a decathlon.**

**Proofread Words** Circle the correct spelling of each word.

| 8. esport | axport | (export) |
| 9. terace | (terrace) | terrece |
| 10. emport | amport | (import) |
| 11. (decade) | decad | deckade |
| 12. aduit | (audit) | audet |
| 13. (dictionary) | dictionary | dictionery |
| 14. portabel | (portable) | portible |

| 15. jursdiction | juresdiction | (jurisdiction) |
| 16. (territory) | terratory | terretory |
| 17. Dicimber | (December) | Dacember |
| 18. trenspart | trenspert | (transport) |
| 19. (contradict) | contredict | controdict |
| 20. (audition) | aduition | audetin |

**School + Home**

**Home Activity** Your child identified misspelled list words. Ask your child to say five list words, tell the Latin root for each, and then spell and define each word.

Name _____

# Commas

**Directions** Read the passage. Then read each question. Circle the letter of the correct answer.

# Tales of Old

(1) Tales about medieval times usually share very similar elements. (2) Often, these tales involve royalty, such as a king a queen a prince or a lovely princess. (3) The story may tell of <u>a damsel in distress, a terrible plague, or a knight in shining armor.</u> (4) The kingdom's wizard, sometimes called Merlin, concocts potions and breaks witches' spells. (5) The bravest knight rides a white horse across the drawbridge while the wicked army plans its attack. (6) The proud king lives in a tall castle, while the poor serfs dwell in cold, leaky cottages. (7) Yes these tales are often quite similar, but they are always entertaining.

**1** What change, if any, should be made in sentence 2?

**A** Insert commas after the words *king, queen,* and *prince*

**B** Insert commas after the words *king* and *queen*

**C** Change *royalty,* to **royalty**

**D** Make no change

**2** In sentence 3, the underlined portion is an example of which?

**A** Direct address

**B** Appositive

**C** Series

**D** Introductory phrase

**3** What change, if any, should be made in sentence 7?

**A** Insert comma after *tales are* and *often*

**B** Insert a comma after *Yes*

**C** Remove comma after *similar*

**D** Make no change

**4** Which sentence in this passage includes an appositive?

**A** Sentence 1

**B** Sentence 3

**C** Sentence 4

**D** Sentence 5

**5** Which sentence shows incorrect use of a comma?

**A** Ivy, do you like reading about kings and queens?

**B** Yes but I prefer more modern stories.

**C** My brother, a fan of fairy tales, has read all these books.

**D** I have read the first, second, and third books in the series.

© Pearson Education, Inc., 5

**Home Activity** Your child prepared for taking tests on commas. Ask your child to give example sentences to teach you about the four uses of commas he or she learned.

# Fact and Opinion

- **Statements of fact** are objective, not personal. They can be proved true or false.
  **Statements of opinion** are personal judgments or beliefs. They cannot be proved true or false.
- Statements of opinion can be valid or faulty. **Valid** statements can be supported by facts and common sense. **Faulty** statements cannot.
- Examine statements of opinion by using your prior knowledge. Based on what you have seen or read or what you know, ask, *Is the statement valid or faulty?*

**Directions** Read the following passage. Then complete the chart below.

During the 1930s, ocean liners were a way of traveling in luxury. I'm sure that only the finest craftsmen were allowed to contribute to the most luxurious of these floating palaces. Immigrants as well as the wealthy traveled aboard these ocean liners. The ships were the most beautiful vessels on the water. The era of the transatlantic ocean liner continued from the 1920s until the 1960s. Each of us should learn more about the splendor of these ships.

## Possible answers given for 1, 3–5.

| Statement of Opinion | Support | Valid or Faulty? |
|---|---|---|
| I'm sure that only the finest craftsmen were allowed to contribute to the most luxurious of these floating palaces. | 1. **Ship builders would probably use the best craftsmen they could find to build their ships.** | 2. **Valid** |
| 3. **Each of us should learn more about the splendor of these ships.** | 4. **Some people are not interested in ships.** | 5. **Faulty** |

© Pearson Education, Inc., 5

**Home Activity** Your child identified statements of fact and opinion in a nonfiction passage. Work with your child to identify the statements of fact and opinion in a short magazine article. Challenge him or her to ask questions to check whether statements of opinion are supported by facts.

# Writing • Book Review

## Babe Ruth Was No Baby

I knew Babe Ruth was a famous baseball player before I read the book *Babe Ruth: One of Baseball's Greatest* by Guernsey Van Riper. But I did not know what a hard life Babe Ruth had as a boy. This book is a biography about Babe Ruth. I liked how this author gave a lot of detail about Babe's childhood. It tells how Babe was a tough boy and then turned his power into being a tough baseball player.

It is funny that his first name was George, but his nickname was Babe, like a small child. Babe was always big and strong even when he was a little boy. *Babe Ruth* explains that Babe got into trouble many times because his parents did not watch him. They ran a restaurant with rough customers. For example, in the book a neighbor named Mrs. Callahan says, "And the things that go on in that restaurant! The men seem to do nothing but fight and talk loudly." She felt, "It's certainly the wrong place for a headstrong boy like that George Ruth. One of these days, I've a mind to call to the police." Babe was only seven years old when she said that.

When Babe grew older, he kept getting into trouble. Finally, a teacher thought Babe would be good at baseball. He was right! Babe stopped being difficult when he used his strength to hit homeruns.

This biography is entertaining and shows an important lesson about how to use what you have to do well in life. The author shows through Babe's life how someone can take a problem and turn it into a success.

I think everyone will enjoy this book. Learning how someone famous started out poor and always in trouble and then worked to make something of himself is an inspiration.

1. What book is being reviewed? Who is the author?

   *Babe Ruth: One of Baseball's Greatest*; Guernsey Van Riper.

2. Which paragraph gives details about Babe Ruth's childhood? Circle two details.

   paragraph two; Possible answers: his first name was George, but his nickname was Babe. Babe was always big and strong even when he was a little boy.

3. Why does the reviewer think people will want to read this book?

   The story of a boy who started out poor and always in trouble but then made something of himself is inspiring.

# Vocabulary

**Directions** Choose the word from the box that best matches each definition. Write the word on the line.

criticizing _____

1. finding fault with; disapproving of; blaming

explosion _____

2. act of bursting with a loud noise; a blowing up

drenching _____

3. wetting thoroughly; soaking

era _____

4. a period of time or history

cruised _____

5. traveled at the speed at which the vehicle operates best

> **Check the Words You Know**
>
> ___criticizing
> ___cruised
> ___drenching
> ___era
> ___explosion
> ___hydrogen

**Directions** Choose the word from the box that best matches each clue. Write the word on the line.

drenching _____

6. This is said of extremely heavy rain.

era _____

7. An example of this is the colonial period or the Middle Ages.

explosion _____

8. A bomb could make this happen.

hydrogen _____

9. This element combines with oxygen to make water.

cruised _____

10. This describes how a ship might have moved along the water.

## Write an E-mail Message

On a separate sheet of paper, write an e-mail message you might send from a ship after witnessing the eruption of a volcano. Use as many vocabulary words as you can.

**E-mail messages should include words from the vocabulary list and details about the sights and sounds of a volcano's eruption.**

**Home Activity** Your child identified and used vocabulary words from *The Hindenburg*. Read a story or nonfiction article with your child. Have him or her point out unfamiliar words. Work together to try to figure out the meaning of each word by using other words that appear near it.

## Quotations and Quotation Marks

A **direct quotation** gives a person's exact words and is enclosed in **quotation marks (" ")**. Direct quotations begin with capital letters and end with proper punctuation. End punctuation is inside the closing quotation marks. Words that tell who is speaking are set off from the quotation by punctuation.

- When the quotation comes last in a sentence, set it off with a comma.
  Jamie asked, "What was the *Hindenburg?*"

- When the quotation comes first in a sentence, a comma, question mark, or exclamation mark sets off the quotation.
  "It was a dirigible," replied May. "It was enormous!" she added.

- When the quotation is interrupted by words that tell who is speaking, use two sets of quotation marks. Notice that words telling who is speaking are followed by punctuation. Use a comma if the second part of the quotation does not begin a new sentence.
  "Dirigibles were lighter than air," he added, "because they were filled with hydrogen."

- Use end punctuation and a capital letter if the second part of the quotation does begin a new sentence.
  "Isn't hydrogen flammable?" asked Jamie. "What kept it from exploding?"

**Directions** Rewrite each sentence. Add quotation marks where they are needed.

1. Are the blimps dirigibles? asked Max.

   **"Are the blimps dirigibles?" asked Max.**

2. No, they aren't, explained Vi, because they aren't rigid.

   **"No, they aren't," explained Vi, "because they aren't rigid."**

**Directions** Write each sentence correctly. Add capital letters, quotation marks, and other punctuation as needed.

3. Vi said the framework is like a skeleton

   **Vi said, "The framework is like a skeleton."**

4. fabric covers it she added like skin

   **"Fabric covers it," she added, "like skin."**

**Home Activity** Your child learned about quotations and quotation marks. With your child, find quotations in a newspaper or magazine article. Have your child highlight the quotation marks and other punctuation and explain why they are used.

# Related Words

| Spelling Words | | | | |
|---|---|---|---|---|
| clean | cleanse | inspire | inspiration | legal |
| legality | define | definition | please | pleasant |
| combine | combination | human | humanity | organ |
| organist | crime | criminal | recognize | recognition |

**Words in Context** Write the list words that complete the sentence.

I use the **(1)** _____ of other artists to **(2)** _____ me. (inspiration, inspire)

1. __inspiration__    2. __inspire__

The **(3)** _____ looked tiny as she stood in front of the **(4)** _____. (organ, organist)

3. __organist__    4. __organ__

**(5)** _____ the eggs and sugar; add the flour and spices to the **(6)** _____. (combine, combination)

5. __Combine__    6. __combination__

She said, "Jake, **(7)** _____ be **(8)** _____ to your Aunt Martha." (please, pleasant)

7. __please__    8. __pleasant__

"I'm not a **(9)** _____," he said. "I didn't commit the **(10)** _____." (crime, criminal)

9. __criminal__    10. __crime__

**Definitions** Write the list word that has the same meaning as the word or phrase.

11. dirt free __clean__    12. wash __cleanse__

13. word's meaning __definition__    14. person __human__

15. identify something __recognize__    16. specify meaning __define__

17. lawfulness __legality__    18. allowed by law __legal__

19. appreciation, fame __recognition__    20. quality of being human __humanity__

© Pearson Education, Inc., 5

**School + Home**

**Home Activity** Your child wrote related words that are spelled similarly but pronounced differently. Say list words and have your child say and spell the list word that is related.

# Scoring Rubric: Reviews

| | 4 | 3 | 2 | 1 |
|---|---|---|---|---|
| **Focus/Ideas** | Summarizes the main idea, includes a thesis supported by data from the book | Mostly summarizes the main idea and a thesis mostly by data from the book | Somewhat summarizes main idea, may have a thesis with some data from book | Lacks a summary or main idea; no thesis; no data from book |
| **Organization** | Includes a strong introduction, body and conclusion | Includes basic introduction, body, and conclusion | Includes weak introduction, body, and conclusion | No introduction, body, and/or conclusion |
| **Voice** | Involved throughout | Involved most of the time | Tries to be involved | No involvement |
| **Word Choice** | Language matches purpose closely | Language matches purpose well | Language only partly matches purpose | Language does not match purpose |
| **Sentences** | Clear and complete | Mostly clear and complete | Somewhat clear and complete | Neither clear nor complete |
| **Conventions** | Few to no errors in use of quotations and quotation marks and in spelling of related words | Moderate errors in use of quotations and quotation marks and in spelling of related words | Several errors in use of quotations and quotation marks and in spelling of related words | Consistently incorrect use of quotations and quotation marks and spelling of related words |

Name_____

# Vocabulary • Unfamiliar Words

- When you see an **unfamiliar word** while reading, use context clues, or words around the unfamiliar word, to figure out its meaning.
- Context clues include definitions, explanations, and synonyms (words that have the same or nearly the same meaning as other words).

**Directions** Read the following passage. Then answer the questions below.

In the early 1900s, many people were criticizing the Wright brothers for trying to make a flying machine. These people accused the Wright brothers of trying to do something humans were not meant to do. However, the brothers kept working on their invention, even in drenching, soaking rain. In 1903, they finally created an airplane with a propeller and a gas engine. They controlled the speed of the aircraft by increasing or decreasing the spark in the engine. This caused an explosion, or bursting, of fuel that drove the propeller. When they finally got a propeller-driven machine into the air, they cruised at a very slow speed, traveling at only about one mile an hour. Still, the Wright brothers' plane opened up a whole new era of transportation, the age of the airplane.

**1.** What does *criticizing* mean? What clues help you to determine its meaning?

**"accusing"; *accused,* along with what people were saying about the Wright brothers, hint at the meaning of the word.**

**2.** What does *drenching* mean? What clue helps you determine the meaning?

**"soaking"; This synonym appears in the same sentence.**

**3.** What clue helps you to determine the meaning of *explosion*? What does this word mean?

**A synonym for *explosion* is given immediately after the word. *Explosion* means "bursting."**

**4.** What context clue helps you determine the meaning of *cruised*?

**The word *traveling* helps to clarify the meaning of *cruised.***

**5.** What does *era* mean? How can you use context clues to determine the meaning?

**"a period of time"; The synonym *age* and the identification of a period of history help to determine the word's meaning.**

© Pearson Education, Inc., 5

**Home Activity** Your child identified and used context clues to understand new words in a nonfiction passage. Work with your child to identify unfamiliar words in another article. Then have him or her find context clues to help with understanding the new words. Confirm the meanings with the glossary in the back of your book or a dictionary.

# Map/Globe/Atlas

- A **map** is a drawing of a place that shows where something is or where something happened. You may see different kinds of maps. These include picture maps, road maps, political maps, physical maps, and special-purpose maps. Look carefully at a map's **legend,** or key. It explains any symbols used in the map. It also shows directions as well as a scale of distance.

- An **atlas** is a book of maps.

- A **globe** is a sphere with a map of the world on it. Because the Earth is round, globes give a more accurate picture of the size and shape of the Earth than flat maps do.

**Directions** Study the following map. Then use the map to answer the questions below.

1. On May 20, 1937, Amelia Earhart took off on an airplane flight that she hoped would make her the first person to fly around the world. She began in Oakland, California. What was her last stop in the United States?

   **Her last stop in the United States was Miami, Florida.**

2. Where did she land next?

   **Next Earhart landed at San Juan.**

3. About how far was her flight across the United States? How do you know?

   **Her flight across the United States was about 5,200 km; The**

   **distance can be calculated using the map's legend.**

4. On which continents did she land along the way to Lae, New Guinea?

   **North America, South America, Africa, Asia, and Australia**

5. On July 1, 1937, Amelia Earhart left Lae, New Guinea. What was her next intended stop? How far is this place from New Guinea?

   **Amelia Earhart was supposed to land at Howland Island, which**

   **is about 4,000 km east of New Guinea in the Pacific Ocean.**

**Directions**  Study the following map. Then use the map to answer the questions below.

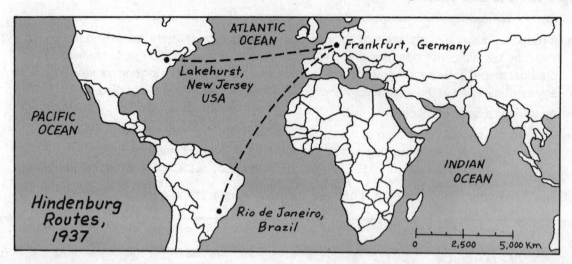

6. The *Hindenburg* was a German airship that flew passengers during the 1930s. What does this map show? How do you know?

**The map shows the routes the *Hindenburg* traveled during 1937.**

**The title of the map gives this information.**

7. From what city in Europe did the *Hindenburg* fly? Across what body of water did the *Hindenburg* fly?

**The flights began in Frankfurt, Germany. The flights crossed the**

**Atlantic Ocean.**

8. According to the map, what were the *Hindenburg*'s two destinations in 1937?

**The *Hindenburg*'s two destinations were Lakehurst, New Jersey,**

**USA, and Rio de Janeiro, Brazil.**

9. What was the approximate distance of the route to each of these destinations?

**Frankfurt to Lakehurst: approximately 6,400 km; Frankfurt to**

**Rio de Janeiro: approximately 9,600 km**

10. Is this map similar to a globe? Which term would you use to describe this map—a road map, a political map that shows the borders of countries, or a physical map that shows elevations and other details of the land?

**The map is different from a globe because it is not curved like a**

**globe. It is a political map that shows countries' borders.**

**Home Activity**  Your child learned about using maps as resources. Look at a road map together. Ask your child to determine distances and plot out routes to destinations you specify.

# Related Words

**Proofread an Article** Circle six spelling errors and one sentence containing punctuation errors. Write the corrections on the lines.

**Spelling Words**

clean
cleanse
inspire
inspiration
legal
legality
define
definition
please
pleasant

combine
combination
human
humanity
organ
organist
crime
criminal
recognize
recognition

## Courts

The United States Supreme Court is the highest court in the land. Often it is asked to determine the (legalaty) of a law. The Supreme Court has the right to either (reconize) or deny any appeal submitted to it. (Some times) it (difines) conditions under which an existing law may be (leagle) or illegal. The Constitution and laws of each state establish the state courts. These state courts handle (criminul) cases. States also usually have courts that handle specific legal matters. (These include juvenile court; family court; and others.)

1. **legality**     2. **recognize**

3. **sometimes**     4. **defines**

5. **legal**     6. **criminal**

7. **These include juvenile court, family court, and others.**

**Proofread Words** Circle the correct spelling of the word.

8. crim          crieme          (crime)

9. (recognition)   raconition      reconition

10. plese        (please)         pleeze

11. orgunist     (organist)       orgenist

12. humen        homan           (human)

13. enspire      (inspire)        inspir

14. orgun        argon           (organ)

15. (humanity)   humenety        humenity

16. (combination) comination      cumination

**Frequently Misspelled Words**

sometimes
everything
maybe
a lot

**Home Activity** Your child identified misspelled words. Write the first four letters of a list word and have your child write the two related words.

© Pearson Education, Inc., 5

## Quotations and Quotation Marks

**Directions** Read the passage. Then read each question. Circle the letter of the correct answer.

# Up In the Air

(1) "I'm going on a hot-air balloon ride," said Sherry. (2) "Wow!" That's so cool!" exclaimed Phillip. (3) "He added earnestly, "Do you think I could come along?" (4) That afternoon, Sherry asked her father if Phillip could go with them in the balloon. (5) "Sure answered her father, "as long as he isn't afraid of heights!" (6) Phillip had never been in a balloon or an airplane, and he was very excited. (7) "Thank you so much," he said. "For letting me go along for the ride!"

**1** What change, if any, should be made in sentence 1?

  **A** Change *"I'm going* to **I'm going**

  **B** Change *ride,"* to **ride"**

  **C** Change *ride,"* to **ride."**

  (**D**) Make no change

**2** What change, if any, should be made in sentence 2?

  **A** Change **"Wow!"** to **"Wow,"**

  **B** Change *That's* to **"That's**

  (**C**) Change **"Wow!"** to **"Wow!**

  **D** Make no change

**3** What change, if any, should be made in sentence 3?

  (**A**) Remove quotation marks from the beginning of the sentence

  **B** Remove all quotation marks from the sentence

  **C** Change *"He added earnestly,* to **He added earnestly**

  **D** Make no change

**4** Which is the correct form of sentence 5?

  **A** "Sure" answered her father, "as long as he isn't afraid of heights!"

  **B** "Sure, answered her father, as long as he isn't afraid of heights!"

  **C** "Sure" answered her father "as long as he isn't afraid of heights!"

  (**D**) "Sure," answered her father, "as long as he isn't afraid of heights!"

**5** What is the correct form of sentence 7?

  **A** "Thank you so much," he said. "For letting me go along for the ride!"

  (**B**) "Thank you so much," he said, "for letting me go along for the ride!"

  **C** "Thank you so much he said for letting me go along for the ride!"

  **D** "Thank you so much, he said, for letting me go along for the ride!"

**Home Activity** Your child prepared for taking tests on quotations and quotation marks. Have your child interview you about your day and write your reply as a quotation, beginning with *He/She said* and using quotation marks correctly.

# Sequence

- **Sequence** is the order of events in a selection. Dates and times of day or clue words such as *first, next,* and *then* can help you follow the sequence of events.

- Clue words such as *meanwhile* and *during* signal events happening at the same time.

**Directions** Read the following passage. Then complete the diagram.

> Will was nervous about playing the clarinet at a school performance for the first time. For five months, he had been taking lessons and learning to make notes come alive. But once the performance started, he got nervous. What if he played at the wrong time or forgot the notes? When the time came for his number, he forgot about all the people watching and just felt good about the music. Then when he heard the applause, he felt even better.

## Possible answers given.

**Sequence of Events**

1. **Will had been taking lessons for five months.**

⬇

2. **The performance started, and he got nervous.**

⬇

3. **He thought only of the music, and he felt good.**

⬇

4. **He felt even better after getting applause.**

5. What do you know about the clarinet or playing in a school performance? Explain how your prior knowledge helps you to understand the story. **Possible answer:**

**I know that sometimes clarinets make loud squeaking noises during performances. That would make me nervous, too.**

**Home Activity** Your child identified the sequence of a story and the prior knowledge he or she had of the subject matter. Work with your child to identify the sequence of the events in a short story. Encourage your child to describe the prior knowledge he or she has of the story's subject matter.

# Writing • Personal Narrative

**Key Features of a Personal Narrative**

- tells a real story about a personal experience
- includes details that help readers understand the experience
- uses first-person point of view (*I, me*)
- reveals author's voice through thoughts and feelings

## A Surprise for Mom

My mom works really hard at a job she loves. She's a chef, and her food is delicious! On her days off, she cooks me fancy pizzas or anything else I want.

A couple of months ago, a thought hit me: "My mom needs someone to cook for her." That's when I hatched my plan. My mom's best friend Trish is also a chef, so I asked her to teach me how to cook a special dinner for Mother's Day.

You should know that I was clueless in the kitchen. Trish had to start from the beginning. First we planned the menu. Then I worked on techniques like reading recipes, measuring ingredients, and cutting vegetables safely. When I moved on to actually cooking, I had trouble with everything! I made mistakes like flipping food out of the pan and burning sauces. However, Trish was really patient with me, and slowly I mastered each dish.

When Mother's Day arrived, I got busy as soon as Mom left for work. She always makes a huge brunch at the restaurant and comes home exhausted.

This time, however, when Mom got home the house smelled great. I had her favorite CD playing and the table set. The first part of our meal, salad, was ready to serve.

Mom was astonished. She ate every bit of food. I was so happy! My hard work had made me more than a successful cook. It had made me a son who could finally give goodness back to his mom.

1. What thoughts about his mother does the author share with the reader in paragraphs one and two?

   **In paragraph one, he thinks his mom works really hard. In paragraph two, he thinks his mom needs someone to cook for her.**

2. What details in paragraph five help you feel like you are a part of this experience? Underline sentences that appeal to your senses.

# Vocabulary

**Directions** Choose the word from the box that best matches each definition below. Write the word on the line.

**secondhand**_____ 1. not new; used already by someone else

**jammed**_____ 2. made music with other musicians without having practiced

**fidgety**_____ 3. restless; uneasy

**bass**_____ 4. the largest, lowest sounding stringed instrument in an orchestra or band

**forgetful**_____ 5. apt to forget; having a poor memory

**Directions** Choose the word from the box that best completes each sentence below. Write the word on the line shown to the left.

**jammed**_____ 6. The trio of jazz musicians _____, or played music together.

**nighttime**_____ 7. They met during the _____ after working all day.

**bass**_____ 8. One musician played both a trumpet and a stringed _____.

**clarinet**_____ 9. Another musician played the _____, a favorite woodwind.

**secondhand**_____ 10. The third musician's instrument was a used, or _____, saxophone.

## Write a Review

On a separate sheet of paper, write a review you might compose after you go to a music concert or performance. Use as many vocabulary words as you can.

**Reviews should include words from the vocabulary list and comments about a musical performance.**

**Home Activity** Your child identified and used vocabulary words from *Sweet Music in Harlem*. Read a story or nonfiction article with your child. Have him or her point out unfamiliar words. Work together to try to figure out the meaning of each word by using other words that appear near it.

# Punctuation

You have already learned about punctuation such as commas, quotation marks, and end marks. Here are some other kinds of punctuation.

- A **colon** (:) is used to introduce a list of items. It is also used to separate hours and minutes in expressions of time. In addition, it is used after the salutation in a business letter.
  Use these ingredients: two eggs, one cup of flour, and a stick of butter.
  10:30 A.M.        9:15 P.M.        Dear Ms. Glover:        Sir:

- A **hyphen** (-) is used in some compound words. Two common uses are numbers from twenty-one to ninety-nine and compound words that are thought of as one word.
  old-time music        best-known book        forty-nine        five-year-old boy

- A **semicolon** (;) can be used to join two independent clauses instead of a comma and a conjunction.
  Jazz is a mixture of different types of music; New Orleans was its birthplace.

- **Italics** or **underlining** is used for titles of books, newspapers, magazines, and works of art. Because you cannot write italics, underline titles in your writing.
  the *Chicago Tribune* (newspaper)        *Time for Kids* (magazine)
  *or*        the Chicago Tribune        Time for Kids

- A **dash** (—) sets off information or a comment that interrupts the flow of a sentence.
  Jazz had developed many styles—bebop and Dixieland, for example—by the 1940s.

**Directions** Rewrite each sentence on the lines. Add punctuation where it is needed.

1. Jinny is writing a how to book titled You Can Do Most Anything.

**Jinny is writing a how-to book titled You Can Do Most Anything.**

2. The first show is at 800 P.M. the second is at 1030 P.M.

**The first show is at 8:00 P.M.; the second is at 10:30 P.M.**

3. Cuthbert we call him Chip is my best friend.

**Cuthbert—we call him Chip—is my best friend.**

4. Mae made a last minute effort to learn twenty two songs.

**Mae made a last-minute effort to learn twenty-two songs.**

**Home Activity** Your child learned about punctuation. Have your child explain and model a use for colons and semicolons.

© Pearson Education, Inc., 5

Name _____

# Easily Confused Words

| Spelling Words | | | | |
|---|---|---|---|---|
| quiet | quite | finely | finally | except |
| accept | than | then | since | sense |
| affect | effect | from | form | later |
| latter | adapt | adopt | medal | metal |

**Definitions** Write the list word that means the same as each word or phrase.

1. silent
2. at last
3. receive
4. shape
5. a type of award

1. __quiet__
2. __finally__
3. __accept__
4. __form__
5. __medal__

**Words in Context** Write a list word to finish each sentence.

6. How will this score ___ my grade?
7. I'll see you ___.
8. They plan to ___ a child soon.
9. By ___ we should know the results of the race.
10. My aunt has a good ___ of humor.
11. I think this project is not ___ finished yet.
12. This piano has been very ___ tuned.
13. Everyone was there ___ me.
14. I would rather go to a movie ___ do my homework.
15. I haven't seen her ___ last year.
16. What ___ will this poor test score have on my overall grade?
17. I like to walk home ___ school.
18. I prefer the former choice to the ___.
19. It is important to be able to ___ to new situations.
20. The magnet picked up the ___ pieces.

6. __affect__
7. __later__
8. __adopt__
9. __then__
10. __sense__
11. __quite__
12. __finely__
13. __except__
14. __than__
15. __since__
16. __effect__
17. __from__
18. __latter__
19. __adapt__
20. __metal__

**Home Activity** Your child matched words with definitions and finished sentences. Ask your child to define the word *adapt*.

**Time Line**

**Date**

# Vocabulary • Homographs

- When you are reading, you might see a **homograph**. Homographs are words that are spelled the same but have different meanings and sometimes different pronunciations. For example, *object* can mean both "to protest" and "a thing."
- Use context clues, or words around the unfamiliar word, to figure out its meaning. Context clues include definitions, explanations, and synonyms.
- A dictionary is a book to help you find words you do not know.

**Directions** Read the following passage about jazz music. Then answer the questions below.

> Jeb played bass, a low-sounding stringed instrument, in a jazz quartet. Along with his bass, the group also had a clarinet, a trombone, and a piano. Every night when the group jammed, or made music without practicing, they would attract interest. Soon a crowd would gather. Usually they'd get so deeply involved in the music that they'd get forgetful of the time. Before they realized it, instead of nighttime it would be close to daytime.

1. *Bass* can refer to a musical instrument or a fish. What clues help you to determine the meaning in this passage?

   **Bass is explained in the sentence as a "low-sounding stringed instrument," and the context is about music.**

2. In this context, is *jam* a noun referring to a fruit spread or a verb referring to playing music without practicing? What clues help you to determine the meaning?

   **Jam is a verb referring to playing music, because the context is about music and the word is defined in the sentence.**

3. Use one of the homographs in the passage twice in a sentence, showing both its meanings.

   **Possible answer: I brought jam sandwiches to the jam session.**

4. Which meaning of the homograph *close* is used in the last sentence: "shut" or "near to"?

   **Close means "near to" in the last sentence.**

5. *Interest* can mean "a feeling of concern or curiosity" or "money paid for the use of money." How do context clues indicate its meaning in the passage?

   **Interest means "a feeling of concern or curiosity." The fact that a crowd gathers shows concern or curiosity.**

**Home Activity** Your child identified and used context clues to understand homographs in a passage. Work with your child to identify homographs in an article. Then your child can find context clues to help with the understanding of the new words. Confirm the meanings with your child.

# Poster/Announcement

- **Posters** and **announcements** announce events. The events may be one time only, or they may be continuing, as with club and organization meetings.
- Usually, posters and announcements answer these questions: Who? What? When? Where? Why?
- To emphasize information, posters and announcements may use color and large type size.
- When you write a poster or announcement, include only important information.

**Directions** Use this poster to answer the questions.

| Who is performing at this event? Who is sponsoring the event? | 1. Wynton Marsalis is performing. Jazz Junction is sponsoring the event. |
|---|---|
| What is the event? What is the cost? | 2. The event is a concert. The cost is $25 to $35. |
| When is the event? | 3. The event will be held on June 12, 13, and 14. |
| Where is the event? | 4. The event is in Festival Hall. |
| Why is the event being held? | 5. The event is being held to raise funds for the Children's Wishes Foundation. |

Name_____

**Directions** Use this announcement to answer the questions.

# JOIN TODAY!

## Armstrong School
# Junior
# Jazz Club

This organization is dedicated to
the appreciation of jazz music.
Guest speakers, refreshments, and lots
of music are all part of the fun!

**Come and bring your instrument!**

**Room 201**
**3:30 P.M. Every Tuesday**

6. What is the purpose of this announcement?

**to attract new members to the Junior Jazz Club**

7. What is the event? Why do you think the event takes place?

**The event is a meeting of the Junior Jazz Club. The purpose is to**

**encourage appreciation for jazz and to share an interest in jazz.**

8. When and where does the event take place?

**The meetings are every Tuesday at 3:30 P.M. in Room 201.**

9. What does this announcement emphasize? How and why is this emphasis made?

**The name of the club and the message "join today" are in large**

**type because they are the most important parts.**

10. On a separate sheet of paper, write an announcement for a school event.

**Announcements should include the who, what, when, where,**

**and why of the event.**

**Home Activity** Your child learned about reading posters. Point out a poster to your child, and ask him or her how the poster answers these questions about the event it announces: Who? What? When? Where? Why? Talk about how to compose a poster for a school or community event.

# Easily Confused Words

**Proofread a Dialogue** Circle six spelling mistakes in the article below. Write them correctly. Find a sentence with a misplaced comma. Write the sentence correctly.

**Spelling Words**

quiet
quite
finely
finally
except
accept
than
then
since
sense

affect
effect
from
form
later
latter
adapt
adopt
medal
metal

My Brother the Hero

When my brother (finely) got back (form) serving overseas, my family was happy and proud. We attended a ceremony where we watched him (except) a (metal.) When he stood up to receive his award, we were very (quite.) (Latter,) we went out to dinner to celebrate his return.

1. **finally**
2. **from**
3. **accept**
4. **medal**
5. **quiet**
6. **Later**
7. **Later, we went out to dinner to celebrate his return.**

**Proofread Words** Circle the word that is spelled correctly. Write it on the line.

8. axcept (accept)    8. **accept**
9. adupt (adapt)    9. **adapt**
10. adoped (adopt)    10. **adopt**
11. (affect) afect    11. **affect**
12. (except) exsept    12. **except**
13. finaly (finally)    13. **finally**
14. (sense) sence    14. **sense**
15. (then) thun    15. **then**

**Frequently Misspelled Words**

where
were

**Home Activity** Your child identified misspelled words. Ask your child to pick a list word and use it in a sentence.

# Punctuation

**Directions** Read the passage. Then read each question. Circle the letter of the correct answer.

# Jazzing It Up

(1) Jazz was created as a blend of several musical genres; New Orleans was where it began. (2) African Americans migrated to northern cities New York and Chicago, most importantly and brought jazz with them. (3) During the Great Depression—from 1929 to the early 1940s—jazz gained popularity and began to change. (4) A new form of jazz emerged at this time () big band. (5) Big band music—also called "swing"—helped people forget about the problems caused by the Depression. (6) Best-known for this type of jazz were Bennie Goodman and Count Basie. (7) *Magazines* like Down Beat helped launch the careers of: many great musicians.

**1** What change, if any, should be made in sentence 2?

**(A)** Insert (—) before *New York* and after *importantly*

**B** Insert (—) before *New York* and after *Chicago*

**C** Insert (;) before *New York* and after *importantly*

**D** Make no change

**2** In sentence 3, what is the function of the phrase *from 1929 to the early 1940s*?

**A** The phrase tells more about *jazz gained popularity*

**(B)** The phrase tells more about *the Great Depression*

**C** The phrase tells what happened during the Great Depression

**D** The phrase has no function

**3** What form of punctuation should replace the parentheses in sentence 4?

**A** Semicolon (;)

**(B)** Colon (:)

**C** Hyphen (-)

**D** Dash (—)

**4** What change, if any, should be made in sentence 6?

**A** Change *Best-known* to **Best known**

**B** Change *Best-known* to **Bestknown**

**C** Change *were* to **were:**

**(D)** Make no change

**5** What is the correct form of sentence 7?

**A** *Magazines* like Down Beat helped launch the careers of: many great musicians.

**B** *Magazines* like *Down Beat* helped launch the careers of: many great musicians.

**(C)** Magazines like *Down Beat* helped launch the careers of many great musicians.

**D** Magazines; like Down Beat—helped launch the careers of many great musicians.

**Home Activity** Your child prepared for taking tests on punctuation. Have your child make index cards for the colon, semicolon, dash, hyphen, and italics and then search books and magazines for examples of the use of each mark.

© Pearson Education, Inc., 5

# Suffixes *-ous, -sion, -ion, -ation*

| Spelling Words | | | | |
|---|---|---|---|---|
| famous | imagination | various | tension | invasion |
| invention | education | decision | humorous | creation |
| election | nervous | relaxation | exhibition | occupation |
| furious | explanation | conversation | attraction | destination |

**Antonyms** Write the list word that has the opposite or nearly the opposite meaning.

1. serious          **humorous**
2. relaxed          **nervous**
3. repulsion        **attraction**
4. unknown          **famous**
5. destruction      **creation**
6. calm             **furious**
7. uncertainty      **decision**
8. alike            **various**

**Words in Context** Complete each sentence with a list word.

9. Reading, writing, and math are important parts of your **education** .
10. The lightbulb was a marvelous **invention** .
11. Nursing is a helpful **occupation** .
12. In a good **conversation** , everyone has a chance to speak.
13. We saw a(n) **exhibition** of modern art at the museum.
14. Some people play card games for **relaxation** .
15. The beach is a popular summer **destination** .
16. Our picnic was ruined by a(n) **invasion** of ants.
17. You must use your **imagination** to write a compelling poem.
18. It is important for citizens to vote in each **election** .
19. Stretching a rubber band increases its **tension** .
20. You must have a good **explanation** for missing soccer practice.

**Home Activity** Your child has been learning to spell words with suffixes. Call out some of the list words and ask your child to give a synonym or antonym for each word.

# Modifiers

**Directions** Underline the adjectives, adverbs, and prepositional phrases in each sentence. (Do not underline the articles *a* and *the*.)

1. <u>Little</u> bats migrate <u>from central Mexico</u>.

2. Free-tails are <u>medium-sized</u> bats that live <u>in colonies</u>.

3. They roost <u>annually</u> <u>under the Congress Avenue Bridge</u>.

4. The <u>helpful</u> Free-tails eat moths and other <u>harmful</u> pests.

5. <u>Concerned</u> people <u>in Austin</u> want to save the <u>shrinking</u> bat population.

**Directions** Write *adverb, adjective,* or *prepositional phrase* to identify each underlined modifier. Write *adjective* or *adverb* to identify how a prepositional phrase is used.

6. Our science class studied <u>different</u> species.     **adjective**

7. Insects live <u>everywhere</u>.     **adverb**

8. Some insects blend <u>perfectly</u> with their environments.     **adverb**

9. Some insects are harmful because they feed <u>on our crops.</u>     **prepositional phrase—adverb**

10. The bat is a very <u>useful</u> creature.     **adjective**

11. Many harmful insects are eaten <u>by bats.</u>     **prepositional phrase—adverb**

12. The ladybug, <u>with its cheerful colors</u>, is my favorite insect.     **prepositional phrase— adjective**

**Directions** Underline the misplaced modifier in each sentence. Rewrite the sentence, and put the modifier where it belongs.

13. Farmers fight harmful insects <u>in airplanes called crop dusters</u>.

**Farmers in airplanes called crop dusters fight harmful insects.**

14. They <u>only</u> want to kill harmful insects and not useful ones.

**They want to kill only harmful insects and not useful ones.**

15. Crops are poisonous to bats <u>sprayed with pesticides</u>.

**Crops sprayed with pesticides are poisonous to bats.**

# Final Syllable -*ant*, -*ent*, -*ance*, -*ence*

**Spelling Words**

| | | | | |
|---|---|---|---|---|
| important | difference | intelligent | confidence | hesitant |
| experience | instance | evidence | conference | consistent |
| ignorant | absence | pollutant | insurance | excellence |
| entrance | appearance | clearance | ambulance | persistent |

**Analogies** Write the word that completes each comparison.

1. Happiness is to sadness as presence is to **absence** _____.

2. Sweet is to sour as educated is to **ignorant** _____.

3. Rose is to flower as smoke is to **pollutant** _____.

4. Trip is to journey as example is to **instance** _____.

5. Night is to day as exit is to **entrance** _____.

6. Pretty is to lovely as smart is to **intelligent** _____.

7. Doctor is to hospital as paramedic is to **ambulance** _____.

8. Heat is to cold as sameness is to **difference** _____.

9. Game is to sport as meeting is to **conference** _____.

10. Difficult is to easy as insignificant is to **important** _____.

**Words in Context** Complete each sentence with a list word.

11. The car repairs were paid for by the **insurance** _____ company.

12. The jury considered the **evidence** _____ against the man on trial.

13. Bright autumn colors gave the trees a lovely **appearance** _____.

14. The soccer players liked the referee because his calls were **consistent** _____.

15. Confronting a bear must be a frightening **experience** _____.

16. Because he was shy, Will was **hesitant** _____ to meet people.

17. There was a(n) **clearance** _____ sale of snow boots at the end of the winter.

18. That baseball player has much **confidence** _____ in his ability.

19. At the spring assembly, the best students were rewarded for **excellence** _____.

20. To succeed in your goal, you must be **persistent** _____.

**Home Activity** Your child learned to spell words with the final syllables -*ant*, -*ent*, -*ance*, and -*ence*. Ask your child to find an example of a word with each ending in a magazine and then spell each word without looking at the magazine.

# Conjunctions

**Directions** Underline the conjunction in each sentence.

1. Scientists look for facts <u>and</u> solve problems.

2. All problems are different, <u>but</u> each problem takes time to solve.

3. Scientists search for answers in an orderly <u>and</u> exact way.

4. They use scientific method, <u>or</u> a systematic approach to problem solving.

5. Eventually, they form a hypothesis, <u>but</u> this is not the end.

6. They must analyze the data <u>and</u> draw a conclusion.

**Directions** Underline the conjunction in ( ) that completes each sentence.

7. Is a scientific truth a theory (and, <u>or</u>) a law?

8. A theory may be logical, (or, <u>but</u>) a law is widely accepted.

9. Newton's ideas about motion are called laws, (and, <u>but</u>) Einstein's idea about relativity is called a theory.

10. Both Newton (<u>and</u>, or) Einstein used scientific method.

**Directions** Use the conjunction *and, but,* or *or* to join each pair of sentences. Write the new sentences. Remember to add a comma.

11. The reindeer population grew large. Then most of the reindeer died suddenly.
    **The reindeer population grew large, but then most of the reindeer died suddenly.**

12. Were the reindeer diseased? Did they starve?
    **Were the reindeer diseased, or did they starve?**

13. The animals had lost weight. Their bone marrow contained no fat.
    **The animals had lost weight, and their bone marrow contained no fat.**

14. The reindeer had eaten all the island's food. Then disaster struck.
    **The reindeer had eaten all the island's food, and then disaster struck.**

# Latin Roots

| Spelling Words | | | | |
|---|---|---|---|---|
| portable | audience | decade | territory | auditorium |
| dictionary | terrace | reporter | December | contradict |
| export | decimal | audit | transport | audition |
| prediction | import | jurisdiction | decathlon | terrain |

**Classifying** Write the list word that belongs in each group.

1. state, country, region, **territory**

2. patio, deck, balcony, **terrace**

3. September, October, November, **December**

4. week, month, year, **decade**

5. races, hurdle, shot put, **decathlon**

6. aquarium, solarium, gymnasium, **auditorium**

7. writer, investigator, researcher, **reporter**

8. integer, fraction, whole number, **decimal**

9. thesaurus, encyclopedia, handbook, **dictionary**

10. court, claims, civil, **jurisdiction**

**Synonyms** Write the list word that has the same or nearly the same meaning.

11. tryout **audition**

12. forecast **prediction**

13. ground **terrain**

14. onlookers **audience**

15. move **transport**

16. check **audit**

17. send **export**

18. dispute **contradict**

19. moveable **portable**

20. bring in **import**

**Home Activity** Your child has learned to spell words with Latin roots. Take turns brainstorming a word that has one of the list word roots. Look up each word in the dictionary to confirm that it comes from a Latin word.

# Commas

**Directions** Add commas to each sentence where they are needed.

1. Rafael has joined the Fleet Feet, a traveling soccer team.

2. He will have to buy shoes, a uniform, and a ball.

3. Dad, how can I earn money?

4. Well, son, you could do more chores around the house.

5. Rafael washed the car, walked the dog, and watered the garden.

6. He also received money as gifts from his aunt, grandparents, and parents.

**Directions** Rewrite each sentence. Add commas where they are needed.

7. "Anna are you a good money manager?"

   **"Anna, are you a good money manager?"**

8. In general people are better at spending than saving.

   **In general, people are better at spending than saving.**

9. Most people need a budget a plan for keeping track of their income and expenses.

   **Most people need a budget, a plan for keeping track of their income and expenses.**

10. I spend my money on lunches books and supplies.

    **I spend my money on lunches, books, and supplies.**

11. George a friend who does not have a budget is always short of money.

    **George, a friend who does not have a budget, is always short of money.**

12. "By the way George you owe me fifty cents."

    **"By the way, George, you owe me fifty cents."**

# Related Words

| Spelling Words | | | | |
|---|---|---|---|---|
| clean | inspire | legal | define | please |
| cleanse | inspiration | legality | definition | pleasant |
| combine | human | organ | crime | recognize |
| combination | humanity | organist | criminal | recognition |

**Analogies** Write the word that completes each sentence.

1. Pepper is to salt as dirty is to **clean** .

2. Beast is to animal as person is to **human** .

3. Stop is to go as separate is to **combine** .

4. Violin is to violinist as organ is to **organist** .

5. Good-bye is to hello as thank you is to **please** .

6. Exhilaration is to excitement as encouragement is to **inspiration** .

7. Individual is to single as mixture is to **combination** .

8. Tool is to hammer as instrument is to **organ** .

9. Earth is to world as mankind is to **humanity** .

10. Unwind is to relax as unlawful is to **criminal** .

**Synonyms** Write the list word that has the same or nearly the same meaning.

11. wash       **cleanse**

12. lawful      **legal**

13. meaning     **definition**

14. agreeable   **pleasant**

15. acknowledgement  **recognition**

**Antonyms** Write the list word that has the opposite or nearly the opposite meaning.

16. not notice    **recognize**

17. discourage    **inspire**

18. confuse      **define**

19. unlawfulness   **legality**

20. legal       **crime**

**Home Activity** Your child has learned to spell related words. Read several pairs of words from the list. Ask your child to explain how knowing the spelling of one word in the pair can help in spelling the other word.

Name _____

# Quotations and Quotation Marks

**Directions** Write *C* if the sentence uses quotation marks and other punctuation correctly. Write *NC* if it is not correct.

1. "Are you going to take a vacation," asked Aaron?  ___NC___

2. "I usually fly to my grandparents' home in Michigan," said Pat.  ___C___

3. "Do you like to fly," asked Aaron, "or would you rather take a train?"  ___C___

4. "Pat replied, I like different things about both."  ___NC___

5. "A train lets you see more things," she explained. "However, an airplane is quicker."  ___C___

**Directions** Write each sentence correctly. Add capital letters, quotation marks, and other punctuation as needed.

6. when does our flight take off asked Nina

**"When does our flight take off?" asked Nina.**

7. it is scheduled to leave at 8:00 A.M. said Mom

**"It is scheduled to leave at 8:00 A.M.," said Mom.**

8. she added that means we should be at the airport by 6:00 A.M.

**She added, "That means we should be at the airport by 6:00 A.M."**

9. no way cried Nina that's too early

**"No way!" cried Nina. "That's too early!"** *or* early."

10. it is early agreed Mom however, we have to allow plenty of time

**"It is early," agreed Mom. "However, we have to allow plenty of time."**

11. after we check our bags she suggested we can have breakfast

**"After we check our bags," she suggested, "we can have breakfast."**

12. that sounds good said Nina can I buy a magazine to read

**"That sounds good," said Nina. "Can I buy a magazine to read?"**

# Easily Confused Words

| Spelling Words | | | | |
|---|---|---|---|---|
| quiet | except | since | from | adapt |
| quite | accept | sense | form | adopt |
| finely | than | affect | later | medal |
| finally | then | effect | latter | metal |

**Antonyms** Write the list word that has the opposite or nearly the opposite meaning.

1. coarsely    **finely**

2. reject    **accept**

3. earlier    **later**

4. noisy    **quiet**

5. now    **then**

**Synonyms** Write the list word that has the same or nearly the same meaning.

6. result    **effect**

7. reward    **medal**

8. very    **quite**

9. because    **since**

10. select    **adopt**

**Analogies** Write the word that completes each comparison.

11. First is to last as former is to **latter**.

12. Start is to begin as at last is to **finally**.

13. In is to out as to is to **from**.

14. Milk is to drink as iron is to **metal**.

15. Buy is to purchase as influence is to **affect**.

16. North is to direction as sight is to **sense**.

17. Also is to too as but is to **except**.

18. Gift is to present as shape is to **form**.

19. Work is to labor as change is to **adapt**.

20. Log is to dog as fan is to **than**.

**Home Activity** Your child has learned to spell sound-alike words. Ask your child to name three pairs of list words, spell each word, and explain how they differ in meaning.

Name _____

# Punctuation

**Directions** Match the punctuation with a description of its use.

___**D**___ 1. italics (underlining)

___**B**___ 2. colons (:)

___**E**___ 3. dashes (—)

___**A**___ 4. semicolons (;)

___**C**___ 5. hyphens (-)

**A** join clauses without a conjunction

**B** introduce a list, express hours and minutes, and appear after the salutation in a business letter

**C** join some compound words

**D** set off titles of books, magazines, and works of art

**E** set off words that interrupt the sentence

**Directions** Rewrite each sentence. Add the missing punctuation marks.

6. I'm always losing things I can usually find them in a few minutes.

**I'm always losing things; I can usually find them in a few minutes.**

7. I have lost several things this week six notebooks, twenty one pencils, and my America Sings book.

**I have lost several things this week: six notebooks, twenty-one pencils, and my America Sings book.**

8. Now my jacket it's the one with the gold buttons is missing.

**Now my jacket—it's the one with the gold buttons—is missing.**

9. It could be in the car it might be in my locker.

**It could be in the car; it might be in my locker.**

10. There's one thing this ten year old will never forget. School ends at 345 P.M.!

**There's one thing this ten-year-old will never forget. School ends at 3:45 P.M.!**

# KWL Chart

**Directions** Fill out this KWL chart to help you organize your ideas.

Topic _____

| What I **K**now | What I **W**ant to Know | What I **L**earned |
|---|---|---|
| Answers should include details about each element of the research report. | | |

**Controlling Question** _____

# Topic and Detail Sentences

**Directions** Decide how you will organize your paragraphs. Then write a topic sentence and supporting details for each paragraph.

**Paragraph 1**
Topic Sentence **Answers should include clear topic sentences, each supported by at least two detail sentences.**
Detail Sentences _____
_____
_____
_____

**Paragraph 2**
Topic Sentence _____
_____
Detail Sentences _____
_____
_____
_____

**Paragraph 3**
Topic Sentence _____
_____
Detail Sentences _____
_____
_____
_____

**Paragraph 4**
Topic Sentence _____
_____
Detail Sentences _____
_____
_____
_____

# Combining Sentences

**Directions** Use the word in parentheses to combine each pair of sentences. Remember to capitalize the first word of each new sentence and to add a comma when necessary. **Possible answers:**

1. (because) You can't see faults. They are far below the surface of the Earth.

   **You can't see faults because they are far below the surface of the Earth.**

2. (when) An earthquake occurs. Parts of the Earth's crust suddenly break and shift.

   **An earthquake occurs when parts of the Earth's crust suddenly break and shift.**

3. (or) Are all earthquake waves the same? Are there different kinds of earthquake waves?

   **Are all earthquake waves the same, or are there different kinds of earthquake waves?**

4. (and) The Richter scale measures energy released. The Mercali scale measures the results of an earthquake.

   **The Richter scale measures energy released, and the Mercali scale measures the results of an earthquake.**

5. (but) Today geologists can neither predict nor prevent earthquakes. One day they hope to do both.

   **Today geologists can neither predict nor prevent earthquakes, but one day they hope to do both.**

# Peer and Teacher Conferencing Research Report

**Directions** Read your partner's essay. Refer to the Revising Checklist as you write your comments or questions. Offer compliments as well as revision suggestions. Then take turns talking about each other's draft. Give your partner your notes. After you and your teacher talk about your essay, add your teacher's comments to the notes.

## Revising Checklist

**Focus/Ideas**
☐ Is the research report focused on one topic?
☐ Are there enough details?

**Organization**
☐ Does each paragraph have a topic sentence and supporting detail sentences?

**Voice**
☐ Is the report interesting to read?

**Word Choice**
☐ Has the writer paraphrased the material?

**Sentences**
☐ Have some short simple sentences been combined into compound or complex sentences to improve flow and clarity?

**Things I Thought Were Good** _____

_____

_____

**Things I Thought Could Be Improved** _____

_____

_____

**Teacher's Comments** _____

_____